Real Analysis

About the Author

PATRICK M. FITZPATRICK

(Ph.D., Rutgers University) held post-doctoral positions at the Courant Institute of New York University and the University of Chicago. Since 1975 he has been a member of the Mathematics Department at the University of Maryland at College Park, where he is now Professor of Mathematics and Associate Chairman for Undergraduate Studies. He has also held Visiting Professorships at the University of Paris and the University of Florence. Professor Fitzpatrick's principal research interest, on which he has written more than fifty research articles, is nonlinear functional analysis.

Real Analysis

Patrick M. Fitzpatrick
UNIVERSITY OF MARYLAND

PWS Publishing Company

I(T)P An International Thomson Publishing Company

Boston • Albany • Bonn • Cincinnati • Detroit • London • Madrid • Melbourne
Mexico City • New York • Paris • San Francisco • Singapore • Tokyo • Toronto • Washington

PWS PUBLISHING COMPANY
20 Park Plaza, Boston, MA 02116-4324

I$\textcircled{T}$P ™

International Thomson Publishing
The trademark ITP is used under license.

 This book is printed on recycled, acid-free paper

For more information, contact:
PWS Publishing Co.
20 Park Plaza
Boston, MA 02116

International Thomson Publishing Europe
Berkshire House I68-I73
High Holborn
London WC1V 7AA
England

Thomas Nelson Australia
102 Dodds Street
South Melbourne, 3205
Victoria, Australia

Nelson Canada
1120 Birchmont Road
Scarborough, Ontario
Canada M1K 5G4

International Thomson Editores
Campos Eliseos 385, Piso 7
Col. Polanco
11560 Mexico D.F., Mexico

International Thomson Publishing GmbH
Königswinterer Strasse 418
53227 Bonn, Germany

International Thomson Publishing Asia
221 Henderson Road
#05-10 Henderson Building
Singapore 0315

International Thomson Publishing Japan
Hirakawacho Kyowa Building, 31
2-2-1 Hirakawacho
Chiyoda Ku, Tokyo 102
Japan

Library of Congress Cataloging-in-Publication Data

Fitzpatrick, Patrick
    Real analysis / Patrick M. Fitzpatrick.
      p. cm.
    Includes index.
    ISBN 0-534-92611-8
    1. Mathematical analysis. I. Title.
QA300.F638   1995
$515^1.83$—dc20
                     95-20041
                     CIP

Sponsoring Editor: *Steve Quigley*
Production Editor: *Monique A. Calello*
Editorial Assistant: *John Ward*
Marketing Manager: *Marianne Rutter*
Manufacturing Manager: *Ellen Glisker*
Interior Designer: *Catherine Hawkes*
Cover Designer: *Kathleen Wilson*

Interior Illustrator: *Hayden Graphics*
Compositor: *Atlis Graphics & Design, Inc.*
Cover Illustration: *"Cities of the Plain," watercolor,*
© Richard C. Karwoski, The Image Bank
Cover Printer: *Henry N. Sawyer Co., Inc.*
Text Printer: *R.R. Donnelley & Sons–Crawfordsville*

Printed and bound in the United States of America
95 96 97 98 99—10 9 8 7 6 5 4 3 2 1

TO BRIDGET, PATRICK, KERA, AND MICHAEL

In order to put his system into mathematical form at all, Newton had to devise the concept of differential quotients and propound the laws of motion in the form of differential equations—perhaps the greatest advance in thought that a single individual was ever privileged to make.

Albert Einstein

from an essay

On the one hundredth anniversary of Maxwell's birth

James Clerk Maxwell: A Commemorative Volume

Contents

The Real Numbers   6

Sequences of Real Numbers   23

Continuous Functions and Limits   42

Differentiation   68

The Elementary Functions as Solutions of Differential Equations   98

Integration   113

The Second Fundamental Theorem and Its Consequences   141

Approximation by Taylor Polynomials   165

The Convergence of Sequences and Series of Functions   192

Consequences of the Field and Positivity Axioms   A1

Answer Section   A7

Preface

The goal of this book is to rigorously present the fundamental concepts of mathematical analysis for functions of a single variable in the clearest, simplest way, within the context of illuminating examples and stimulating exercises. It is a text suitable for an introductory course in mathematical analysis, for students who have taken an elementary calculus sequence. I hope that the student will assimilate a precise understanding of the subject, together with an appreciation of its coherence and significance.

Mathematical analysis has been seminal in the development of many branches of science. Indeed, the importance of the applications of the computational algorithms that are a part of the subject often leads to courses in which familiarity with implementing these algorithms is emphasized at the expense of the ideas that underlie the subject. While these techniques are very important, without a genuine understanding of the concepts that are at the heart of these algorithms, it is possible to make only limited use of these computational possibilities.

I have tried to emphasize the unity of the subject. Mathematical analysis is not a collection of isolated facts and techniques, but is, instead, a coherent body of knowledge. Beyond the intrinsic importance of the actual subject, the study of mathematical analysis instills habits of thought that are essential for a proper understanding of many areas of pure and applied mathematics.

At the beginning of this course it is necessary to establish a base on which the subsequent proofs will be built. It has been my experience that in order to cover, within the allotted time, a substantial amount of analysis, it is not possible to provide a detailed construction of the real numbers starting with a serious treatment of set theory. I have chosen to codify the properties of the real numbers as three groups of axioms. In the Preliminaries, the arithmetic and order properties are codified in the Field and Positivity Axioms; a detailed discussion of the consequences of these axioms, which certainly are familiar to the student, is provided in the Appendix. The least familiar of these axioms, the Completeness Axiom, is presented in the first section of the first chapter, Section 1.1.

Another important issue in a first course in analysis is the way that the elementary functions are introduced. The students will be familiar with the properties of the logarithmic and trigonometric functions and their inverses, although, most probably, they will not have seen a rigorous analysis of these functions. In Chapter 5, the natural logarithm, the sine, and the cosine functions are introduced as the (unique) solutions of particular differential equations; on the provisional assumption that these equations have solutions, an analytic derivation of the properties of these functions and their inverses is provided. Later, after the differentiability properties of functions defined by integrals and by power series have been established, it is proven that these differential equations do indeed have solutions, and so the provisional assumptions of Chapter 5 are removed.

The beginning chapter is devoted to properties of the real numbers. Then, in Chapter 2, sequences are studied. Monotonicity and linearity properties of convergent sequences are established, and the Completeness Axiom is recast as the Bolzano-Weierstrass Theorem and the Nested Interval Theorem for convergent sequences. The material from this chapter is used repeatedly throughout the book. For instance, in Chapter 3, continuity of functions and limits of functions are defined in terms of sequential convergence. The linearity properties of convergent sequences from Chapter 2 immediately imply corresponding linearity properties for continuous functions, limits, derivatives, and later, in Chapter 7, for integrals.

In the third chapter, the essential properties of continuous functions are established and, in a concluding section, limits of functions are treated. Chapter 4 is devoted to differentiation. In Section 4.5, Darboux's Theorem is proven: It asserts that in order for a real-valued function, defined on an open interval, to be the derivative of another function, it is necessary that the given function possess the intermediate value property. This is the first result regarding the solvability of differential equations.

As I already mentioned, in Chapter 5, the elementary functions are introduced as the (unique) solutions of particular differential equations; solely on this basis, an analytic derivation of the properties of these functions and their inverses is provided.

Integration is studied in Chapters 6 and 7. The integral is defined in terms of Darboux sums, and later its property of being the limit of appropriate sequences of Riemann sums is established. The relationship between integration and differentiation is described in two theorems, which I call the First and the Second Fundamental Theorems of Calculus. This is done to emphasize the distinction between the formula for evaluating the integral of a function that is known to be the derivative of another function and the related, but different, matter of understanding the conditions under which a given function is the derivative of some other function and providing integral representations of solutions of differential equations. The study of the approximation of functions by Taylor polynomials is the subject of Chapter 8. In Chapter 9, we consider a sequence of functions that converges to a limit function and study the way in which the limit function inherits properties possessed by the functions that are the terms of the sequence; the distinction between pointwise and uniform convergence is emphasized. This concludes this book. In my *Advanced Calculus: A Course in Mathematical Analysis*, the present book is continued to cover mathematical analysis of functions of several variables.

Each course in mathematical analysis will have its own particular character, depending on the taste of the teacher, the composition of the class, the length of the course, and the text. While this book certainly presents a particular viewpoint of analysis, I hope that it also permits, through emphasis and selection, a reasonable range of flexibility. In addition to the absolutely essential topics, other important topics have been arranged in such a way that selections can be made without disturbing the coherence of the course. As two examples of such optional topics, I mention the approximation methods for estimating integrals and the Weierstrass Approximation Theorem. Precise estimates for the errors incurred in the approximation of integrals were always present in the classical courses in mathematical analysis. Nowadays, they do not appear so frequently. In view of the recent growth in computational capability and the attendant need to estimate errors in approximation methods, this topic seems to me worthy of consideration for inclusion in a course. This material is presented in the last section of Chapter 7; the last two chapters are independent of this section. An approximation theorem of quite a different flavor is the Weierstrass Approximation Theorem. This stands as one of the singular jewels of classical analysis. It can be presented as a companion to the discussion of approximation of functions by Taylor polynomials. The theorem is proven in the last section of Chapter 8; the last chapter is independent of this section.

I cannot overemphasize the importance of the exercises. To achieve a genuine understanding of the material it is necessary that the student work many problems. The problems are designed to be challenging and to stimulate the student to carefully reread the relevant sections to properly assimilate the material. Many of the problems foreshadow future developments.

Acknowledgments

Preliminary versions of portions of this book, in note form, have been used in their classes by a number of my colleagues. The book has been improved by their comments about the notes and also by suggestions from other colleagues. Accepting sole responsibility for the final manuscript, I warmly thank Professors James Alexander, Stuart Antman, John Benedetto, Ken Berg, Michael Boyle, Joel Cohen, Jeffrey Cooper, Craig Evans, Seymour Goldberg, Paul Green, Denny Gulick, David Hamilton, Chris Jones, Adam Kleppner, John Millson, Umberto Neri, Jacobo Pejsachowicz, Dan Rudolph, Jerome Sather, James Schafer, and Daniel Sweet.

I would also like to thank the following reviewers for their comments and criticisms: Professors Bruce Barnes, University of Oregon; John Van Eps, California Polytechnic State University-San Luis Obispo; Christopher E. Hee, Eastern Michigan University; Gordon Melrose, Old Dominion University; Claudio Morales, University of Alabama; Harold R. Parks, Oregon State University; Steven Michael Shubert, Bowling Green State University; William Yslas Velez, University of Arizona; Clifford E. Weil, Michigan State University; and W. Thurmon Whitney, University of New Haven.

It is a pleasure to thank Ms. Jaya Nagendra for her excellent typing of various versions of the manuscript, and also to thank the editorial and production personnel at PWS Publishing Company for their considerate and expert assistance in making the manuscript into a book.

Finally, I am especially grateful to a teacher of mine and to a student of mine. As an undergraduate at Rutgers I was very fortunate to have Professor John Bender as my teacher. He introduced me to mathematical analysis. Moreover, his personal encouragement was what led me to pursue mathematics as a lifetime study. It is not possible to adequately express my debt to him. I also wish to single out for special thanks one of the many students who have contributed to this book. Alan Preis was a great help to me in the final preparation of the manuscript. His assistance and our stimulating discussions in this final phase made what could have been a very tiresome task into a pleasant one.

Patrick M. Fitzpatrick

Preliminaries

Sets and Functions

For a set A, the membership of the element x in A is denoted by $x \in A$ or x in A, and the nonmembership of x in A is denoted by $x \notin A$. A member of A is often called a *point* in A. Two sets are the same if and only if they have the same members. Frequently sets will be denoted by braces, so that $\{x \mid \text{proposition about } x\}$ is the set of all elements x such that the proposition about x is true.

If A and B are sets, then A is called a *subset* of B if and only if each member of A is a member of B, and we denote this by $A \subseteq B$ or by $B \supseteq A$. The *union* of two sets A and B, written $A \cup B$, is the set of all elements that belong either to A or to B; that is, $A \cup B = \{x \mid x \text{ in } A \text{ or } x \text{ in } B\}$. The word *or* is used here in the nonexclusive sense, so that points that belong to both A and B belong to $A \cup B$. The *intersection* of A and B, denoted by $A \cap B$, is the set of all points that belong to both A and B; that is, $A \cap B = \{x \mid x \text{ in } A \text{ and } x \text{ in } B\}$. Given sets A and B, the *complement* of A in B, denoted by $B \backslash A$, is the set of all points in B that are not in A. In particular, for a set B and a point x_0, $B \backslash \{x_0\}$ denotes the set of points in B that are not equal to x_0. The set that has no members is called the *empty set* and is denoted by $\emptyset$.

Given two sets A and B, by a *function* from A to B we mean a correspondence that associates with each point in A a point in B. Frequently we denote such a function by $f: A \to B$, and for each point x in A, we denote by $f(x)$ the point in B that is associated with x. We call the set A the *domain* of the function $f: A \to B$ and we define the *image* of $f: A \to B$, denoted by $f(A)$, to be $\{y \mid y = f(x) \text{ for some point } x \text{ in } A\}$. If $f(A) = B$, the function $f: A \to B$ is said to be *onto*. If for each point y in $f(A)$ there is exactly one point x in A such that $y = f(x)$, the function $f: A \to B$ is said to be *one-to-one*. A function $f: A \to B$ that is both one-to-one and onto is said to be *invertible*. For an invertible function $f: A \to B$, for each point y in $f(B)$ there is exactly one point x in A such that $f(x) = y$, and this point is denoted by $f^{-1}(y)$; this correspondence defines the function $f^{-1}: B \to A$, which is called the *inverse function* of the function $f: A \to B$.

The Field Axioms for the Real Numbers

In order to rigorously develop analysis, it is necessary to understand the foundation on which it is constructed; this foundation is the set of real numbers, which we will denote by $\mathbb{R}$. Of course, the reader is quite familiar with many properties of the real numbers. However, in order to clarify the basis of our development, it is very useful to codify the properties of $\mathbb{R}$. We will assume that the set of real numbers $\mathbb{R}$ satisfies three groups of axioms: the Field Axioms, the Positivity Axioms, and the Completeness Axiom. A discussion of the Completeness Axiom, which is perhaps the least familiar to the reader, will be deferred until Chapter 1. We will now describe the Field Axioms and the Positivity Axioms and some of their consequences.

For each pair of real numbers a and b, a real number is defined that is called the *sum* of a and b, written $a + b$, and a real number is defined that is called the *product* of a and b, denoted by ab. These operations satisfy the following collection of axioms.

The Field Axioms

Commutativity of Addition: For all real numbers a and b,

$$a + b = b + a.$$

Associativity of Addition: For all real numbers a, b, and c,

$$(a + b) + c = a + (b + c).$$

The Additive Identity: There is a real number, which is denoted by 0, such that

$$0 + a = a + 0 = a \quad \text{for all real numbers } a.$$

The Additive Inverse: For each real number a, there is a real number b such that

$$a + b = 0.$$

Commutativity of Multiplication: For all real numbers a and b,

$$ab = ba.$$

Associativity of Multiplication: For all real numbers a, b, and c,

$$(ab)c = a(bc).$$

The Multiplicative Identity: There is a real number, which is denoted by 1, such that

$$1a = a1 = a \quad \text{for all real numbers } a.$$

The Multiplicative Inverse: For each real number $a \neq 0$, there is a real number b such that

$$ab = 1.$$

The Distributive Property: For all real numbers a, b, and c,

$$a(b + c) = ab + ac.$$

The Nontriviality Assumption:

$$1 \neq 0.$$

The Field Axioms are simply a record of the properties that one has always assumed about addition and multiplication of real numbers.

From the Field Axioms it follows* that there is only one number that has the property attributed to 0 in the Additive Identity Axiom. Moreover, it also follows that for each real number a,

$$a0 = 0a = 0,$$

and that for any real numbers a and b,

$$\text{if} \quad ab = 0, \quad \text{then} \quad a = 0 \quad \text{or} \quad b = 0.$$

The Additive Inverse Axiom asserts that for each real number a, there is a solution of the equation

$$a + x = 0.$$

One can show that this equation has only one solution; we denote it by $-a$ and call it the *additive inverse* of a. For each pair of numbers a and b, we define their *difference,* denoted by $a - b$, by

$$a - b \equiv a + (-b).$$

The Field Axioms also imply that there is only one number having the property attributed to 1 in the Multiplicative Identity Axiom. For a real number $a \neq 0$, the Multiplicative Inverse Axiom asserts that the equation

$$ax = 1$$

has a solution. One can show there is only one solution; we denote it by a^{-1} and call it the *multiplicative inverse* of a. We then define for each pair of numbers a and $b \neq 0$ their *quotient,* denoted by a/b, as

$$\frac{a}{b} \equiv ab^{-1}.$$

It is an interesting algebraic exercise to verify the implications of the Field Axioms that we have just mentioned and also to verify the following familiar consequences of these same axioms: For any real numbers a and $b \neq 0$,

$$-(-a) = a, \quad (b^{-1})^{-1} = b, \quad \text{and} \quad (-b)^{-1} = -b^{-1}.$$

---

*Verification of these and of subsequent assertions in these Preliminaries is provided in Appendix A.

The Positivity Axioms for the Real Numbers

In the real numbers there is a natural notion of order: greater than, less than, and so on. A convenient way to codify these properties is by specifying axioms satisfied by the set of positive numbers.

The Positivity Axioms

There is a set of real numbers, denoted by $\mathcal{P}$, called the set of *positive numbers*. It has the following two properties:

P1 If a and b are positive, then ab and $a + b$ are also positive.

P2 For a real number a, exactly one of the following three alternatives is true:

$$a \text{ is positive,} \quad -a \text{ is positive,} \quad a = 0.$$

The Positivity Axioms lead in a natural way to an ordering of the real numbers: For real numbers a and b, we define $a > b$ to mean that $a - b$ is positive, and $a \geq b$ to mean that $a > b$ or $a = b$. We then define $a < b$ to mean that $b > a$, and $a \leq b$ to mean that $b \geq a$.

Using the Field Axioms and the Positivity Axioms, it is possible to establish the following familiar properties of inequalities (see Appendix A):

(i) For each real number $a \neq 0$, $a^2 > 0$. In particular, $1 > 0$, since $1 \neq 0$ and $1 = 1^2$.

(ii) For each positive number a, its multiplicative inverse a^{-1} is also positive.

(iii) If $a > b$, then

$$ac > bc \quad \text{if} \quad c > 0,$$

and

$$ac < bc \quad \text{if} \quad c < 0.$$

Interval Notation

For a pair of real numbers a and b such that $a < b$, we define

$$(a, b) \equiv \{x \text{ in } \mathbb{R} \mid a < x < b\},$$
$$[a, b] \equiv \{x \text{ in } \mathbb{R} \mid a \leq x \leq b\},$$
$$(a, b] \equiv \{x \text{ in } \mathbb{R} \mid a < x \leq b\},$$

and

$$[a, b) \equiv \{x \text{ in } \mathbb{R} \mid a \leq x < b\}.$$

Moreover, it is convenient to use the symbols ∞ and $-\infty$ in the following manner. We define

$$[a, \infty) \equiv \{x \text{ in } \mathbb{R} \mid a \leq x\},$$
$$(-\infty, b] \equiv \{x \text{ in } \mathbb{R} \mid x \leq b\},$$
$$(a, \infty) \equiv \{x \text{ in } \mathbb{R} \mid a < x\},$$
$$(-\infty, b) \equiv \{x \text{ in } \mathbb{R} \mid x < b\},$$

and

$$(-\infty, \infty) \equiv \mathbb{R}.$$

The reader should be very careful to observe that although we have defined, say, $[a, \infty)$, we have *not* defined the symbols ∞ and $-\infty$. In particular, we have *not* adjoined additional numbers to $\mathbb{R}$.

It will also be convenient to set $[a, a] \equiv \{a\}$. In general, when we write $[a, b]$ or (a, b), unless another meaning is explicitly mentioned, it is assumed that a and b are real numbers such that $a < b$.

Each of the sets listed above is called an *interval*. In the analysis of functions $f : A \to \mathbb{R}$, where A is a set of real numbers, a special role is played by those functions that have an interval as their domain A. In particular, intervals of the form (a, b), which we call *open intervals,* or of the form $[a, b]$, which we call *closed intervals,* will frequently be the domains of the functions that we will study.

The Real Numbers

The Completeness Axiom: The Natural, Rational, and Irrational Numbers

A rigorous understanding of mathematical analysis must be based on a proper understanding of the set of real numbers. The purpose of this first chapter is to establish the fundamental properties of the set $\mathbb{R}$ of real numbers.

The properties of addition and multiplication of real numbers have been codified in the Preliminaries as the Field Axioms. The set of real numbers is also equipped with the concept of order, and the properties of order and inequality have been codified in the Preliminaries as the Positivity Axioms. Many interesting properties of the real numbers are consequences of the Field and Positivity Axioms. However, an additional axiom is necessary. To explain why this is so, let us now introduce some special subsets of $\mathbb{R}$.

The subsets of $\mathbb{R}$ that we will now define are the natural numbers, the integers, and the rationals. Of course, these are already familiar to the reader: The natural numbers are the numbers 1, 2, 3, and so on. However, it is necessary to make this statement more precise, and a convenient way of doing so is to first introduce the concept of an *inductive set.*

DEFINITION   *A set S of real numbers is said to be inductive provided that*

(i) *the number* 1 *is in S*

and

(ii) *if the number x is in S, the number x* + 1 *is also in S.*

The whole set of real numbers $\mathbb{R}$ is inductive. Also, using just the fact that the number 1 is greater than the number 0, it follows that the set $\{x \text{ in } \mathbb{R} \mid x \geq 0\}$ is inductive, as is the set $\{x \text{ in } \mathbb{R} \mid x \geq 1\}$. The set of *natural numbers*, denoted by $\mathbb{N}$, is defined as the intersection of all inductive subsets of $\mathbb{R}$. The set $\mathbb{N}$ itself is inductive. To see this, observe that the number 1 belongs to $\mathbb{N}$, since 1 belongs to every inductive set. Furthermore, if the number k belongs to $\mathbb{N}$, then k belongs to every inductive set; thus, $k + 1$ belongs to every inductive set, and therefore $k + 1$ belongs to $\mathbb{N}$. Thus $\mathbb{N}$ is inductive and, by definition, it is contained in every other inductive set.

We define the set of *integers*, denoted by $\mathbb{Z}$, to be the set of numbers consisting of the natural numbers, their negatives, and the number 0. The set of *rational numbers*, denoted by $\mathbb{Q}$, is defined to be the set of quotients of integers. Now it is a little tedious, but not really difficult, to prove that the set of rational numbers satisfies the Field Axioms and the Positivity Axioms. However, it is not possible to develop calculus using only rational numbers. For instance, it will be necessary to conclude that a polynomial that attains both positive and negative values must also attain the value 0. This is not true if one considers only rational numbers. For example, consider the polynomial defined by $p(x) = x^2 - 2$ for all real numbers x. Then $p(0) < 0$ and $p(2) > 0$. However, as has been known since antiquity, there is no rational number x having the property that $x^2 = 2$; that is, there is no rational number x such that $p(x) = 0$. Before giving the classical proof of this assertion, we first note the following two properties of the integers:

- Each rational number z may be expressed as $z = m/n$, where m and n are integers and either m or n is odd.

- If q is an integer and q^2 is even, then q is even.

The proofs of these properties are outlined in Exercises 23 and 24 of Section 1.3.

PROPOSITION 1.1

There is no rational number whose square equals 2.

Proof   We will suppose that the proposition is false and derive a contradiction. Suppose there is a rational number x such that $x^2 = 2$. We may express x as $x = m/n$, where m and n are integers and either m or n is odd. Since $m^2/n^2 = 2$, we have $m^2 = 2n^2$. Thus m^2 is even, so m is also even. We now express m as $m = 2k$ where k is an integer. Since $m^2 = 2n^2$, we have $4k^2 = 2n^2$. Thus n^2 is even, so n is also even. Hence both m and n are even. But we initially chose these integers so that at least one of them was odd.

The assumption that the proposition is false has led to a contradiction, so the proposition must be true.   ∎

Thus there is no rational number x such that $x^2 = 2$, and hence it is not possible to prove even the simplest geometric result concerning the intersection of the graph of a polynomial and the x-axis (that is, points where $x^2 - 2 = 0$) if we restrict ourselves to rational numbers. Worse yet, even the Pythagorean Theorem fails if we restrict ourselves to rational numbers: If r is the length of the hypotenuse of a right-angled triangle whose other two sides have length 1, then $r^2 = 2$, and so the length of the hypotenuse is not a rational number.

We need an additional axiom for the real numbers that at the very least assures us that there are real numbers whose square equals 2. The final axiom will be the Completeness Axiom. In order to state this axiom, we first need the following.

DEFINITION   *A nonempty set S of real numbers is said to be bounded above provided that there is a number c having the property that*

$$x \le c \quad \text{for all } x \text{ in } S.$$

Such a number c is called an upper bound for S.

It is clear that if a number c is an upper bound for a set S, then every number greater than c is also an upper bound for this set. For a nonempty set S of numbers that is bounded above, among all of the upper bounds for S it is not at all obvious why there should be a smallest, or least, upper bound. In fact, the assertion that there is such a least upper bound will be the final axiom for the real numbers.

The Completeness Axiom

Suppose that S is a nonempty set of real numbers that is bounded above. Then among the set of upper bounds for S there is a smallest, or least, upper bound.

For a nonempty set S of real numbers that is bounded above, the *least upper bound* of S, the existence of which is asserted by the Completeness Axiom, will be denoted by l.u.b. S. Sometimes the least upper bound of S is also called the *supremum* of S and is denoted by sup S.

It is worthwhile to note explicitly that if the number b is an upper bound for the set S, then in order to verify that $b = $ l.u.b. S it is necessary to show that b is less than any other upper bound for S. This task, however, is equivalent to showing that each number smaller than b is not an upper bound for S. This observation will be used frequently, so we will record it here as the following.

PROPOSITION 1.2   Suppose that S is a nonempty set of real numbers that is bounded above, and that the number b is an upper bound for S. Then the following three assertions are equivalent:

(i) $b = $ l.u.b. S.

(ii) If d is any upper bound for the set S, then $b \le d$.

(iii) If a is any number less than b, then a is not an upper bound for S, so there is a number x in S such that $a < x \le b$.

At first glance, it is not at all apparent that the Completeness Axiom will help our development of analysis. Perhaps the best way to illustrate the role to be played by this final axiom is to prove that with the Completeness Axiom there is necessarily a real number x such that $x^2 = 2$, and so, in particular, there are real numbers that are not rational. Such numbers are called *irrational*.

In preparation for the proof of the next proposition, it is useful to observe that from the difference of squares formula, $a^2 - b^2 = (a - b)(a + b)$, it follows that for any two nonnegative numbers a and b, $a \leq b$ if and only if $a^2 \leq b^2$.

PROPOSITION 1.3

Let c be a positive number. Then there is a positive number whose square is c.

Proof

Define $S = \{x \text{ in } \mathbb{R} \mid x > 0 \text{ and } x^2 < c\}$. First, observe that the set S is nonempty: If $c > 1$, then the number 1 is in S, whereas if $c \leq 1$, then the number $c/2$ is in S. Second, observe that the set S is bounded above: If the number x is in S, then x and $c + 1$ are positive numbers such that $x^2 < c < (c + 1)^2$, so $x < c + 1$. Thus the number $c + 1$ is an upper bound for S.

By the Completeness Axiom, the set S has a least upper bound. We define

$$b = \text{l.u.b. } S,$$

and note that b is positive. The Positivity Axiom P2 implies that either $b^2 < c$, $b^2 > c$, or $b^2 = c$. We will argue by contradiction to show that the first two possibilities do not occur and therefore $b^2 = c$.

First suppose that $b^2 < c$. We will choose a suitably small positive number r such that $(b + r)^2$ is also less than c. Thus the number $b + r$, which is larger than b, belongs to S, contradicting the choice of b as an upper bound for S. Hence it cannot be the case that $b^2 < c$. To see how to choose such a number r, observe that if r is any positive number less than 1,

$$
\begin{aligned}
(b + r)^2 &= b^2 + 2rb + r^2 \\
&< b^2 + r(2b + 1) \\
&= c - (c - b^2) + r(2b + 1).
\end{aligned}
$$

Hence $(b + r)^2 < c$ if r is any positive number that is smaller than 1 and also smaller than $(c - b^2)/(2b + 1)$.

Now suppose that $b^2 > c$. We will choose a suitably small positive number t less than b such that $(b - t)^2$ is also greater than c. Hence $(b - t)^2 > x^2$ for all x in S, and so, because $b - t$ is positive, it follows that $(b - t) > x$ for all x in S. This means that the number $b - t$ is an upper bound for S, contradicting the choice of b as the least upper bound for S. Thus it cannot be the case that $b^2 > c$. To see how to choose such a number t, observe that if t is any positive number, then

$$
\begin{aligned}
(b - t)^2 &= b^2 - 2tb + t^2 \\
&= c + (b^2 - c) - 2tb + t^2 \\
&> c + (b^2 - c) - 2tb.
\end{aligned}
$$

Thus it suffices to choose for t any positive number that is smaller than b and is also smaller than $(b^2 - c)/2b$.

We have shown that it is not possible that $b^2 < c$ or that $b^2 > c$. We therefore conclude that $b^2 = c$.   ■

We will see in Chapter 3 that, in fact, the above proposition is a corollary of a much more general result, called the Intermediate Value Theorem.

For a positive number c, there is only one positive number whose square equals c. To see why this is so, just observe that if a and b are positive numbers each of whose square is c, then $0 = a^2 - b^2 = (a - b)(a + b)$. Since $a + b > 0$, it follows that $a = b$. As usual, we denote the positive number whose square is c by $\sqrt{c}$. We define $\sqrt{0} \equiv 0$.

DEFINITION   *A nonempty set S of real numbers is said to be bounded below provided that there is a number b having the property that*

$$b \leq x \quad \text{for all } x \text{ in } S.$$

Such a number b is called a lower bound for S.

It is clear that if a number b is a lower bound for a set S, then every number less than b is also a lower bound for S. We will now use the Completeness Axiom to show that for a nonempty set of numbers S that is bounded below, among the lower bounds for the set there is a *greatest lower bound*, which is denoted by g.l.b. S. Sometimes the greatest lower bound of S is called the *infimum* of S and is denoted by inf S.

THEOREM 1.4   Suppose that S is a nonempty set of real numbers that is bounded below. Then among the set of lower bounds for S there is a largest, or greatest, lower bound.

Proof   We will consider the set obtained by "reflecting" the set S about the number 0; that is, we will consider the set $T = \{x \text{ in } \mathbb{R} \mid -x \text{ in } S\}$.

For any number x, $b \leq x$ if and only if $-x \leq -b$. Thus a number b is a lower bound for S if and only if the number $-b$ is an upper bound for T. Since the set S has been assumed to be bounded below, it follows that the set T is bounded above. The Completeness Axiom asserts that there is a least upper bound for T, which we will denote by c. Since lower bounds of S occur as negatives of upper bounds for T, the number $-c$ is the greatest lower bound for S. ■

The following result will play an important part in our development of integration.

THEOREM 1.5   **The Dedekind Gap Theorem**   Suppose that S and T are nonempty sets of real numbers having the property that

$$s \leq t \quad \text{for all } s \text{ in } S \text{ and } t \text{ in } T. \tag{1.1}$$

Then
$$\sup S \leq \inf T. \tag{1.2}$$

Moreover, the following three assertions are equivalent:

(i) There is exactly one real number c having the property that

$$s \leq c \leq t \quad \text{for all } s \text{ in } S \text{ and } t \text{ in } T.$$

(ii) $\sup S = \inf T$.

(iii) For each positive number ϵ, there are numbers s in S and t in T such that $t - s < \epsilon$.

Proof   From (1.1) it follows that every member of T is an upper bound for the set S. Since the number sup S is the smallest upper bound for the set S, we have sup $S \leq t$ for all t in T. Thus the number sup S is a lower bound for the set T. Being a lower bound, it is less than or equal to the greatest lower bound; that is, the inequality (1.2) holds.

We leave the proof of the equivalence of (i) and (ii) as an exercise; we will prove the equivalence of (ii) and (iii).

Suppose that (ii) holds. Let ϵ be any positive number. Since sup S is the smallest upper bound for S, the number sup $S - \epsilon/2$ is not an upper bound for S. Thus there is a number s in S such that $s > \sup S - \epsilon/2$. Similarly, since inf T is the largest lower bound for T, the number inf $T + \epsilon/2$ is not a lower bound for T. Thus there is a number t in T such that $t < \inf T + \epsilon/2$. Hence

$$t - s < (\inf T + \epsilon/2) - (\sup S - \epsilon/2) = \epsilon.$$

This proves assertion (iii).

Finally, we prove that (iii) implies (ii). Suppose that (iii) holds. Let ϵ be any positive number. Then we can choose numbers s in S and t in T such that $t - s < \epsilon$. But then

$$0 \leq \inf T - \sup S \leq t - s < \epsilon.$$

It follows that sup $S = \inf T$, for otherwise, by choosing $\epsilon = (\inf T - \sup S)/2$, we contradict the preceding inequality. This proves assertion (ii). ∎

EXERCISES

1.   Let A be a set of real numbers that is bounded above, and let B be a nonempty subset of A. Prove that sup $A \geq \sup B$. (*Hint:* Define $a = \sup A$ and show that a is an upper bound for B.)

2.   Suppose that A is a nonempty set of real numbers that is both bounded above and bounded below, and that inf $A = \sup A$. Prove that the set A consists of exactly one number.

3.   For a positive number c, show that if x is any number such that $x^2 = c$, then either $x = \sqrt{c}$ or $x = -\sqrt{c}$.

4.   Prove that the sum of rational numbers is rational. Also prove that the sum of a rational and an irrational number must be irrational.

5.   For a set A of numbers, a member c of A is called the *maximum* of A provided that it is an upper bound for A. Prove that a set A of numbers has a maximum if and only if it is bounded above and sup A belongs to A. Give an example of a set A of numbers that is nonempty and bounded above but has no maximum.

6.   Prove that $\sqrt{3}$ is not a rational number. (*Hint:* Follow the idea of the proof of Proposition 1.1.)

7. Let a, b, and c be real numbers such that $a \neq 0$, and consider the quadratic equation

$$ax^2 + bx + c = 0.$$

Prove that a number x is a solution of this equation if and only if

$$(2ax + b)^2 = b^2 - 4ac.$$

Suppose that $b^2 - 4ac > 0$. Prove that the quadratic equation has exactly two solutions, given by

$$x = \frac{-b + \sqrt{b^2 - 4ac}}{2a} \quad \text{and} \quad x = \frac{-b - \sqrt{b^2 - 4ac}}{2a}.$$

8. In the preceding exercise, now suppose that $b^2 - 4ac < 0$. Prove that there are no real numbers that are solutions of the quadratic equation.

9. Define $S = \{x \text{ in } \mathbb{R} \mid x^2 < x\}$. Prove that $\sup S = 1$.

10. Prove that there is a positive number x such that $x^3 = 3$. (*Hint:* Follow the proof of Proposition 1.3.)

1.2   The Archimedean Property and the Density of the Rationals and the Irrationals

We will devote this section to a more precise description of the way the natural numbers, the rational numbers, and the irrational numbers are situated in the set of real numbers. By its very definition, the set $\mathbb{N}$ of natural numbers is inductive and is contained in every other inductive set. Thus:

If A is a set of natural numbers that is inductive, then $A = \mathbb{N}$.   (1.3)

Some elementary properties of the natural numbers follow immediately from this observation. For instance, if n is a natural number, then $n \geq 1$; this follows from (1.3) if we observe that since the number 1 is greater than the number 0, the set $A = \{n \text{ in } \mathbb{N} \mid n \geq 1\}$ is an inductive subset of $\mathbb{N}$, and hence is equal to $\mathbb{N}$. Also, the interval $(1, 2)$ contains no natural numbers; this also follows from (1.3) if we observe that the set $\{1\} \cup \{n \text{ in } \mathbb{N} \mid n \geq 2\}$ is an inductive subset of $\mathbb{N}$, and hence is equal to $\mathbb{N}$.

Arguments that are based on the above property (1.3) occur so frequently that it is useful to formalize them as follows.

Principle of Mathematical Induction

For each natural number n, let S(n) be some mathematical assertion. Suppose that S(1) is true. Also suppose that whenever k is a natural number such that S(k) is true, then S(k + 1) is also true. Then S(n) is true for every natural number n.

Proof Define $A = \{k$ in $\mathbb{N} \mid S(k)$ is true$\}$. The assumptions mean precisely that A is an inductive subset of $\mathbb{N}$. According to (1.3), $A = \mathbb{N}$. Thus $S(n)$ is true for every natural number n. ∎

For a set A of numbers, a member of A that is a lower bound for A is called the *minimum* of A, and a member of A that is an upper bound for A is called the *maximum* of A. It is important to distinguish between *minimum* and *infimum*, and between *maximum* and *supremum*. The Completeness Axiom asserts that a nonempty set A of real numbers that is bounded above always has a supremum. However, in general, the number sup A need not be a member of A, so A need not have a maximum. For instance, the interval $(0, 1)$ has no maximum, since its supremum lies outside of the interval. Similarly, although Theorem 1.4 asserts that each nonempty set of real numbers that is bounded below has an infimum, such a set need not have a minimum. However, for sets of natural numbers we can say more. In fact, every nonempty set of natural numbers has a minimum, and every nonempty set of natural numbers that is bounded above has a maximum. In order to verify these two assertions, it is useful first to prove the following.

LEMMA 1.6 Suppose that n is a natural number. Then the interval $(n, n + 1)$ contains no natural numbers.

Proof We will prove this by induction. Let the assertion of the lemma be the inductive statement $S(n)$. We have already observed that $S(1)$ is true. Now suppose that k is a natural number such that $S(k)$ is true. Then we claim that $S(k + 1)$ must also be true. Indeed, if $S(k + 1)$ is not true, then there is a natural number m such that $k + 1 < m < k + 2$, in which case $m - 1$ is a natural number (see Exercise 9) with $k < m - 1 < k + 1$, which contradicts the inductive hypothesis $S(k)$. Thus $S(k + 1)$ is true. By the Principle of Mathematical Induction, $S(n)$ is true for every natural number n. ∎

For a natural number n, it will be convenient to denote by $\{1, \ldots, n\}$ the set of natural numbers k such that $1 \le k \le n$.

PROPOSITION 1.7 Let n be a natural number and let $A \subseteq \{1, \ldots, n\}$ be nonempty. Then the set A has a minimum and a maximum.

Proof We will also prove this by induction. Let the assertion of the proposition be the inductive statement $S(n)$. If $n = 1$, then $A = \{1\}$, so the number 1 is both a minimum and a maximum for the set A. Thus $S(1)$ is true.

Now let k be a natural number such that $S(k)$ is true; that is, suppose that every nonempty subset of $\{1, \ldots, k\}$ has a minimum and a maximum. To prove $S(k + 1)$, we select a nonempty subset A of, $\{1, \ldots, k + 1\}$, and show that it has a maximum and a minimum. First we will show that A has a maximum. If $k + 1$ belongs to A, then $k + 1$ is the maximum of A. If $k + 1$ does not belong to A, then, by Lemma 1.6, $A \subseteq \{1, \ldots, k\}$, so by the inductive assumption, the set A has a maximum. Now we need to show that A has a minimum. If the set $A \cap \{1, \ldots, k\}$ is empty, then, again using Lemma 1.6, we conclude that $A = \{k + 1\}$, so $k + 1$ is its minimum. Otherwise, the set $A \cap \{1, \ldots, k\}$ is nonempty, so by the inductive assumption, $A \cap \{1, \ldots, k\}$ has a minimum, and this minimum is also a minimum for A. Thus $S(k+1)$ is true. By the Principle of Mathematical Induction, $S(n)$ is true for every natural number n. ∎

PROPOSITION 1.8   Every nonempty set of natural numbers has a minimum.

Proof   Let A be a nonempty set of natural numbers. Since the set A is nonempty, we may select a number n in A. Then the set $A \cap \{1, \ldots, n\}$ is a nonempty subset of $\{1, \ldots, n\}$, and so, according to Proposition 1.7, it has a minimum. This minimum for $A \cap \{1, \ldots, n\}$ is also a minimum for A. ∎

Of course, it is not the case that each nonempty set of natural numbers has a maximum. For example, the set $\mathbb{N}$ itself does not have a maximum, since if n is any natural number, then $n+1$ is a natural number that is greater than n. Moreover, the set $\mathbb{N}$ of natural numbers is not bounded above. It is rather surprising that in order to prove this we will need to use the Completeness Axiom.

THEOREM 1.9   **The Archimedean Property**   For any number c, there is a natural number n that is greater than c.

Proof   We will suppose that the theorem is false and derive a contradiction. Suppose that there is no natural number that is greater than c. Then, using the Positivity Axiom P2, we conclude that

$$n \le c \quad \text{for every natural number } n.$$

Thus the set $\mathbb{N}$ of natural numbers is bounded above. The Completeness Axiom asserts that $\mathbb{N}$ has a least upper bound. Denote the least upper bound of $\mathbb{N}$ by b.

Since b is the smallest upper bound for $\mathbb{N}$, the number $b - 1/2$ is not an upper bound for $\mathbb{N}$. Thus we can choose a positive integer n that is greater than $b - 1/2$. But then $n + 1 > (b - 1/2) + 1 > b$, so $n + 1$ is a natural number that is larger than b. This contradicts the choice of b as an upper bound for $\mathbb{N}$. This contradiction proves the result. ∎

The Archimedean Property is often stated as follows: For each pair of positive numbers a and b, there is a natural number n such that $na > b$. This is clearly equivalent to the above formulation.

COROLLARY 1.10   For each positive number ϵ, there is a natural number n such that $1/n < \epsilon$.

Proof   Let ϵ be a positive number. Then the number $1/\epsilon$ is also positive. By the Archimedean Property, there is a natural number n such that $n > 1/\epsilon$, which means that $1/n < \epsilon$. ∎

We conclude this section with a theorem about the distribution in $\mathbb{R}$ of the rational numbers and the irrational numbers.

DEFINITION   *A set S of real numbers is said to be dense in* $\mathbb{R}$ *provided that every interval* $I = (a, b)$, *where* $a < b$, *contains a member of S.*

THEOREM 1.11   The set of rational numbers and the set of irrational numbers are *both* dense in $\mathbb{R}$.

Proof   Let a and b be real numbers such that $a < b$. We need to show that the interval (a, b) contains both a rational and an irrational number. We will consider only the case when $0 \le a < b$, because the other cases follow easily from this one.

First we will show that the interval (a, b) contains a rational number. According to Corollary 1.10, we can choose a natural number m such that $1/m$ is less than the length of the interval; that is, $1/m < b - a$. Again using the Archimedean Property, we can choose another natural number n such that $n/m > b$.

Define A to be the set of natural numbers k such that $k/m < b$. Since $1/m < b - a < b$, the number 1 belongs to the set A. Thus A is nonempty. The natural number n was chosen such that $n/m > b$, so every member of A is less than n. Proposition 1.7 asserts that the set A has a maximum. Denote the maximum by j. We will show that the rational number j/m is in the interval (a, b).

Since j is in A, $j/m < b$. Thus it only remains to show that $j/m > a$. However, since j is the maximum of the set A, the integer $j + 1$ is not in A, and this means that $(j + 1)/m \ge b$. This inequality, together with the inequality $1/m < b - a$, gives us

$$\frac{j}{m} \ge b - \frac{1}{m} > b - (b - a) = a.$$

It remains to find an irrational number in the interval (a, b). Once more using Corollary 1.10, since $b - j/m > 0$, we can choose a natural number ℓ such that

$$\frac{\sqrt{2}}{\ell} < b - \frac{j}{m}.$$

Since $\sqrt{2}$ is irrational, the number

$$\frac{j}{m} + \frac{\sqrt{2}}{\ell}$$

is also irrational. (This assertion is a consequence of Exercise 4 of Section 1.1.) The natural number ℓ was chosen to be large enough to ensure that this irrational number lies in the interval (a, b). ∎

EXERCISES

1.   Verify that the sets $A = \{n \text{ in } \mathbb{N} \mid n \ge 1\}$ and $B = \{1\} \cup \{n \text{ in } \mathbb{N} \mid n \ge 2\}$ are inductive.
2.   Let A be a nonempty set of real numbers that is bounded below. Prove that the set A has a minimum if and only if the number $\inf A$ belongs to A.
3.   For each of the following two sets, find the maximum, minimum, infimum, and supremum, if they are defined: (a) $\{1/n \mid n \text{ in } \mathbb{N}\}$, (b) $\{x \text{ in } \mathbb{R} \mid x^2 < 2\}$. Justify your conclusions.
4.   Suppose that the number a has the property that for every natural number n, $a \le 1/n$. Prove that $a \le 0$.
5.   Given a real number a, define $S = \{x \mid x \text{ in } \mathbb{Q}, x < a\}$. Prove that $a = \sup S$.

6. Prove that every bounded, nonempty set of natural numbers has a maximum.
7. In the proof of Theorem 1.11, we considered only the case of an interval of the form (a, b), where $0 \leq a < b$. Use this case to prove the other cases.
8. Prove that the Archimedean Property is equivalent to Corollary 1.10.
9. Let n be a natural number greater than 1. Prove that $n - 1$ is also a natural number. (*Hint*: Prove that the set $\{n \mid n = 1 \text{ or } n \text{ in } \mathbb{N} \text{ and } n - 1 \text{ in } \mathbb{N}\}$ is inductive.)

1.3   Three Inequalities and Three Algebraic Identities

At the heart of many arguments in analysis lies the problem of estimating the sizes of various quotients, differences, and sums. In order to do so, it is useful to have available a small storehouse of inequalities and algebraic identities. In this section, we will derive three useful inequalities and three useful algebraic identities that will be used frequently throughout this book.

Recall that for a real number x, its *absolute value*, denoted by $|x|$, is defined by

$$|x| = \begin{cases} x & \text{if } x \geq 0 \\ -x & \text{if } x < 0. \end{cases}$$

Directly from this definition and from the Positivity Axioms for $\mathbb{R}$, it follows that if c and d are any numbers such that d is nonnegative, then

$$|c| \leq d \quad \text{if and only if} \quad -d \leq c \leq d. \tag{1.4}$$

Given a pair of real numbers a and b, we will often need to estimate the size of $|a + b|$. The following important inequality provides estimates, from above and from below, for the size of the absolute value of the sum of two numbers.

THEOREM 1.12   For any pair of numbers a and b,

$$|a| - |b| \leq |a + b| \leq |a| + |b|. \tag{1.5}$$

Proof   We will first prove the right-hand inequality, $|a + b| \leq |a| + |b|$. Using (1.4), we see that this is equivalent to the assertion that

$$-|a| - |b| \leq a + b \leq |a| + |b|.$$

In fact, it follows from (1.4) that

$$-|x| \leq x \leq |x| \quad \text{for all real numbers } x.$$

This is sufficient to prove the preceding inequality.

Now the left-hand inequality in (1.5) is a consequence of the right-hand inequality in (1.5). Indeed,

$$|a| = |(a + b) + (-b)| \leq |a + b| + |b|,$$

since we have just shown that the absolute value of the sum is less than or equal to the sum of the absolute values. Thus, $|a| - |b| \leq |a + b|$.   ∎

For later reference, we name each of the inequalities in (1.5).

The Triangle Inequality

For any two numbers a and b,

$$|a + b| \leq |a| + |b|.$$

The Reverse Triangle Inequality

For any two numbers a and b,

$$|a + b| \geq |a| - |b|.$$

For any two numbers x and y, we define the *distance* between x and y to be $|x - y|$. We explicitly record the following three properties of distance, the first two of which follow directly from the definition of absolute value, and the last of which follows from the Triangle Inequality if we set $a = x - z$ and $b = z - y$.

PROPOSITION For any numbers x, y, and z,
1.13

$$|x - y| = |y - x|,$$

$$|x - y| \geq 0, \quad \text{and} \quad |x - y| = 0 \quad \text{if and only if} \quad x = y,$$

and

$$|x - y| \leq |x - z| + |z - y|.$$

In the geometric language of distance between points, given a number a and a positive number r, the set of numbers x such that $|x - a| < r$ consists of all the numbers whose distance from a is less than r. From (1.4) we see that this set consists exactly of the interval $(a - r, a + r)$.

For a natural number n and any number a, as usual, we write a^n to denote the product of a multiplied by itself n times. We will need a number of inequalities and algebraic identities involving such powers. We begin with the following important inequality.

Bernoulli's Inequality

For each natural number n and each number a such that $a \geq -1$,

$$(1 + a)^n \geq 1 + na.$$

Proof We will give an inductive proof of this inequality. Fix $a \geq -1$. For each natural number n, let $S(n)$ be the assertion of the above inequality. Then $S(1)$ is clearly true. Now let k be a natural number such that $S(k)$ is true; that is, $(1+a)^k \geq 1 + ka$. We need to show that $S(k+1)$ is true. However,

$$(1+a)^{k+1} = (1+a)^k(1+a) \geq (1+ka)(1+a),$$

since $a + 1 \geq 0$ and $S(k)$ is true. Hence, since

$$(1+ka)(1+a) = 1 + (k+1)a + ka^2 \geq 1 + (k+1)a,$$

we see that $S(k+1)$ is true. By the Principle of Mathematical Induction, $S(n)$ is true for every natural number n. ∎

A simple algebraic identity that we will find very useful is the following.

Difference of Powers Formula

For any natural number n and any numbers a and b,

$$a^n - b^n = (a-b)(a^{n-1} + a^{n-2}b + \cdots + ab^{n-2} + b^{n-1}).$$

It is easy to verify this formula, just by expanding the right-hand side. Indeed,

$$(a-b)(a^{n-1} + a^{n-2}b + \cdots + ab^{n-2} + b^{n-1})$$
$$= a^n + a^{n-1}b + a^{n-2}b^2 + \cdots + a^2b^{n-2} + ab^{n-1}$$
$$\quad - a^{n-1}b - a^{n-2}b^2 - \cdots - a^2b^{n-2} - ab^{n-1} - b^n$$
$$= a^n - b^n.$$

The special case of the Difference of Powers Formula that arises when we set $a = 1$ and $b = r$ becomes, upon rewriting, the following.

Geometric Sum Formula

For any natural number n and any number $r \neq 1$,

$$1 + r + r^2 + \cdots + r^{n-1} = \frac{1 - r^n}{1 - r}.$$

It will be useful to have a formula that expresses powers of the sum of the numbers a and b in terms of the powers of a and of b. In order to state this formula, we need to introduce factorial notation. For each natural number n we define the *factorial* of n, denoted by $n!$, as follows: We define $1! \equiv 1$, and if k is any natural number for which $k!$ has been defined, we then define $(k+1)! \equiv (k+1)k!$. By the Principle of Mathematical Induction, the symbol $n!$ is defined for all natural numbers n. It is convenient to define $0! \equiv 1$. We also need to introduce, for each pair of nonnegative integers n and k such that $n \geq k$, the *binomial coefficient* $\binom{n}{k}$, which is defined by the formula

$$\binom{n}{k} \equiv \frac{n!}{k!(n-k)!}.$$

We have the following formula for $(a+b)^n$, a proof of which is outlined in Exercises 18 and 19.

The Binomial Formula

For each natural number n and each pair of numbers a and b,

$$(a+b)^n = \binom{n}{0}a^n + \binom{n}{1}a^{n-1}b + \binom{n}{2}a^{n-2}b^2 + \cdots + \binom{n}{n-1}ab^{n-1} + \binom{n}{n}b^n.$$

Let us close this chapter by recalling the summation notation. For a natural number n and numbers $a_0, a_1, \ldots, a_n$, we define

$$\sum_{k=0}^{n} a_k \equiv a_0 + a_1 + \cdots + a_n.$$

This notation condenses many formulas. For example, in this summation notation, the three algebraic formulas we have described become:

The Difference of Powers Formula

$$a^n - b^n = (a-b)\sum_{k=0}^{n-1} a^{n-1-k}b^k.$$

The Geometric Sum Formula

$$\sum_{k=0}^{n-1} r^k = \frac{1-r^n}{1-r} \quad if\, r \neq 1.$$

The Binomial Formula

$$(a+b)^n = \sum_{k=0}^{n} \binom{n}{k}a^{n-k}b^k.$$

EXERCISES

1. Let a be a positive number. Prove that if x is a number such that $|x - a| < a/2$, then $x > a/2$.
2. Let a and b be numbers such that $|a - b| \leq 1$. Prove that $|a| \leq |b| + 1$.
3. Let $a, b, c,$ and d be numbers such that $|c| \neq |d|$. Prove that
$$\left|\frac{a+b}{c+d}\right| \leq \frac{|a| + |b|}{||c| - |d||}.$$
4. For a natural number n and any two nonnegative numbers a and b, use the Difference of Powers Formula to prove that
$$a \leq b \quad \text{if and only if} \quad a^n \leq b^n.$$
5. In the case when $a \geq 0$, show that Bernoulli's Inequality is a consequence of the Binomial Formula.
6. Write out the Difference of Powers Formula explicitly for $n = 2, 3,$ and 4.

7. Write out the Binomial Formula explicitly for $n = 2, 3$, and 4.

8. For a natural number n and numbers a and b such that $a \geq b \geq 0$, prove that

$$a^n - b^n \geq nb^{n-1}(a - b).$$

9. Using the fact that the square of a real number is nonnegative, prove Cauchy's Inequality: For any numbers a and b,

$$ab \leq \frac{1}{2}(a^2 + b^2).$$

Use Cauchy's Inequality to prove that if $a \geq 0$ and $b \geq 0$, then

$$\sqrt{ab} \leq \frac{1}{2}(a + b).$$

10. Let $a, b,$ and c be nonnegative numbers. Prove the following inequalities:

(a) $ab + bc + ca \leq a^2 + b^2 + c^2.$

(b) $8abc \leq (a + b)(b + c)(c + a).$

(c) $abc(a + b + c) \leq a^2b^2 + b^2c^2 + c^2a^2.$

11. (a)   For numbers $a, b,$ and c, prove that

$$1 + a + b + c \geq 1 - |a| - |b| - |c|.$$

(b)   For any numbers $c_0, c_1,$ and c_2, consider the polynomial defined by

$$p(x) = x^3 + c_2x^2 + c_1x + c_0 \quad \text{for all } x.$$

Prove that there is a positive number r such that

$$p(x) > 0 \quad \text{for all } x \geq r.$$

(*Hint:* Factor out x^3 and use part (a).)

12. A function $f: \mathbb{R} \to \mathbb{R}$ is called *strictly increasing* provided that $f(u) > f(v)$ for all numbers u and v such that $u > v$.

(a)   Define $p(x) = x^3$ for all x. Prove that the polynomial $p: \mathbb{R} \to \mathbb{R}$ is strictly increasing.

(b)   Fix a number c and define $q(x) = x^3 + cx$ for all x. Prove that the polynomial $q: \mathbb{R} \to \mathbb{R}$ is strictly increasing if and only if $c \geq 0$. (*Hint:* For $c < 0$, consider the graph to understand why it is not strictly increasing, and then prove it is not increasing.)

13. Let n be a natural number and $a_1, a_2, \cdots, a_n$ be positive numbers. Prove that

$$(1 + a_1)(1 + a_2) \cdots (1 + a_n) \geq 1 + a_1 + a_2 + \cdots + a_n$$

and that

$$(a_1 + a_2 + \cdots + a_n)\left(a_1^{-1} + a_2^{-1} + \cdots + a_n^{-1}\right) \geq n^2.$$

14. Rewrite the Geometric Sum Formula and replace n with $n + 1$ to show that for every natural number n,

$$\frac{1}{1-r} = 1 + r + \cdots + r^n + \frac{r^{n+1}}{1+r} \quad \text{if} \quad r \neq 1.$$

(a)   Use the above formula to find a formula for

$$\frac{1}{1+x^2} + \frac{1}{(1+x^2)^2} + \cdots + \frac{1}{(1+x^2)^n}.$$

(b)   Also, show that if $a \neq 0$, then

$$\frac{1}{a} = 1 + (1-a) + (1-a)^2 + \frac{(1-a)^3}{a}.$$

15. Use the Principle of Mathematical Induction to prove the following equalities for each natural number n:

(a) $\displaystyle\sum_{k=1}^{n} k = \frac{n(n+1)}{2}.$

(b) $\displaystyle\sum_{k=1}^{n} k^2 = \frac{n(n+1)(2n+1)}{6}.$

16. Let n be a natural number. Find a formula for $\sum_{k=1}^{n} k(k+1)$.

17. Let n be a natural number. Prove that

$$1^3 + 2^3 + \cdots + n^3 = (1 + 2 + \cdots + n)^2.$$

18. Prove that if n and k are natural numbers such that $k \leq n$, then

$$\binom{n+1}{k} = \binom{n}{k-1} + \binom{n}{k}.$$

19. Use the formula in the preceding exercise to provide an inductive proof of the Binomial Formula.

20. Prove that if n is a natural number greater than 1, then $n - 1$ is also a natural number. (*Hint:* Prove that the set $\{n \mid n = 1 \text{ or } n \text{ in } \mathbb{N} \text{ and } n - 1 \text{ in } \mathbb{N}\}$ is inductive.)

21. Prove that if n and m are natural numbers such that $n > m$, then $n - m$ is also a natural number. (*Hint:* Prove this by induction on m, making use of the preceding exercise.)

22. Let a be a nonzero number and m and n be integers. Prove the following equalities:

(a) $a^{m+n} = a^m a^n$

(b) $(ab)^n = a^n b^n$

23. A natural number n is called *even* if it can be written as $n = 2k$ for some other natural number k, and is called *odd* if either $n = 1$ or $n = 2k + 1$ for some other natural number k.

(a)   Prove that each natural number n is either odd or even.

(b)   Prove that if m is a natural number, then $2m > 1$.

(c)   Prove that a natural number n cannot be both odd and even. (*Hint:* Recall that if n and m are natural numbers such that $m > n$, then $m - n$ is also a natural number.)

(d) Suppose that $k_1, k_2, \ell_1,$ and ℓ_2 are natural numbers such that ℓ_1 and ℓ_2 are odd. Prove that if $2^{k_1}\ell_1 = 2^{k_2}\ell_2$, then $k_1 = k_2$ and $\ell_1 = \ell_2$.

24. (a) Prove that if n is a natural number, then $2^n > n$.
    (b) Prove that if n is a natural number, then

$$n = 2^{k_0}\ell_0$$

for some odd natural number ℓ_0 and some nonnegative integer k_0. (*Hint:* If n is odd, let $k = 0$ and $\ell = n$; if n is even, let $A = \{k$ in $\mathbb{N} \mid n = 2^k\ell$ for some ℓ in $\mathbb{N}.\}$ By (a), $A \subseteq \{1, 2, \ldots, n\}$. Choose k_0 to be the maximum of A.)

25. Prove that the preceding two exercises are sufficient to prove the assertions that preceded the proof of the irrationality of $\sqrt{2}$.

26. A real number of the form $m/2^n$ where m and n are integers, is called a *dyadic rational.* Prove that the set of dyadic rationals is dense in $\mathbb{R}$.

Sequences of Real Numbers

2.1 The Convergence of Sequences

Two of the central topics in the analysis of real-valued functions of a real variable are the differentiation and integration of functions that have as their domain an interval of real numbers. Sequences of real numbers are also important and, in fact, properties of general functions can be deduced from an understanding of sequences. Accordingly, in this chapter we will study sequences of real numbers, and in Chapter 3 we will turn to the study of general functions.

DEFINITION   *A sequence of real numbers is a real-valued function whose domain is the set of natural numbers.*

Since in the first nine chapters we will be considering only sequences of real numbers, we will abbreviate *sequence of real numbers* by writing *sequence*. Also, rather than denoting a sequence with standard functional notation, such as $f: \mathbb{N} \to \mathbb{R}$, it is customary to use subscripts, replacing $f(n)$ with a_n, and denoting a sequence by $\{a_n\}$. A natural number n is called an *index* for the sequence, and the number a_n associated with the index n is called the nth *term* of the sequence.

Often sequences are defined by presenting an explicit formula. Thus, for example, $\{1/n\}$ denotes the sequence that has, for each index n, an nth term equal to $1/n$. The sequence $\{1 + (-1)^n\}$ has, for each index n, an nth term equal to $1 + (-1)^n$, so the nth term of this sequence equals 0 if the index n is odd, and equals 2 if the index n is even.

Frequently sequences are defined in a less explicit manner, as in the following example.

EXAMPLE 2.1   For each natural number n, define a_n to be the largest natural number that is less than or equal to $\sqrt{n^3}$. Proposition 1.7 of Chapter 1 implies that every bounded nonempty set of natural numbers has a maximum, so that for each natural number n there is a largest natural number that is less than or equal to $\sqrt{n^3}$. Thus the sequence $\{a_n\}$ is properly defined. We leave it as an exercise for the reader to find the first four terms of this sequence.   □

We now give an example of a sequence $\{a_n\}$ that is defined recursively; that is, the sequence is defined by defining the first term a_1, then defining a_{n+1} whenever n is a natural number such that the nth term a_n is defined. By the Principle of Mathematical Induction, the nth term a_n is defined for every natural number n, and thus the sequence $\{a_n\}$ is properly defined.

EXAMPLE 2.2   Define $a_1 = 1$. If n is a natural number such that a_n has been defined, then define

$$a_{n+1} = \begin{cases} a_n + 1/n & \text{if } a_n^2 \le 2 \\ a_n - 1/n & \text{if } a_n^2 > 2. \end{cases}$$

This formula defines the sequence recursively. We leave it as an exercise for the reader to find the first four terms of this sequence.   □

EXAMPLE 2.3   Let r be any number. Define the sequence $\{s_n\}$ by

$$s_n = \sum_{k=1}^{n} r^k \quad \text{for every natural number } n.$$ □

EXAMPLE 2.4   Define the sequence $\{s_n\}$ by

$$s_n = \sum_{k=1}^{n} \frac{1}{k} \quad \text{for every natural number } n.$$ □

The two preceding sequences are formed in the following manner: Given a sequence $\{c_n\}$, define a new sequence $\{s_n\}$ by the formula

$$s_n = \sum_{k=1}^{n} c_k \quad \text{for every natural number } n. \tag{2.1}$$

Sequences formed in this manner are called *infinite series*.

We will be interested in sequences $\{a_n\}$ that have the following property: "As n gets large, the a_n's approach a fixed number." We make this precise as follows.

DEFINITION   *A sequence $\{a_n\}$ is said to converge to the number a provided that for every positive number ϵ there is a natural number N such that*

$$|a_n - a| < \epsilon \quad \text{for all integers } n \geq N.$$

Now, a given sequence may or may not converge. But if a sequence does converge, it cannot converge to more than one point. Indeed, suppose the sequence $\{a_n\}$ converges to a and to a'. Observe that the Triangle Inequality implies that

$$|a - a'| \leq |a_n - a| + |a_n - a'| \quad \text{for every natural number } n. \tag{2.2}$$

Let $\epsilon > 0$. Since the sequence $\{a_n\}$ converges to a, we may choose a natural number N_1 such that $|a_n - a| < \epsilon$ for all integers $n \geq N_1$. Also, since the sequence $\{a_n\}$ converges to a', we may choose a natural number N_2 such that $|a_n - a'| < \epsilon$ for all integers $n \geq N_2$. Choose n to be a natural number greater than both N_1 and N_2. From inequality (2.2) and the choice of N_1 and N_2, it follows that

$$|a - a'| \leq |a_n - a| + |a_n - a'| < \epsilon + \epsilon = 2\epsilon.$$

Thus $a = a'$, since otherwise, by letting $\epsilon = |a - a'|/2$, we contradict the preceding inequality.

If the sequence $\{a_n\}$ converges to the number a, we call a the *limit of the sequence* $\{a_n\}$, and write

$$\lim_{n \to \infty} a_n = a.$$

PROPOSITION 2.1   The sequence $\{1/n\}$ converges to 0; that is, $\lim_{n \to \infty} 1/n = 0$.

Proof   Let $\epsilon > 0$. We need to find a natural number N such that

$$\left| \frac{1}{n} - 0 \right| < \epsilon \quad \text{for all integers } n \geq N;$$

that is, $1/n < \epsilon$ if $n \geq N$. But by the Archimedean Property of $\mathbb{R}$, we may select a natural number N such that $N > 1/\epsilon$. Thus $1/N < \epsilon$, and hence

$$\frac{1}{n} \leq \frac{1}{N} < \epsilon \quad \text{for all integers } n \geq N. \qquad \blacksquare$$

EXAMPLE 2.5   The sequence $\{(-1)^n\}$ does not converge. To see this, we argue by contradiction. Suppose that the sequence $\{(-1)^n\}$ converges to a number a. Taking $\epsilon = 1$, it follows from the definition of convergence that there is a natural number N such that

$$|(-1)^n - a| < 1 \quad \text{for all integers } n \geq N.$$

In particular, $1 - a \leq |1 - a| = |(-1)^{2N} - a| < 1$, so $a > 0$. On the other hand, we also have $1 + a \leq |1 + a| = |(-1)^{2N+1} - a| < 1$, so $a < 0$. This contradiction shows that the sequence $\{(-1)^n\}$ does not converge. $\qquad \square$

EXAMPLE 2.6   The sequence $\{2/n^2 + 4/n + 3\}$ converges to 3; that is,

$$\lim_{n\to\infty} \left[\frac{2}{n^2} + \frac{4}{n} + 3 \right] = 3.$$

In order to verify this assertion, we choose $\epsilon > 0$. Then we need to find a natural number N such that

$$\left| \frac{2}{n^2} + \frac{4}{n} + 3 - 3 \right| < \epsilon \quad \text{for all integers } n \geq N. \tag{2.3}$$

Observe that

$$\left| \frac{2}{n^2} + \frac{4}{n} + 3 - 3 \right| = \frac{2}{n^2} + \frac{4}{n} \leq \frac{6}{n} \quad \text{for every natural number } n.$$

Now, by the Archimedean Property of $\mathbb{R}$, we may select a natural number N such that $N > 6/\epsilon$. Thus $6/N < \epsilon$, and so

$$\left| \frac{2}{n^2} + \frac{4}{n} + 3 - 3 \right| \leq \frac{6}{n} \leq \frac{6}{N} < \epsilon \quad \text{for all integers } n \geq N,$$

and so (2.3) holds.   □

We will soon prove a general result, Theorem 2.5, that will allow us to analyze the previous example, and others like it, in a very simple manner.

PROPOSITION 2.2   For any number c such that $|c| < 1$, the sequence $\{c^n\}$ converges to 0; that is,

$$\lim_{n\to\infty} c^n = 0.$$

Proof   Let $\epsilon > 0$. We need to find a natural number N such that

$$|c^n - 0| < \epsilon \quad \text{for all integers } n \geq N.$$

Observe that since $0 < |c| < 1$, if we set $d = 1/|c| - 1$, it follows that $|c| = 1/(1 + d)$ and d is positive. Hence, using Bernoulli's Inequality, we obtain the inequality

$$|c|^n = \frac{1}{(1 + d)^n} \leq \frac{1}{1 + nd} \leq \frac{1}{nd} \quad \text{for every natural number } n. \tag{2.4}$$

Using the Archimedean Property of $\mathbb{R}$, we may choose a natural number N such that $N > 1/\epsilon d$. Consequently, since the numbers d and ϵ are positive, $1/Nd < \epsilon$, and hence, by inequality (2.4),

$$|c^n - 0| = |c|^n \leq \frac{1}{nd} \leq \frac{1}{Nd} < \epsilon \quad \text{for all integers } n \geq N. \quad ■$$

It is usually the case that after first examining some particular examples of a concept, we then find it useful to prove some general results. We will now prove that the sum of convergent sequences converges to the sum of the limits, the product of convergent sequences converges to the product of the limits, and, when all quotients are defined, the quotient of convergent sequences converges to the quotient of the limits. To do so, it is convenient first to introduce a definition and prove two preliminary lemmas.

DEFINITION   *A sequence $\{a_n\}$ is said to be bounded provided that there is a number M such that*

$$|a_n| \leq M \quad \text{for every natural number } n.$$

LEMMA 2.3   Every convergent sequence is bounded.

Proof   Let $\{a_n\}$ be a sequence that converges to the number a. Taking $\epsilon = 1$, it follows from the definition of convergence that we may select a natural number N such that

$$|a_n - a| < 1 \quad \text{for all integers } n \geq N.$$

Thus, using the Reverse Triangle Inequality, we have

$$|a_n| - |a| \leq |a_n - a| < 1 \quad \text{for all integers } n \geq N,$$

from which it follows that

$$|a_n| \leq 1 + |a| \quad \text{for all integers } n \geq N.$$

Define $M = \max\{1 + |a|, |a_1|, \ldots, |a_{N-1}|\}$. Then

$$|a_n| \leq M \quad \text{for every natural number } n.$$

Thus the sequence $\{a_n\}$ is bounded. ∎

LEMMA 2.4   Suppose that the sequence $\{b_n\}$ converges to the nonzero number b. Then there is a natural number N such that

$$|b_n| > \frac{|b|}{2} \quad \text{for all integers } n \geq N.$$

Proof   Since $|b|/2$ is positive, we may take $\epsilon = |b|/2$ and use the definition of convergence of a sequence to choose a natural number N such that

$$|b_n - b| < \frac{|b|}{2} \quad \text{for all integers } n \geq N.$$

Thus, using the Reverse Triangle Inequality, we have

$$|b| - |b_n| \leq |b_n - b| < \frac{|b|}{2} \quad \text{for all integers } n \geq N,$$

from which it follows that

$$|b_n| > \frac{|b|}{2.} \quad \text{for all integers } n \geq N.$$ ∎

THEOREM 2.5 Suppose that the sequence $\{a_n\}$ converges to the number a and that the sequence $\{b_n\}$ converges to the number b. Then the sequence $\{a_n + b_n\}$ converges, and

$$\text{(i)} \quad \lim_{n\to\infty} [a_n + b_n] = a + b.$$

Also, the sequence $\{a_n b_n\}$ converges, and

$$\text{(ii)} \quad \lim_{n\to\infty} [a_n b_n] = ab.$$

Moreover, if $b_n \neq 0$ for all n and $b \neq 0$, then the sequence $\{a_n/b_n\}$ converges, and

$$\text{(iii)} \quad \lim_{n\to\infty} \left[\frac{a_n}{b_n}\right] = \frac{a}{b}.$$

Proof of (i) Let $\epsilon > 0$. We need to find a natural number N such that

$$|(a_n + b_n) - (a + b)| < \epsilon \quad \text{for all integers } n \geq N.$$

In order to do so, we first observe that for every natural number n,

$$|(a_n + b_n) - (a + b)| = |(a_n - a) + (b_n - b)|,$$

and hence, by the Triangle Inequality,

$$|(a_n + b_n) - (a + b)| \leq |a_n - a| + |b_n - b|. \tag{2.5}$$

Since the sequence $\{a_n\}$ converges to a, we may choose a natural number N_1 such that

$$|a_n - a| < \frac{\epsilon}{2} \quad \text{for all integers } n \geq N_1,$$

and since the sequence $\{b_n\}$ converges to b, we may choose a natural number N_2 such that

$$|b_n - b| < \frac{\epsilon}{2} \quad \text{for all integers } n \geq N_2.$$

Define $N = \max\{N_1, N_2\}$. Then from inequality (2.5) and the choice of N_1 and N_2, it follows that if $n \geq N$, then

$$|(a_n + b_n) - (a + b)| \leq |a_n - a| + |b_n - b| < \frac{\epsilon}{2} + \frac{\epsilon}{2} = \epsilon.$$

Proof of (ii) Let $\epsilon > 0$. We need to find a natural number N such that

$$|a_n b_n - ab| < \epsilon \quad \text{for all integers } n \geq N.$$

In order to do so, we first observe that for every natural number n,

$$a_n b_n - ab = a_n b_n - a_n b + a_n b - ab = a_n(b_n - b) + b(a_n - a),$$

and hence, by the Triangle Inequality,

$$|a_n b_n - ab| \leq |a_n||b_n - b| + |b||a_n - a|. \tag{2.6}$$

Lemma 2.3 asserts that every convergent sequence is bounded. Thus we may choose a number M such that $|a_n| \leq M$ for every natural number n. This choice of M, together with inequality (2.6), implies that for every natural number n,

$$|a_n b_n - ab| \leq M|b_n - b| + |b||a_n - a|. \tag{2.7}$$

Since the sequence $\{b_n\}$ converges to b, we may choose a natural number N_1 such that

$$|b_n - b| < \frac{\epsilon}{2(M+1)} \quad \text{for all integers } n \geq N_1,$$

and since the sequence $\{a_n\}$ converges to a, we may choose a natural number N_2 such that

$$|a_n - a| < \frac{\epsilon}{2(|b|+1)} \quad \text{for all integers } n \geq N_2.$$

Let $N = \max\{N_1, N_2\}$. From inequality (2.7) and the choices of N_1 and N_2, it follows that if $n \geq N$, then

$$|a_n b_n - ab| \leq M|b_n - b| + |b||a_n - a| < \epsilon.$$

Proof of (iii)   Using (iii), it is clear that it suffices to prove that the sequence $\{1/b_n\}$ converges to $1/b$. Let $\epsilon > 0$. We need to find a natural number N such that

$$\left| \frac{1}{b_n} - \frac{1}{b} \right| < \epsilon \quad \text{for all integers } n \geq N.$$

In order to do so, first observe that for every natural number n,

$$\frac{1}{b_n} - \frac{1}{b} = \frac{b - b_n}{bb_n}.$$

According to Lemma 2.4, we can choose a natural number N, such that

$$|b_n| > \frac{|b|}{2} \quad \text{for all integers } n \geq N_1.$$

Thus,

$$\left| \frac{1}{b_n} - \frac{1}{b} \right| = \left| \frac{b - b_n}{bb_n} \right| \leq \frac{2}{|b|^2} |b_n - b| \quad \text{for all integers } n \geq N_1. \tag{2.8}$$

Since the sequence $\{b_n\}$ converges to b and the number $\epsilon |b|^2 / 2$ is positive, we can choose a natural number N_2 such that

$$|b_n - b| < \frac{\epsilon |b|^2}{2} \quad \text{for all integers } n \geq N_2. \tag{2.9}$$

Define $N = \max\{N_1, N_2\}$. From the inequalities (2.8) and (2.9), it follows that if $n \geq N$, then

$$\left| \frac{1}{b_n} - \frac{1}{b} \right| \leq \frac{2}{|b|^2} |b_n - b| < \epsilon. \qquad \blacksquare$$

For convenient reference, it is useful to name the assertions in the preceding theorem. For convergent sequences $\{a_n\}$ and $\{b_n\}$, we have:

The Sum Property

$$\lim_{n\to\infty}[a_n + b_n] = \lim_{n\to\infty} a_n + \lim_{n\to\infty} b_n.$$

The Product Property

$$\lim_{n\to\infty}[a_n b_n] = \lim_{n\to\infty} a_n \cdot \lim_{n\to\infty} b_n.$$

The Quotient Property

If $b_n \neq 0$ for all natural numbers n, and $b \neq 0$, then

$$\lim_{n\to\infty}\left[\frac{a_n}{b_n}\right] = \frac{\lim_{n\to\infty} a_n}{\lim_{n\to\infty} b_n}.$$

Furthermore, from the sum and product properties of convergent sequences we also get the following:

The Difference Property

$$\lim_{n\to\infty}[a_n - b_n] = \lim_{n\to\infty} a_n - \lim_{n\to\infty} b_n$$

and, more generally,

The Linearity Property

For any two numbers α and β,

$$\lim_{n\to\infty}[\alpha a_n + \beta b_n] = \alpha \lim_{n\to\infty} a_n + \beta \lim_{n\to\infty} b_n.$$

We have already shown that

$$\lim_{n\to\infty}\frac{1}{n} = 0, \quad \text{and that if} \quad |c| < 1, \quad \text{then} \quad \lim_{n\to\infty} c^n = 0.$$

It is clear that a constant sequence converges to its constant value. These particular sequence calculations, together with Theorem 2.5, allow us to calculate the limits of many other sequences.

EXAMPLE 2.7 The preceding remarks, together with Theorem 2.5, imply that

$$\lim_{n\to\infty}\left[\left(\frac{3}{4}\right)^n + \frac{2}{n} - 6\right] = \lim_{n\to\infty}\left[\left(\frac{3}{4}\right)^n\right] + 2\lim_{n\to\infty}\left[\frac{1}{n}\right] - \lim_{n\to\infty}[6] = -6. \quad \square$$

Theorem 2.5 describes the behavior of convergent sequences with respect to addition, multiplication, and division; that is, it relates convergence of sequences to the field properties of $\mathbb{R}$. We now turn to a description of the way in which the limit of a convergent sequence inherits order properties that are possessed by the individual terms of the sequence, in that we will show the relationship between convergence of sequences and the order properties of $\mathbb{R}$.

LEMMA 2.6   Suppose that the sequence $\{d_n\}$ converges to the number d, and that $d_n \geq 0$ for every natural number n. Then $d \geq 0$.

Proof   We will suppose that the conclusion is false and derive a contradiction. Indeed, suppose that $d < 0$. Letting $\epsilon = |d|/2$, we see that $\epsilon > 0$ and that $d + \epsilon = d/2 < 0$. Thus, the interval $(d - \epsilon, d + \epsilon)$ consists entirely of negative numbers, so no term of the sequence $\{d_n\}$ belongs to this interval. Therefore, the sequence $\{d_n\}$ cannot converge to d. This is a contradiction; thus, d must be nonnegative.   ■

The preceding lemma asserts that a convergent sequence of nonnegative numbers has a limit that is also nonnegative. It is not always true that a convergent sequence of positive numbers has a limit that is also positive. For instance, $\{1/n\}$ is a sequence of positive numbers that converges to 0.

THEOREM 2.7   Let the sequence $\{a_n\}$ converge to a, the sequence $\{b_n\}$ converge to b, and the sequence $\{c_n\}$ converge to c. Suppose that

$$a_n \leq c_n \leq b_n \quad \text{for every natural number } n.$$

Then

$$a \leq c \leq b.$$

Proof   The difference property of convergent sequences implies that the sequence $\{b_n - c_n\}$ converges to $b - c$. By assumption, $\{b_n - c_n\}$ is a sequence of nonnegative numbers. The preceding lemma implies that its limit is also nonnegative; that is, $c \leq b$. The very same argument, applied to the sequence $\{c_n - a_n\}$, shows that $a \leq c$.   ■

COROLLARY 2.8   Let a and b be real numbers such that $a < b$. Suppose that the sequence $\{c_n\}$ converges to c, and that

$$a \leq c_n \leq b \quad \text{for every natural number } n.$$

Then $a \leq c \leq b$.

Proof   Define $a_n = a$ and $b_n = b$ for every natural number n. The conclusion follows from the preceding theorem applied to the sequences $\{a_n\}$, $\{b_n\}$, and $\{c_n\}$.   ■

In the proof of the next theorem, we will use the observation that given a number ℓ and a positive number r, for any number x,

$$|x - \ell| < r \quad \text{if and only if} \quad \ell - r < x < \ell + r.$$

THEOREM 2.9   **The Squeezing Principle**   Let $\{a_n\}$, $\{b_n\}$, and $\{c_n\}$ be sequences such that

$$a_n \leq c_n \leq b_n \quad \text{for every natural number } n.$$

Suppose that the sequences $\{a_n\}$ and $\{b_n\}$ converge to the same limit ℓ. Then the sequence $\{c_n\}$ also converges to ℓ.

Proof   Let $\epsilon > 0$. We need to find a natural number N such that

$$\ell - \epsilon < c_n < \ell + \epsilon \quad \text{for all integers } n \geq N. \tag{2.10}$$

Since the sequence $\{a_n\}$ converges to ℓ, we can select a natural number N_1 such that

$$\ell - \epsilon < a_n < \ell + \epsilon \quad \text{for all integers } n \geq N_1.$$

In particular,

$$\ell - \epsilon < a_n \quad \text{for all integers } n \geq N_1. \tag{2.11}$$

On the other hand, since the sequence $\{b_n\}$ also converges to ℓ, we can select a natural number N_2 such that

$$\ell - \epsilon < b_n < \ell + \epsilon \quad \text{for all integers } n \geq N_2.$$

In particular,

$$b_n < \ell + \epsilon \quad \text{for all integers } n \geq N_2. \tag{2.12}$$

Define $N = \max\{N_1, N_2\}$. From inequalities (2.11) and (2.12) and the assumption that $a_n \leq c_n \leq b_n$ for every natural number n, it follows that if $n \geq N$, then

$$\ell - \epsilon < a_n \leq c_n \leq b_n < \ell + \epsilon.$$

Thus we have found a natural number N such that (2.10) holds. ∎

EXERCISES

1. Using only the Archimedean Property of $\mathbb{R}$, give a direct "ϵ–N" verification of the following limits:
   (a) $\lim\limits_{n\to\infty} \dfrac{1}{\sqrt{n}} = 0$
   (b) $\lim\limits_{n\to\infty} \dfrac{1}{n+5} = 0$

2. Using only the Archimedean Property of $\mathbb{R}$, give a direct "ϵ–N" verification of the convergence of the following sequences:
   (a) $\left\{\dfrac{2}{\sqrt{n}} + \dfrac{1}{n} + 3\right\}$
   (b) $\left\{\dfrac{n^2}{n^2+n}\right\}$

3. Prove that the sequence $\{a_n\}$ converges to a if and only if the sequence $\{|a_n - a|\}$ converges to 0.

4. Let the sequence $\{b_n\}$ converge to b. Suppose that the sequence $\{a_n\}$ and the number a have the property that there is a number M and a natural number N such that

   $$|a_n - a| \leq M|b_n - b| \quad \text{for all integers } n \geq N.$$

   Prove that the sequence $\{a_n\}$ converges to a.

5. Suppose that the sequence $\{a_n\}$ converges to a. Use the Reverse Triangle Inequality to prove that the sequence $\{|a_n|\}$ converges to $|a|$.

6. Suppose $\{a_n\}$ is a sequence of nonnegative numbers that converges to a. Prove that the sequence $\{\sqrt{a_n}\}$ converges to $\sqrt{a}$. (*Hint:* Consider the cases $a = 0$ and $a > 0$ separately.)

7. If the sequence $\{a_n^2\}$ converges, does the sequence $\{a_n\}$ also necessarily converge?

8. (a)   Prove that if $0 < r < 1$, then

$$\lim_{n \to \infty} \sqrt{n} r^n = 0.$$

(*Hint:* Follow the proof that $\lim_{n \to \infty} r^n = 0$.)

(b)   Prove that if $0 < r < 1$, then

$$\lim_{n \to \infty} n r^n = 0.$$

(*Hint:* if $a = \sqrt{r}$, then $n r^n = (\sqrt{n} a^n)(\sqrt{n} a^n)$.)

9.   Prove that

$$\lim_{n \to \infty} n^{1/n} = 1.$$

(*Hint:* Define $\alpha_n = n^{1/n} - 1$ and show that $n = (1 + \alpha_n)^n \geq 1 + [n(n-1)/2]\alpha_n^2$.)

10.   Suppose that the sequence $\{a_n\}$ converges to a. Give necessary and sufficient conditions for the sequence $\{(-1)^n a_n\}$ to converge. Prove your assertion.

11.   Prove that the Archimedean Property of $\mathbb{R}$ is equivalent to the fact that $\lim_{n \to \infty} 1/n = 0$.

12.   We have proven that $\lim_{n \to \infty} c^n = 0$ if $|c| < 1$. Prove that the sequence $\{c^n\}$ does not converge if $|c| > 1$.

13.   Let $\{a_n\}$ be a sequence of real numbers. Suppose that for each positive number c there is a natural number N such that

$$a_n > c \quad \text{for all integers } n \geq N.$$

When this is so, the sequence $\{a_n\}$ is said to *converge to infinity*, and we write

$$\lim_{n \to \infty} a_n = \infty.$$

Prove the following:

(a) $\displaystyle\lim_{n \to \infty} [n^3 - 4n^2 - 100n] = \infty$ (b) $\displaystyle\lim_{n \to \infty} \left[\sqrt{n} - \frac{1}{n^2} + 4 \right] = \infty$

14.   Discuss the convergence of each of the following sequences:

(a) $\{\sqrt{n+1} - \sqrt{n}\}$ (b) $\{(\sqrt{n+1} - \sqrt{n})\sqrt{n}\}$ (c) $\{(\sqrt{n+1} - \sqrt{n})n\}$

15.   Define the sequence $\{s_n\}$ by

$$s_n = \frac{1}{2 \cdot 1} + \frac{1}{3 \cdot 2} + \cdots + \frac{1}{(n+1)(n)} \quad \text{for every natural number } n.$$

Prove that

$$\lim_{n \to \infty} s_n = 1.$$

16.   Let the sequences $\{a_n\}$ and $\{b_n\}$ have the property that

$$\lim_{n \to \infty} [a_n^2 + b_n^2] = 0.$$

Prove that

$$\lim_{n \to \infty} a_n = \lim_{n \to \infty} b_n = 0.$$

17.   Suppose that the sequence $\{a_n\}$ converges to a and that $|a| < 1$. Prove that the sequence $\{(a_n)^n\}$ converges to 0.

18.   We have proven that the sequence $\{1/n\}$ converges to 0 and that it does not converge to any other number. Use this to prove that none of the following assertions is equivalent to the definition of convergence of a sequence $\{a_n\}$ to the number a.

(a)   For some $\epsilon > 0$ there is a natural number N such that

$$|a_n - a| < \epsilon \quad \text{for all integers } n \geq N.$$

(b)   For each $\epsilon > 0$ and each natural number N,

$$|a_n - a| < \epsilon \quad \text{for all integers } n \geq N.$$

(c)   There is a natural number N such that for every number $\epsilon > 0$,

$$|a_n - a| < \epsilon \quad \text{for all integers } n \geq N.$$

19.   For the sequence defined in Example 2.2, prove that for every integer n, $|a_n - \sqrt{2}| < 1/n$. Use this property to show that the sequence converges to $\sqrt{2}$.

20.   (The convergence of Cesaro averages.) Suppose that the sequence $\{a_n\}$ converges to a. Define the sequence $\{\sigma_n\}$ by

$$\sigma_n = \frac{a_1 + a_2 + \cdots + a_n}{n} \quad \text{for every natural number } n.$$

Prove that the sequence $\{\sigma_n\}$ also converges to a.

2.2 Monotone Sequences, the Bolzano-Weierstrass Theorem, and the Nested Interval Theorem

In Section 2.1 we showed that $\lim_{n \to \infty} 1/n = 0$, and that $\lim_{n \to \infty} c^n = 0$ provided that $|c| < 1$. It is clear that constant sequences converge to their constant value. Thus, using the sum, product, and quotient properties of convergent sequences, we can combine these three examples to obtain further examples of convergent sequences. It will be important to analyze more general sequences. We now turn to the task of providing criteria that are sufficient to determine that a sequence converges, but that do not require any explicit knowledge of the proposed limit.

DEFINITION   *A sequence $\{a_n\}$ is said to be monotonically increasing provided that*

$$a_{n+1} \geq a_n \quad \text{for every natural number } n.$$

A sequence $\{a_n\}$ is said to be monotonically decreasing provided that

$$a_{n+1} \leq a_n \quad \text{for every natural number } n.$$

A sequence $\{a_n\}$ is called monotone if it is either monotonically increasing or monotonically decreasing.

In the preceding section, we proved that if a sequence converges, it must be bounded. Of course, as the sequence $\{(-1)^n\}$ shows, a bounded sequence need not converge. However, in the case of a monotone sequence, there is the following important theorem.

THEOREM 2.10   **The Monotone Convergence Theorem**   A monotone sequence converges if and only if it is bounded.

Proof   We have already proven that a convergent sequence is bounded, so it remains to be shown that if the sequence $\{a_n\}$ is bounded and monotone, it converges. Let us first suppose that the sequence $\{a_n\}$ is monotonically increasing. Then if we define $S = \{a_n \mid n \in \mathbb{N}\}$, by assumption, the set S is bounded above. According to the Completeness Axiom, S has a least upper bound. Define $a = $ l.u.b. S. We claim that the sequence $\{a_n\}$ converges to a. Indeed, let $\epsilon > 0$. We need to find a natural number N such that

$$|a_n - a| < \epsilon \quad \text{for all integers } n \ge N;$$

that is,

$$a - \epsilon < a_n < a + \epsilon \quad \text{for all integers } n \ge N. \tag{2.13}$$

Since the number a is an upper bound for the set S, we have

$$a_n \le a < a + \epsilon \quad \text{for every natural number } n. \tag{2.14}$$

On the other hand, since a is the least upper bound for S, the number $a - \epsilon$ is not an upper bound for S, so there is a natural number N such that $a - \epsilon < a_N$. However, the sequence $\{a_n\}$ is monotonically increasing, so

$$a - \epsilon < a_N \le a_n \quad \text{for all integers } n \ge N. \tag{2.15}$$

From the inequalities (2.14) and (2.15), we obtain the required inequality (2.13). Thus, the sequence $\{a_n\}$ converges to a.

It remains to consider the case when the sequence $\{a_n\}$ is monotonically decreasing. But then the sequence $\{-a_n\}$ is monotonically increasing. By the case just considered, $\{-a_n\}$ converges, and so, using the linearity property of convergent sequences, it follows that $\{a_n\}$ also converges.   ∎

EXAMPLE 2.8   Define

$$s_n = \sum_{k=1}^{n} \frac{1}{k} \cdot \frac{1}{2^k} \quad \text{for every natural number } n.$$

Then it is clear that the sequence $\{s_n\}$ is monotonically increasing. According to the Monotone Convergence Theorem, $\{s_n\}$ converges if and only if it is bounded. We will show that it is bounded. Indeed, using the Geometric Sum Formula, we see that for every natural number n,

$$s_n \le \frac{1}{2} + \left(\frac{1}{2}\right)^2 + \cdots + \left(\frac{1}{2}\right)^n = \frac{1/2 - (1/2)^{n+1}}{1 - 1/2} \le 1.$$

Hence the monotone sequence $\{s_n\}$ is bounded, and so it converges. Observe that we have proven that $\{s_n\}$ converges without explicitly identifying the limit.   □

EXAMPLE 2.9   Define

$$s_n = \sum_{k=1}^{n} \frac{1}{k} \qquad \text{for every natural number } n.$$

The series $\{s_n\}$ is called the *harmonic series*. Again, we see that the sequence $\{s_n\}$ is monotonically increasing. We claim that it is not bounded and hence not convergent. Indeed, to see this, observe that

$$s_2 = 1 + \frac{1}{2} \geq 1 + \frac{1}{2},$$

and that

$$s_4 = s_2 + \frac{1}{3} + \frac{1}{4} \geq 1 + \frac{1}{2} + \frac{1}{2} = 1 + \frac{2}{2},$$

and that in general we have

$$s_{2^n} \geq 1 + \frac{n}{2} \qquad \text{for every natural number } n.$$

From this, using the Archimedean Property of $\mathbb{R}$, it follows that the sequence $\{s_n\}$ is not bounded and hence does not converge.   □

EXAMPLE 2.10   Consider the sequence $\{(1 + 1/n)^n\}$. We claim that this sequence is monotonically increasing. Indeed, using the Binomial Formula from Section 1.3, we see that for all natural numbers n,

$$\left(1 + \frac{1}{n}\right)^n = 1 + n \cdot \frac{1}{n} + \frac{n(n-1)}{1 \cdot 2} \frac{1}{n^2} + \cdots + \frac{n(n-1)\cdots(n-n+1)}{1 \cdot 2 \cdots n} \frac{1}{n^n}$$

$$= 1 + 1 + \frac{1}{1 \cdot 2}\left(1 - \frac{1}{n}\right) + \frac{1}{1 \cdot 2 \cdot 3}\left(1 - \frac{1}{n}\right)\left(1 - \frac{2}{n}\right) + \cdots$$

$$+ \frac{1}{1 \cdot 2 \cdots n}\left(1 - \frac{1}{n}\right)\left(1 - \frac{2}{n}\right)\cdots\left(1 - \frac{n-1}{n}\right).$$

From this, using a similar expansion for $(1 + 1/(n+1))^{n+1}$ and comparing the first $n+1$ terms, we see that for every natural number n,

$$\left(1 + \frac{1}{n}\right)^n < \left(1 + \frac{1}{n+1}\right)^{n+1}.$$

Hence the sequence $\{(1 + 1/n)^n\}$ is monotonically increasing. The above expansion and the Geometric Sum Formula imply that for every natural number n,

$$2 < \left(1 + \frac{1}{n}\right)^n < 2 + \frac{1}{2} + \cdots + \frac{1}{2^{n-1}} < 3.$$

The Monotone Convergence Theorem implies that the sequence $\{(1 + 1/n)^n\}$ converges. The limit of this sequence is one of the important constants of mathematics and is denoted by e. From the above we see that $2 < e \leq 3$. In Chapter 8 we will estimate the number e more precisely.   □

DEFINITION   *Consider a sequence $\{a_n\}$. Let $\{n_k\}$ be a sequence of natural numbers that is strictly increasing; that is,*

$$n_1 < n_2 < n_3 < \cdots .$$

Then the sequence $\{b_k\}$ defined by

$$b_k = a_{n_k} \quad \text{for every natural number } k$$

is called a subsequence of the sequence $\{a_n\}$.

Often a subsequence of $\{a_n\}$ is simply denoted by $\{a_{n_k}\}$, it being implicitly understood that $\{n_k\}$ is a strictly increasing sequence of natural numbers and that the kth term of the sequence $\{a_{n_k}\}$ is a_{n_k}.

A given sequence may or may not be monotone. But, in fact, every sequence has a monotone subsequence. This is not at all obvious. For instance, it is not obvious that the sequence $\{\sin(n)\}$ has a monotone subsequence.

THEOREM 2.11   Every sequence has a monotone subsequence.

Proof   Consider a sequence $\{a_n\}$. We call a natural number m a *peak index* for the sequence $\{a_n\}$ provided that $a_n \leq a_m$ for all integers $n \geq m$.

Either there are only finitely many peak indices for the sequence or there are infinitely many such indices.

Case 1. There are finitely many peak indices. Then we may choose a natural number N such that there are no peak indices greater than N. We will recursively define a monotonically increasing subsequence of $\{a_n\}$. Indeed, define $n_1 = N + 1$. Now suppose that k is a natural number such that positive integers

$$n_1 < n_2 < \cdots < n_k$$

have been chosen such that

$$a_{n_1} < a_{n_2} < \cdots < a_{n_k}.$$

Since $n_k > N$, the index n_k is not a peak index. Hence there is an index $n_{k+1} > n_k$ such that $a_{n_{k+1}} > a_{n_k}$. Thus we recursively define a strictly increasing sequence of positive integers $\{n_k\}$ having the property that the subsequence $\{a_{n_k}\}$ is monotonically increasing.

Case 2. There are infinitely many peak indices. For each natural number k, let n_k be the kth peak index. From the very definition of peak index it follows that the subsequence $\{a_{n_k}\}$ is monotonically decreasing.   ■

THEOREM 2.12   Every bounded sequence has a convergent subsequence.

Proof Let $\{a_n\}$ be a bounded sequence. According to the preceding theorem, we may choose a monotone subsequence $\{a_{n_k}\}$. Since $\{a_n\}$ is bounded, so is its subsequence $\{a_{n_k}\}$. Hence $\{a_{n_k}\}$ is a bounded monotone sequence. According to the Monotone Convergence Theorem, $\{a_{n_k}\}$ converges. ∎

There is a slightly more refined version of Theorem 2.12 that we will find very useful.

For a subset D of $\mathbb{R}$, we say that the sequence $\{a_n\}$ is *a sequence in D* provided that for every natural number n, a_n belongs to D.

THEOREM 2.13 **The Bolzano-Weierstrass Theorem** Let a and b be numbers such that $a < b$. Every sequence in the interval $[a, b]$ has a subsequence that converges to a point in $[a, b]$.

Proof Let $\{x_n\}$ be a sequence in $[a, b]$. Then $\{x_n\}$ is bounded. Hence, by the preceding theorem, there is a subsequence $\{x_{n_k}\}$ that converges. But the sequence $\{x_{n_k}\}$ is a sequence in $[a, b]$, and hence, according to Corollary 2.8, its limit is also in $[a, b]$. ∎

The following result should not be surprising.

PROPOSITION 2.14 Let the sequence $\{a_n\}$ converge to the limit a. Then every subsequence of $\{a_n\}$ also converges to the same limit a.

Proof Let $\{a_{n_k}\}$ be a subsequence of $\{a_n\}$. Let $\epsilon > 0$. We need to find a natural number N such that

$$|a_{n_k} - a| < \epsilon \quad \text{for all integers } k \geq N. \tag{2.16}$$

Since the whole sequence $\{a_n\}$ converges to a, we may choose a natural number N such that

$$|a_n - a| < \epsilon \quad \text{for all integers } n \geq N. \tag{2.17}$$

But observe that since $\{n_k\}$ is a strictly increasing sequence of natural numbers,

$$n_j \geq j \quad \text{for every natural number } j.$$

Thus inequality (2.16) follows from inequality (2.17). Hence the subsequence $\{a_{n_k}\}$ also converges to a. ∎

The sequence $\{a_{n+1}\}$ is a subsequence of $\{a_n\}$. Hence,

$$\text{if } \lim_{n \to \infty} a_n = a, \quad \text{then} \quad \lim_{n \to \infty} a_{n+1} = a \quad \text{as well.}$$

This simple observation can be quite useful in analyzing sequences that are defined recursively.

EXAMPLE 2.11   Define $a_1 = 1$. If n is a natural number for which a_n has been defined, then define

$$a_{n+1} = \frac{1 + a_n}{2 + a_n}.$$

An induction argument shows that $\{a_n\}$ is a sequence of positive numbers. Moreover, directly from the definition of the sequence, it follows that for every natural number n,

$$a_{n+2} - a_{n+1} = \frac{a_{n+1} - a_n}{(2 + a_n)(2 + a_{n+1})}.$$

Since $a_2 < a_1$, the preceding identity and an induction argument show that $\{a_n\}$ is monotonically decreasing. According to the Monotone Convergence Theorem, the sequence $\{a_n\}$ converges. Denote the limit by a. From the fact that $\lim_{n \to \infty} a_{n+1} = a$, and also from the sum, product, and quotient properties of convergent sequences, it follows that

$$a = \lim_{n \to \infty} a_{n+1} = \lim_{n \to \infty} \frac{1 + a_n}{2 + a_n} = \frac{1 + a}{2 + a}.$$

Thus, $a^2 + a - 1 = 0$ and $a \geq 0$. It follows from the quadratic formula that

$$\lim_{n \to \infty} a_n = \frac{-1 + \sqrt{5}}{2}. \qquad \square$$

We finish this section with a geometric consequence of the Monotone Convergence Theorem.

THEOREM 2.15   **The Nested Interval Theorem**   For each natural number n, let a_n and b_n be numbers such that $a_n < b_n$, and consider the interval $I_n = [a_n, b_n]$. Assume that

$$I_{n+1} \subseteq I_n \quad \text{for every natural number } n. \tag{2.18}$$

Also assume that

$$\lim_{n \to \infty} [b_n - a_n] = 0. \tag{2.19}$$

Then there is exactly one point x that belongs to the interval I_n for all n, and both of the sequences $\{a_n\}$ and $\{b_n\}$ converge to this point.

Proof   Assumption (2.18) means precisely that for every natural number n,

$$a_n \leq a_{n+1} < b_{n+1} \leq b_n.$$

In particular, the sequence $\{a_n\}$ is a monotonically increasing sequence that is bounded above by b_1. The Monotone Convergence Theorem implies that the sequence $\{a_n\}$ converges; we will denote its limit by a. Observe that $a_n \leq a$ for every natural number n. A similar argument shows that the monotonically decreasing sequence $\{b_n\}$ converges to a number that we denote by b, and that $b \leq b_n$ for every natural number n. Thus

$$a_n \leq a \text{ and } b \leq b_n \quad \text{for every natural number } n. \tag{2.20}$$

Using assumption (2.19) and the difference property of convergent sequences, we conclude that

$$0 = \lim_{n \to \infty} [b_n - a_n] = b - a.$$

Thus $a = b$. Setting $x = a = b$, it follows from (2.20) that the point x belongs to I_n for every natural number n. There can only be one such point, since the existence of two such points would contradict the assumption (2.19) that the lengths of the intervals converge to 0. ∎

1. Which of the following sequences is monotone? Justify your conclusions.

   (a) $\left\{ n + \dfrac{(-1)^n}{n} \right\}$ (b) $\left\{ \dfrac{(-1)^n}{5n} \right\}$ (c) $\left\{ \dfrac{1}{n^2} + \dfrac{(-1)^n}{3^n} \right\}$

2. For each of the following sequences, find the peak indices. Justify your conclusions.

   (a) $\left\{ \dfrac{1}{n} \right\}$ (b) $\{(-1)^n\}$ (c) $\{(-1)^n n\}$ (d) $\left\{ \dfrac{(-1)^n}{n} \right\}$

3. Prove that the sequence

$$\left\{ 1 + \frac{1}{2!} + \cdots + \frac{1}{n!} \right\}$$

   converges. (We will see later that it converges to $e - 1$.)

4. Suppose that the sequence $\{a_n\}$ is monotone. Prove that $\{a_n\}$ converges if and only if $\{a_n^2\}$ converges. Show that this result does not hold without the monotonicity assumption.

5. Let $\{b_n\}$ be a bounded sequence of nonnegative numbers and r be any number such that $0 \le r < 1$. Define

$$s_n = b_1 r + b_2 r^2 + \cdots + b_n r^n \quad \text{for every natural number } n.$$

   Use the Monotone Convergence Theorem to prove that the series $\{s_n\}$ converges.

6. Let $a > 0$. Prove that the sequence $\{a^{1/n}\}$ converges. Then, by considering the subsequence $\{\sqrt{a^{1/n}}\}$, prove that $\lim_{n \to \infty} a^{1/n} = 1$.

7. Let $\{a_{n_k}\}$ be a subsequence of the sequence $\{a_n\}$. Show that $n_k \ge k$ for every natural number k.

8. For a positive number c, consider the quadratic equation

$$x^2 - x - c = 0, \qquad x > 0.$$

   Define the sequence $\{x_n\}$ recursively by fixing $x_1 > 0$ and then, if n is a natural number for which x_n has been defined, defining

$$x_{n+1} = \sqrt{c + x_n}.$$

   Prove that the sequence $\{x_n\}$ converges monotonically to the solution of the above equation.

9. For a pair of positive numbers α and β, the number $\sqrt{\alpha\beta}$ is called the *geometric mean* of α and β, and the number $(\alpha + \beta)/2$ is called the *arithmetic mean* of α and β. By observing that $(\sqrt{\alpha} - \sqrt{\beta})^2 \ge 0$, show that $(\alpha + \beta)/2 \ge \sqrt{\alpha\beta}$.

10. For a pair of positive numbers a and b, define sequences $\{a_n\}$ and $\{b_n\}$ recursively as follows: Define $a_1 = a$ and $b_1 = b$. If n is a natural number for which a_n and b_n have been defined, define

$$a_{n+1} = \frac{a_n + b_n}{2} \quad \text{and} \quad b_{n+1} = \sqrt{a_n b_n}.$$

11. (a) Use the preceding exercise to prove that for every natural number n,

$$a_n \geq a_{n+1} \geq b_{n+1} \geq b_n.$$

(b) From (a), show that the sequences $\{a_n\}$ and $\{b_n\}$ converge. Then show that $\{a_n\}$ and $\{b_n\}$ have the same limit. This common limit is called the *Gauss Arithmetic-Geometric Mean* of a and b; it occurs as the value of an important elliptic integral involving a and b.

12. A set A of real numbers is called *compact* if whenever $\{x_n\}$ is a sequence in A, there is a subsequence of $\{x_n\}$ that converges to a point in A. Using this terminology, the Bolzano-Weierstrass Theorem may be restated as follows: *If a and b are numbers such that $a \leq b$, the interval $[a, b]$ is compact.* Which of the following sets is compact? Justify your conclusions.

(a) $(0, 1)$ (b) $[0, 1)$ (c) $\mathbb{R}$ (d) $[0, 1] \cup [3, 4]$

3

Continuous Functions and Limits

3.1   Continuity

In Chapter 2, we considered real-valued functions that have as their domain the set of natural numbers; that is, we considered sequences of real numbers. We now begin the study of real-valued functions having as their domain a general subset of $\mathbb{R}$. There is a standard notation: For a set of real numbers D, by

$$f: D \to \mathbb{R}$$

we denote a function whose domain is D, and for each point x in D we denote by $f(x)$ the value that the function assigns to x. When we write $f: D \to \mathbb{R}$ we will assume without further mention that D is a set of real numbers.

Two of the concepts that are essential to an analytic description of functions $f: D \to \mathbb{R}$ are *continuity* and *differentiability*. The first five sections of this chapter are devoted to the study of continuity. In the final section we study limits in preparation for the discussion of differentiability, which we will begin in Chapter 4.

DEFINITION   *A function $f: D \to \mathbb{R}$ is said to be continuous at the point x_0 in D provided that whenever $\{x_n\}$ is a sequence in D that converges to x_0, the image sequence $\{f(x_n)\}$ converges to $f(x_0)$. The function $f: D \to \mathbb{R}$ is said to be continuous provided that it is continuous at every point in D.*

The definition of continuity of the function $f: D \to \mathbb{R}$ at the point x_0 in D is formulated to make precise the intuitive notion that "if x is a point in D that is close to x_0, its image $f(x)$ is close to $f(x_0)$."

FIGURE 3.1

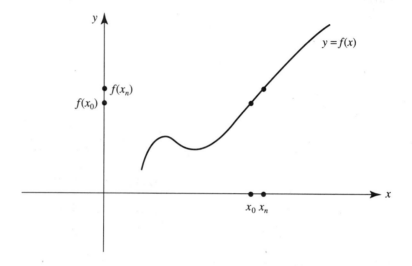

EXAMPLE 3.1   For each number x, define $f(x) = x^2 - 2x + 4$. Then the function $f: \mathbb{R} \to \mathbb{R}$ is continuous. To verify this, we select a point x_0 in $\mathbb{R}$, and we will show that the function is continuous at x_0. Let $\{x_n\}$ be a sequence that converges to x_0. By the sum and product properties of convergent sequences,

$$\lim_{n \to \infty} f(x_n) = \lim_{n \to \infty} [x_n^2 - 2x_n + 4] = x_0^2 - 2x_0 + 4 = f(x_0).$$

Thus, $f: \mathbb{R} \to \mathbb{R}$ is continuous at x_0.   □

EXAMPLE 3.2   Define $f(x) = \sqrt{x}$ for $x \geq 0$. Then the function $f: [0, \infty) \to \mathbb{R}$ is continuous. To verify this, we select a nonnegative number x_0 and let $\{x_n\}$ be a sequence of nonnegative numbers that converges to x_0. But then the sequence $\{\sqrt{x_n}\}$ converges to $\sqrt{x_0}$; that is,

$$\lim_{n \to \infty} f(x_n) = \lim_{n \to \infty} \sqrt{x_n} = \sqrt{x_0} = f(x_0).$$

Thus, $f: [0, \infty) \to \mathbb{R}$ is continuous at x_0.   □

EXAMPLE 3.3 Define the function $f: \mathbb{R} \to \mathbb{R}$ by

$$f(x) = \begin{cases} 1 & \text{if } x \text{ is rational} \\ 0 & \text{if } x \text{ is irrational.} \end{cases}$$

This function is called *Dirichlet's function*. There is no point x_0 in $\mathbb{R}$ at which Dirichlet's function is continuous. Indeed, given a point x_0 in $\mathbb{R}$, for each natural number n, we may, by the density of the rationals and the irrationals (Theorem 1.11), choose a rational number, which we label u_n, in the interval $(x_0, x_0 + 1/n)$ and an irrational number, which we label v_n, in the interval $(x_0, x_0 + 1/n)$. But for each natural number n, $f(u_n) = 1$ and $f(v_n) = 0$, so

$$\lim_{n \to \infty} f(u_n) = 1 \neq 0 = \lim_{n \to \infty} f(v_n).$$

Since both of the sequences $\{u_n\}$ and $\{v_n\}$ converge to x_0, it is not possible for $f: \mathbb{R} \to \mathbb{R}$ to be continuous at x_0. □

Given two functions $f: D \to \mathbb{R}$ and $g: D \to \mathbb{R}$, we define the *sum* $f + g: D \to \mathbb{R}$ and the *product* $fg: D \to \mathbb{R}$ by

$$(f + g)(x) \equiv f(x) + g(x) \quad \text{and} \quad (fg)(x) \equiv f(x)g(x) \quad \text{for all } x \text{ in } D.$$

Moreover, if $g(x) \neq 0$ for all x in D, the *quotient* $f/g: D \to \mathbb{R}$ is defined by

$$(f/g)(x) \equiv \frac{f(x)}{g(x)} \quad \text{for all } x \text{ in } D.$$

The following theorem is an analogue, and also a consequence, of the sum, product, and quotient properties of convergent sequences.

THEOREM 3.1 Suppose that the functions $f: D \to \mathbb{R}$ and $g: D \to \mathbb{R}$ are continuous at the point x_0 in D. Then the sum

$$f + g: D \to \mathbb{R} \quad \text{is continuous at } x_0, \tag{3.1}$$

the product

$$fg: D \to \mathbb{R} \quad \text{is continuous at } x_0, \tag{3.2}$$

and, if $g(x) \neq 0$ for all x in D, the quotient

$$f/g: D \to \mathbb{R} \quad \text{is continuous at } x_0. \tag{3.3}$$

Proof Let $\{x_n\}$ be a sequence in D that converges to x_0. By the definition of continuity,

$$\lim_{n \to \infty} f(x_n) = f(x_0) \quad \text{and} \quad \lim_{n \to \infty} g(x_n) = g(x_0).$$

The sum property of convergent sequences implies that

$$\lim_{n \to \infty} [f(x_n) + g(x_n)] = f(x_0) + g(x_0), \tag{3.4}$$

and the product property of convergent sequences implies that

$$\lim_{n \to \infty} [f(x_n)g(x_n)] = f(x_0)g(x_0). \tag{3.5}$$

If $g(x) \neq 0$ for all x in D, the quotient property of convergent sequences implies that

$$\lim_{n \to \infty} \frac{f(x_n)}{g(x_n)} = \frac{f(x_0)}{g(x_0)}. \tag{3.6}$$

By the definition of continuity, (3.1), (3.2), and (3.3) follow from (3.4), (3.5), and (3.6), respectively. ∎

For a nonnegative integer k and numbers $c_0, c_1, \ldots, c_k$, the function $p \colon \mathbb{R} \to \mathbb{R}$ defined by

$$p(x) = \sum_{i=0}^{k} c_i x^i \quad \text{for all } x \text{ in } \mathbb{R}$$

is called a *polynomial*. If $c_k \neq 0$, $p \colon \mathbb{R} \to \mathbb{R}$ is said to have *degree k*.

It is clear that constant functions are continuous. Moreover, the function $f \colon \mathbb{R} \to \mathbb{R}$ defined by $f(x) = x$ for all x in $\mathbb{R}$ is also continuous. From these two simple observations and the sum, product, and quotient properties of continuous functions asserted by Theorem 1, together with an induction argument, we obtain:

COROLLARY 3.2   Let $p \colon \mathbb{R} \to \mathbb{R}$ be a polynomial. Then $p \colon \mathbb{R} \to \mathbb{R}$ is continuous. Moreover, if $q \colon \mathbb{R} \to \mathbb{R}$ is also a polynomial and $D = \{x \text{ in } \mathbb{R} \mid q(x) \neq 0\}$, then the quotient $p/q \colon D \to \mathbb{R}$ is continuous.

In addition to forming the sum, product, and quotient of functions, there is another useful way to combine functions: They may be *composed*.

DEFINITION   *For functions $f \colon D \to \mathbb{R}$ and $g \colon U \to \mathbb{R}$ such that $f(D)$ is contained in U, we define the composition of $f \colon D \to \mathbb{R}$ with $g \colon U \to \mathbb{R}$, denoted by $g \circ f \colon D \to \mathbb{R}$, by the formula*

$$(g \circ f)(x) \equiv g(f(x)) \quad \text{for all } x \text{ in } D.$$

We have the following composition property for continuous functions.

THEOREM 3.3   For functions $f \colon D \to \mathbb{R}$ and $g \colon U \to \mathbb{R}$ such that $f(D)$ is contained in U, suppose that $f \colon D \to \mathbb{R}$ is continuous at the point x_0 in D and $g \colon U \to \mathbb{R}$ is continuous at the point $f(x_0)$. Then the composition

$$g \circ f \colon D \to \mathbb{R}$$

is continuous at x_0.

Proof   Let $\{x_n\}$ be a sequence in D that converges to x_0. By the continuity of the function $f: D \to \mathbb{R}$ at the point x_0, the sequence $\{f(x_n)\}$ converges to $f(x_0)$. But then $\{f(x_n)\}$ is a sequence in U that converges to $f(x_0)$, so by the continuity of $g: U \to \mathbb{R}$ at the point $f(x_0)$, the sequence $\{g(f(x_n))\}$ converges to $g(f(x_0))$; that is,

$$\lim_{n \to \infty} (g \circ f)(x_n) = (g \circ f)(x_0).$$

Thus, the composition $g \circ f: D \to \mathbb{R}$ is continuous at x_0.   ∎

EXAMPLE 3.4   Define $h(x) = \sqrt{1 - x^2}$ for x in $[-1, 1]$. Then $h: [-1, 1] \to \mathbb{R}$ is continuous. This follows immediately from the continuity of polynomials, the continuity of the square-root function, and the composition property of continuous functions.   □

EXERCISES

1. For a function $f: D \to \mathbb{R}$ and a point x_0 in D, define $A = \{x \text{ in } D \mid x \geq x_0\}$ and $B = \{x \text{ in } D \mid x \leq x_0\}$. Prove that $f: D \to \mathbb{R}$ is continuous at x_0 if and only if $f: A \to \mathbb{R}$ and $f: B \to \mathbb{R}$ are continuous at x_0.

2. Define
$$f(x) = \begin{cases} x^2 & \text{if } x \geq 0 \\ x & \text{if } x < 0. \end{cases}$$
Prove that the function $f: \mathbb{R} \to \mathbb{R}$ is continuous.

3. Define
$$f(x) = \begin{cases} 0 & \text{if } 0 \leq x \leq 1 \\ x & \text{if } 1 < x \leq 2. \end{cases}$$
At what points is the function $f: [0, 2] \to \mathbb{R}$ continuous?

4. Suppose that the function $g: \mathbb{R} \to \mathbb{R}$ is continuous and that $g(x) = 0$ if x is rational. Prove that $g(x) = 0$ for all x in $\mathbb{R}$.

5. Define
$$g(x) = \begin{cases} x^2 & \text{if } x \text{ is rational} \\ -x^2 & \text{if } x \text{ is irrational}. \end{cases}$$
At what points is the function $g: \mathbb{R} \to \mathbb{R}$ continuous?

6. Let the function $f: D \to \mathbb{R}$ be continuous. Then define the function $|f|: D \to \mathbb{R}$ by $|f|(x) = |f(x)|$ for x in D. Prove that the function $|f|: D \to \mathbb{R}$ also is continuous.

7. Let the continuous function $f: D \to \mathbb{R}$ have nonnegative functional values. Define the function $\sqrt{f}: D \to \mathbb{R}$ by $\sqrt{f}(x) = \sqrt{f(x)}$ for x in D. Prove that $\sqrt{f}: D \to \mathbb{R}$ is also continuous.

8. Suppose that the function $f: \mathbb{R} \to \mathbb{R}$ has the property that
$$f(u + v) = f(u) + f(v) \quad \text{for all } u \text{ and } v \text{ in } \mathbb{R}.$$

   (a)   Prove that if $m = f(1)$, then
$$f(x) = mx \quad \text{for all rational numbers } x.$$

   (b)   Use (a) to prove that if $f: \mathbb{R} \to \mathbb{R}$ is continuous, then
$$f(x) = mx \quad \text{for all } x \text{ in } \mathbb{R}.$$

3.2   The Extreme Value Theorem

For a function $f: D \to \mathbb{R}$, we define

$$f(D) = \{y \text{ in } \mathbb{R} \mid y = f(x) \text{ for some } x \text{ in } D\}$$

and call $f(D)$ the *image* of $f: D \to \mathbb{R}$. We say that a function $f: D \to \mathbb{R}$ attains a *maximum value* provided that its image $f(D)$ has a maximum; that is, there is a point x_0 in D such that

$$f(x) \le f(x_0) \quad \text{for all } x \text{ in } D.$$

We will call such a point in D a *maximizer* of the function $f: D \to \mathbb{R}$. Similarly, the function $f: D \to \mathbb{R}$ is said to attain a *minimum value* provided that its image $f(D)$ has a minimum; a point in D at which this minimum value is attained is called a *minimizer* of $f: D \to \mathbb{R}$.

In general, no assertion can be made concerning the existence of a minimum or maximum value for a function $f: D \to \mathbb{R}$. However, in the case when the domain $D = [a, b]$ and the function $f: [a, b] \to \mathbb{R}$ is continuous, we have the following important theorem.

THEOREM 3.4   **The Extreme Value Theorem**   Suppose that the function $f: [a, b] \to \mathbb{R}$ is continuous. Then $f: [a, b] \to \mathbb{R}$ attains both a minimum and a maximum value.

FIGURE 3.2

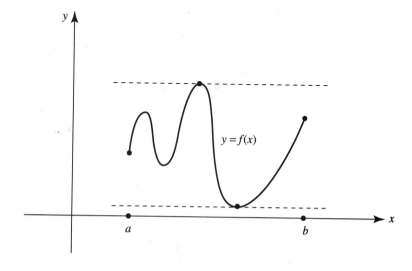

In order to prove this theorem, it is convenient first to prove a weaker result.

LEMMA 3.5

Suppose that the function $f:[a, b] \to \mathbb{R}$ is continuous. Then the image of $f:[a, b] \to \mathbb{R}$ is bounded above; that is, there is a number M such that

$$f(x) \leq M \quad \text{for all } x \text{ in } [a, b].$$

Proof of Lemma 3.5

We will argue by contradiction. Assume there that is no such number M. Let n be a natural number. Then it is not true that

$$f(x) \leq n \quad \text{for all } x \text{ in } [a, b].$$

Thus, there is a point x in $[a, b]$ at which $f(x) > n$. Choose such a point and label it x_n. This defines a sequence $\{x_n\}$ in $[a, b]$ with the property that $f(x_n) > n$ for every natural number n. We can employ the Bolzano-Weierstrass Theorem to find a subsequence $\{x_{n_k}\}$ of $\{x_n\}$ that converges to a point x_0 in $[a, b]$. Since the function $f:[a, b] \to \mathbb{R}$ is continuous at x_0, the image sequence $\{f(x_{n_k})\}$ converges to $f(x_0)$. This contradicts the unboundedness of the sequence $\{f(x_{n_k})\}$. This contradiction proves that the image of $f:[a, b] \to \mathbb{R}$ is bounded above. ∎

Proof of Theorem 3.4

Define $S = f([a, b])$. Then S is a nonempty set of real numbers that, by the preceding lemma, is bounded above. According to the Completeness Axiom, S has a supremum. Define $c = \sup S$. It is necessary to find a point x in $[a, b]$ at which $c = f(x)$.

Let n be a natural number. Then the number $c - 1/n$ is smaller than c, and is therefore not an upper bound for the set S. Thus there is a point x in $[a, b]$ at which $f(x) > c - 1/n$. Choose such a point and label it x_n. From this choice and from the fact that c is an upper bound for S, we see that $c - 1/n < f(x_n) \leq c$ for every natural number n. Hence the sequence $\{f(x_n)\}$ converges to c.

The Bolzano-Weierstrass Theorem asserts that there is a subsequence $\{x_{n_k}\}$ of $\{x_n\}$ that converges to a point x_0 in $[a, b]$. Since $f:[a, b] \to \mathbb{R}$ is continuous at x_0, $\{f(x_{n_k})\}$ converges to $f(x_0)$. But $\{f(x_{n_k})\}$ is a subsequence of $\{f(x_n)\}$, so $c = f(x_0)$. The point x_0 is a maximizer of the function $f:[a, b] \to \mathbb{R}$.

To complete the proof, we observe that the function $-f:[a, b] \to \mathbb{R}$ is also continuous. Consequently, using what we have just proven, we may select a point in $[a, b]$ at which $-f:[a, b] \to \mathbb{R}$ attains a maximum value, and at this point the function $f:[a, b] \to \mathbb{R}$ attains a minimum value. ∎

If one examines the proofs of the preceding lemma and theorem, one sees that the only property of the domain of the function that was used was that each sequence in $[a, b]$ had a subsequence that converged to a point in $[a, b]$. This property is so important that it deserves to be singled out.

DEFINITION

A set K of real numbers is said to be compact provided that every sequence in K has a subsequence that converges to a point in K.

In this new terminology, the Bolzano-Weierstrass Theorem is simply the assertion that if a and b are numbers such that $a < b$, then the set $[a, b]$ is compact.

THEOREM 3.6   Let K be a compact nonempty set of real numbers and suppose that the function $f: K \to \mathbb{R}$ is continuous. Then $f: K \to \mathbb{R}$ attains both a minimum and a maximum value.

Proof   Exercise.   ∎

EXERCISES

1. Find a maximizer for each of the following functions:
    (a) $f: [0, 1] \to \mathbb{R}$, defined by $f(x) = \sqrt{x} + x^{10} + 4$ for $0 \le x \le 1$
    (b) $g: [-1, 1] \to \mathbb{R}$, defined by $g(x) = -x^{10}(x - 1/4)^{24}$ for $-1 \le x \le 1$
    (c) $h: [-1, 1] \to \mathbb{R}$, defined by $h(x) = 4 - 2x^3$ for $-1 \le x \le 1$

2. Let a and b be real numbers with $a < b$. Find a continuous function $f: (a, b) \to \mathbb{R}$ having an image that is unbounded above. Also, find a continuous function $f: (a, b) \to \mathbb{R}$ having an image that is bounded above but that does not attain a maximum value.

3. Decide which of the following subsets of $\mathbb{R}$ is compact:
    (a) $(0, 1)$ (b) $[0, 1)$ (c) $[1, 2] \cup [3, 4]$
    (d) $\mathbb{R}$ (e) $\mathbb{Q} \cap [0, 1]$ (f) $\{1, 2, 3, 4\}$

4. Rewrite the proofs of Lemma 3.5 and Theorem 3.4, with $[a, b]$ replaced by a compact set K, and thereby prove Theorem 3.6.

5. Suppose that K is a nonempty set of real numbers that is not compact. Prove that there is a monotone sequence in K that does not converge to a point in K.

6. Let K be a nonempty set of real numbers that is not compact. Prove that there is a continuous function $g: K \to \mathbb{R}$ that does not attain a maximum value. (*Hint:* By the preceding exercise, we may choose a monotone sequence $\{a_n\}$ in K that does not converge to a point in K. If $\{a_n\}$ is bounded, let a be the point to which the sequence converges, and define $g(x) = 1/|x - a|$ for all x in K. If $\{a_n\}$ is unbounded, define $g(x) = |x|$ for all x in K.)

7. Suppose that the function $f: [0, 1] \to \mathbb{R}$ is continuous, $f(0) > 0$, and $f(1) = 0$. Prove that there is a number x_0 in $(0, 1]$ such that $f(x_0) = 0$ and $f(x) > 0$ for $0 \le x < x_0$.

3.3   The Intermediate Value Theorem

The second important geometric property of the graph of a continuous function that we will establish is that if a continuous function has a domain consisting of an interval, and if its graph contains points that are both above and below a line $y = c$, then, in fact, the function attains the value c on the interval. The heart of the matter lies in the following theorem.

THEOREM 3.7   Suppose that the function $f: [a, b] \to \mathbb{R}$ is continuous. Assume also that

$$f(a) < 0 \quad \text{and} \quad f(b) > 0.$$

Then there is a point x_0 in the open interval (a, b) at which $f(x_0) = 0$.

Proof   We will recursively define a sequence of nested, closed subintervals of $[a, b]$ whose endpoints converge to a point in $[a, b]$ at which $f(x) = 0$.

Let $a_1 = a$ and $b_1 = b$. For a natural number n, suppose that the interval $[a_n, b_n]$ contained in $[a, b]$ has been defined such that $f(a_n) \leq 0$ and $f(b_n) > 0$. Consider the midpoint $c_n = (a_n + b_n)/2$.

- If $f(c_n) \leq 0$, define $a_{n+1} = c_n$ and $b_{n+1} = b_n$.
- If $f(c_n) > 0$, define $a_{n+1} = a_n$ and $b_{n+1} = c_n$.

Observe that for each natural number n,

$$a \leq a_n \leq a_{n+1} < b_{n+1} \leq b_n \leq b,$$

$$f(a_{n+1}) \leq 0 \quad \text{and} \quad f(b_{n+1}) > 0,$$

and

$$(b_{n+1} - a_{n+1}) = \frac{b_n - a_n}{2}.$$

It follows that $(b_n - a_n) = (b - a)/2^{n-1}$ for all n. Thus the sequences $\{a_n\}$ and $\{b_n\}$ satisfy the assumptions of the Nested Interval Theorem (Theorem 2.15 of Chapter 2), so there is a point x_0 in $[a, b]$ to which both $\{a_n\}$ and $\{b_n\}$ converge. Since $f: [a, b] \to \mathbb{R}$ is continuous at x_0, the image sequences $\{f(a_n)\}$ and $\{f(b_n)\}$ converge to $f(x_0)$. It follows that $f(x_0) \leq 0$, since $\{f(a_n)\}$ is a sequence of nonpositive numbers, and that $f(x_0) \geq 0$, since $\{f(b_n)\}$ is a sequence of nonnegative numbers. Consequently, $f(x_0) = 0$.   ∎

FIGURE 3.3(a)

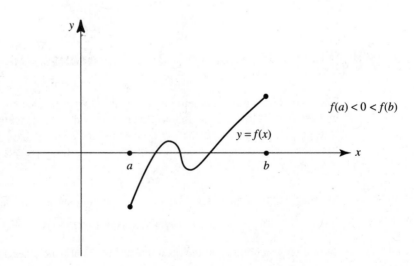

$f(a) < 0 < f(b)$

$y = f(x)$

FIGURE 3.3(b)

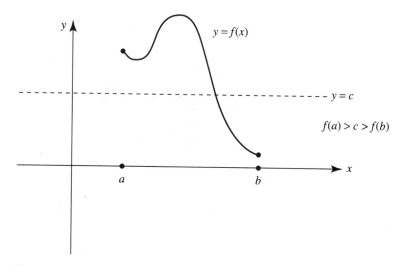

The general Intermediate Value Theorem is obtained from the preceding theorem by a simple algebraic manipulation.

THEOREM 3.8 **The Intermediate Value Theorem** Let the function $f: [a, b] \to \mathbb{R}$ be continuous, and c be a number strictly between $f(a)$ and $f(b)$; that is,

$$f(a) < c < f(b) \quad \text{or} \quad f(b) < c < f(a).$$

Then there is a point x_0 in the open interval (a, b) at which $f(x_0) = c$.

Proof First let us suppose that $f(a) < c < f(b)$. Define the function $g: [a, b] \to \mathbb{R}$ by $g(x) = f(x) - c$ for x in $[a, b]$. Then $g: [a, b] \to \mathbb{R}$ is a continuous function such that $g(a) < 0$ and $g(b) > 0$. We may apply the preceding theorem to conclude that there is a point x_0 in (a, b) at which $g(x_0) = 0$; that is, $f(x_0) = c$. In the case when $f(b) < c < f(a)$, we define $g: [a, b] \to \mathbb{R}$ by $g(x) = c - f(x)$ for x in $[a, b]$ and follow the same argument. ∎

For a natural number n and real numbers $a_0, a_1, \ldots, a_n$, consider the equation

$$a_0 + a_1 x + \cdots + a_n x^n = 0, \qquad x \text{ in } \mathbb{R}. \tag{3.7}$$

In general, of course, this equation might not have any solution. For instance, the equation

$$1 + x^2 = 0, \qquad x \text{ in } \mathbb{R}$$

has no solution. For $n = 1$, we can easily analyze (3.7). For $n = 2$, the quadratic formula permits us to analyze (3.7). For $n = 3$ and $n = 4$, there are explicit formulas similar to, but slightly more complicated than, the quadratic formula for determining the solutions of (3.7). *However, for $n \geq 5$ there cannot be a formula for determining the solutions of (3.7) for arbitrary choices of the coefficients $a_0, a_1, \ldots, a_n$; this follows from a beautiful theorem of Galois, which, unfortunately, lies outside the scope of this book.* Hence,

---

*See I. N. Herstein, *Topics in Algebra*.

even when the function $f: \mathbb{R} \to \mathbb{R}$ is a polynomial, if its degree is greater than 4, it is usually not possible to explicitly determine the solutions of the equation

$$f(x) = 0, \qquad x \text{ in } \mathbb{R}. \tag{3.8}$$

So one can imagine how difficult it is to determine the solutions of equation (3.8) when $f: \mathbb{R} \to \mathbb{R}$ is defined in terms of, say, trigonometric and exponential functions.

However, the Intermediate Value Theorem is useful in the study of equation (3.8). If $f: \mathbb{R} \to \mathbb{R}$ is continuous and we can find numbers a and b with $a < b$ and $f(a) \cdot f(b) < 0$, then (3.8) has a solution in the open interval (a, b). Moreover, the method of proof that we gave for Theorem 3.7, which is called the *bisection method*, provides a recursive method that, after n steps, determines a subinterval of $[a, b]$ of length $(b - a)/2^{n-1}$ that contains a solution of equation (3.8).

EXAMPLE 3.5   Consider the equation

$$x^5 + x + 1 = 0, \qquad x \text{ in } \mathbb{R}.$$

We claim that there is a solution of the above equation. Indeed, define $h: \mathbb{R} \to \mathbb{R}$ by $h(x) = x^5 + x + 1$ for all x in $\mathbb{R}$. Observe that $h(-2) < 0$ and $h(0) > 0$. Thus we may apply the Intermediate Value Theorem to the restriction $h: [-2, 0] \to \mathbb{R}$ to conclude that there is a point x_0 in $(-2, 0)$ that is a solution of this equation. $\qquad\qquad \square$

There is a slightly more general form of the Intermediate Value Theorem that is of interest because it can be generalized to the situation in which one considers real-valued functions of several real variables. Recall that for real numbers a and b with $a < b$ we have called the sets

$$[a, b], (a, b), (a, b], [a, b), (-\infty, b), (-\infty, b], (a, \infty), \text{ and } [a, \infty)$$

intervals. We will also call the empty set, a set consisting of a single member, and the whole set of real numbers *intervals*. It turns out that there is a simple characterization of all intervals: *A subset I of $\mathbb{R}$ is an interval if and only if whenever the points u and v are in I and $u < v$, then the whole interval $[u, v]$ is contained in I* (see Exercise 11). This characterization of a general interval will be useful in the proof of the next result.

THEOREM 3.9   Let I be an interval and suppose that the function $f: I \to \mathbb{R}$ is continuous. Then its image $f(I)$ is an interval.

Proof   Let y_1 and y_2 be points in the image $f(I)$, with $y_1 < y_2$. We must show that $[y_1, y_2]$ is contained in $f(I)$. Indeed, let $y_1 < c < y_2$. Since y_1 and y_2 are in $f(I)$, there are points x_1 and x_2 in I with $f(x_1) = y_1$ and $f(x_2) = y_2$. If we let J be the closed interval having x_1 and x_2 as endpoints, then J is contained in I, since I is an interval. Thus, we can apply the Intermediate Value Theorem to the function $f: J \to \mathbb{R}$ in order to conclude that there is a point x_0 in J at which $f(x_0) = c$. Thus x_0 belongs to I and $f(x_0) = c$. It follows that $[y_1, y_2]$ is contained in $f(I)$. $\qquad\qquad \blacksquare$

In general, it is quite difficult to explicitly determine the image of a function. Consider even the special case when $D = [a, b]$ and the function $f: [a, b] \to \mathbb{R}$ is continuous. According to the Extreme Value Theorem, this function attains maximum and minimum functional values, m and M, and the Intermediate Value Theorem implies that it attains every value between m and M. Thus to find the image of $f: [a, b] \to \mathbb{R}$, one has to determine the maximum and minimum values of this function. Unless the function is relatively simple, it is not possible to explicitly determine these extreme values.

EXERCISES

1. Prove that there is a solution of the equation

    $$x^9 + x^2 + 4 = 0, \qquad x \text{ in } \mathbb{R}.$$

2. Prove that there is a solution of the equation

    $$\frac{1}{\sqrt{x + x^2}} + x^2 - 2x = 0, \qquad x > 0.$$

3. Let $f: [0, \infty) \to \mathbb{R}$ be a continuous function such that $f(0) = 0$ and

    $$f(x) \geq \sqrt{x} \quad \text{for all } x \geq 0.$$

    Show that for each $c > 0$ there is some $x > 0$ such that $f(x) = c$.

4. For a function $f: D \to \mathbb{R}$, a solution of the equation

    $$f(x) = x, \qquad x \text{ in } D$$

    is called a *fixed-point* of $f: D \to \mathbb{R}$. If $f: [-1, 1] \to \mathbb{R}$ is continuous, $f(-1) > -1$, and $f(1) < 1$, show that $f: [-1, 1] \to \mathbb{R}$ has a fixed-point.

5. Suppose that the functions $h: [a, b] \to \mathbb{R}$ and $g: [a, b] \to \mathbb{R}$ are continuous. Observe that a solution of the equation

    $$h(x) = g(x), \qquad x \text{ in } [a, b]$$

    corresponds to a point where the graphs intersect. Show that if $h(a) \leq g(a)$ and $h(b) \geq g(b)$, then this equation has a solution.

6. Suppose that $f: \mathbb{R} \to \mathbb{R}$ is continuous and that its image $f(\mathbb{R})$ is bounded. Prove that there is a solution of the equation

    $$f(x) = x, \qquad x \text{ in } \mathbb{R}.$$

7. Suppose that the function $f: [a, b] \to \mathbb{R}$ is continuous. For a natural number n, let $x_1, \ldots, x_n$ be points in $[a, b]$. Prove that there is a point z in $[a, b]$ at which

    $$f(z) = \frac{f(x_1) + \cdots + f(x_n)}{n}.$$

8. The proof of Theorem 3.7 has a constructive aspect: At the nth stage one has isolated an interval $[a_n, b_n]$ of length $(b - a)/2^{n-1}$ that contains a solution of the equation

    $$f(x) = 0, \qquad x \text{ in } [a, b].$$

    Find an interval of width smaller than $1/8$ that contains a solution of the equation

    $$x^2 = 2, \qquad x > 0.$$

9. Let $p: \mathbb{R} \to \mathbb{R}$ be a polynomial of odd degree. Prove that there is a solution of the equation

$$p(x) = 0, \qquad x \text{ in } \mathbb{R}.$$

10. Suppose that the function $f: [0, 1] \to \mathbb{R}$ is continuous and that its image consists entirely of rational numbers. Prove that $f: [0, 1] \to \mathbb{R}$ is a constant function.

11. Let I be a nonempty set of real numbers that has the property that if u and v are in I with $u < v$, the closed interval $[u, v]$ is contained in I. If I is bounded above, define $b = \sup I$; if I is bounded below, define $a = \inf I$. Prove the following:
    (a) If I is unbounded above and below, then $I = \mathbb{R}$.
    (b) If I is bounded below but not above, then $I = (a, \infty)$ or $I = [a, \infty)$.
    (c) If I is bounded above but not below, then $I = (-\infty, b]$ or $I = (-\infty, b)$.
    (d) If I is bounded, then I is one of the sets $[a, b], (a, b), [a, b), (a, b]$.

3.4   Images and Inverses

DEFINITION   *A function $f: D \to \mathbb{R}$ is said to be one-to-one provided that for each point y in its image $f(D)$, there is exactly one point x in its domain D such that $f(x) = y$.*

It is easy to see that the above definition is equivalent to the assertion that $f: D \to \mathbb{R}$ is one-to-one if when u and v are points in D such that $f(u) = f(v)$, then $u = v$.

For a function $f: D \to \mathbb{R}$ that is one-to-one, by definition, if y is a point in $f(D)$, there is exactly one point x in D such that $f(x) = y$. We will denote this point x by $f^{-1}(y)$, so we have defined the function

$$f^{-1}: f(D) \to \mathbb{R},$$

which we call the *inverse* of the function $f: D \to \mathbb{R}$.

In the analysis of real-valued functions of a single real variable, a particular type of one-to-one function occurs frequently, namely a function whose domain is an interval and that is strictly monotone.

DEFINITION   *The function $f: D \to \mathbb{R}$ is called strictly increasing provided that*

$$f(v) > f(u) \quad \text{for all points } u \text{ and } v \text{ in } D \text{ such that } v > u.$$

The function $f: D \to \mathbb{R}$ is called strictly decreasing provided that

$$f(v) < f(u) \quad \text{for all points } u \text{ and } v \text{ in } D \text{ such that } v > u.$$

A function that is either strictly increasing or strictly decreasing is said to be strictly monotone.

Now it is clear that if $f: D \to \mathbb{R}$ is strictly monotone, it is one-to-one and its inverse $f^{-1}: f(D) \to \mathbb{R}$ is also strictly monotone. We have the following result about the continuity of the inverse.

THEOREM 3.10 Let I be an interval and suppose that the function $f: I \to \mathbb{R}$ is strictly monotone. Then the inverse function $f^{-1}: f(I) \to \mathbb{R}$ is continuous.

Proof We will consider the case when $f: I \to \mathbb{R}$ is strictly increasing. Let $y_0 = f(x_0)$ be a point in $f(I)$. To prove that $f^{-1}: f(I) \to \mathbb{R}$ is continuous at y_0, we will argue by contradiction. Suppose that $f^{-1}: f(I) \to \mathbb{R}$ is not continuous at y_0. Then there is a sequence $\{y_n\}$, with $y_n = f(x_n)$, where x_n is in I for each natural number n, such that $\{y_n\}$ converges to y_0 but $\{x_n\}$ does not converge to x_0. This last assertion means that there is some $\epsilon_0 > 0$ such that $|x_n - x_0| \geq \epsilon_0$ for infinitely many n. We may suppose that $x_0 < x_0 + \epsilon_0 \leq x_n$ for infinitely many n. Since I is an interval, $x_0 + \epsilon_0$ belongs to I, and hence, since $f: I \to \mathbb{R}$ is strictly increasing, $f(x_0) < f(x_0 + \epsilon_0) \leq f(x_n)$ for infinitely many n. Thus the sequence $\{f(x_n)\}$ does not converge to $f(x_0)$. This contradiction proves that $f^{-1}: f(I) \to \mathbb{R}$ is continuous at y_0. ∎

The above theorem is remarkable in that we have not assumed that the function $f: I \to \mathbb{R}$ is continuous! In fact, this theorem can be used to establish the following criterion for a strictly monotone function to be continuous.

THEOREM 3.11 Let I be an interval and suppose that the function $f: I \to \mathbb{R}$ is strictly monotone. Then the function $f: I \to \mathbb{R}$ is continuous if and only if its image $f(I)$ is an interval.

Proof If the function $f: I \to \mathbb{R}$ is continuous, then, according to the Intermediate Value Theorem, as expressed in Theorem 3.9, its image $f(I)$ is an interval.

To prove the converse, suppose that $J = f(I)$ is an interval. Then $f^{-1}: J \to \mathbb{R}$ is strictly monotone. Thus we may apply the preceding theorem, with $f^{-1}: J \to \mathbb{R}$ playing the role of $f: I \to \mathbb{R}$, to conclude that $(f^{-1})^{-1}: f^{-1}(J) \to \mathbb{R}$ is continuous. However, $(f^{-1})^{-1}: f^{-1}(J) \to \mathbb{R}$ is precisely $f: I \to \mathbb{R}$. ∎

PROPOSITION 3.12 For n a natural number, define

$$f(x) = x^n \quad \text{for all } x \geq 0.$$

Then the function $f: [0, \infty) \to \mathbb{R}$ is strictly increasing and continuous, and has image equal to $[0, \infty)$. Moreover, its inverse $f^{-1}: [0, \infty) \to \mathbb{R}$ is continuous.

Proof Let $0 \leq u < v$. Then, according to the Difference in Powers formula,

$$f(v) - f(u) = (v - u) \sum_{k=0}^{n-1} v^{n-1-k} u^k > 0.$$

Thus $f: [0, \infty) \to \mathbb{R}$ is strictly increasing.

To show that $f([0, \infty)) = [0, \infty)$, let $y > 0$. We may select x_0 with $f(x_0) > y$; for instance, if $x_0 = y + 1$, then $f(x_0) = (y + 1)^n > y$. Since $f: [0, \infty) \to \mathbb{R}$ is continuous and $f(0) = 0$, it follows from the Intermediate Value Theorem, applied to the function $f: [0, x_0] \to \mathbb{R}$, that there is a positive number x such that $f(x) = y$.

The continuity of $f^{-1}: [0, \infty) \to \mathbb{R}$ is a consequence of Theorem 3.10. ∎

For a natural number n, if $f^{-1}\colon [0, \infty) \to \mathbb{R}$ is as in the above proposition, as usual, we define $x^{1/n} \equiv f^{-1}(x)$ for $x \geq 0$. Also, for each positive number x and rational number $r = m/n$, where m and n are integers with n positive, we define $x^r \equiv (x^{1/n})^m$.

EXERCISES

1. For n an odd natural number, define $f(x) = x^n$ for all x in $\mathbb{R}$. Prove that the function $f\colon \mathbb{R} \to \mathbb{R}$ is strictly increasing and $f(\mathbb{R}) = \mathbb{R}$.

2. Find the images of each of the following functions:
    (a) $f\colon [0, \infty) \to \mathbb{R}$ defined by $f(x) = 1/(1 + x^2)$ for $x \geq 0$.
    (b) $h\colon (0, 1) \to \mathbb{R}$ defined by $h(x) = 1/(x^2 + 8x)$ for $0 < x < 1$.

3. Define
    $$f(x) = \begin{cases} x & \text{if } x \leq 0 \\ x + 1 & \text{if } x > 0. \end{cases}$$
    Determine $f^{-1}\colon f(\mathbb{R}) \to \mathbb{R}$ and prove that $f^{-1}\colon f(\mathbb{R}) \to \mathbb{R}$ is continuous at 0.

4. (a) Find a continuous function $f\colon (0, 1) \to \mathbb{R}$ with image equal to $\mathbb{R}$.
    (b) Find a continuous function $f\colon (0, 1) \to \mathbb{R}$ with image equal to $[0, 1]$.
    (c) Find a continuous function $f\colon \mathbb{R} \to \mathbb{R}$ that is strictly increasing and has image equal to $(-1, 1)$.

5. Define
    $$f(x) = \begin{cases} 1 + x^2 & \text{if } x > 0 \\ 0 & \text{if } x = 0 \\ -(1 + x^2) & \text{if } x < 0. \end{cases}$$
    Show that the function $f\colon \mathbb{R} \to \mathbb{R}$ is not continuous, but that it has a continuous inverse.

6. Let $D = [0, 1] \cup (2, 3]$ and define $f\colon D \to \mathbb{R}$ by
    $$f(x) = \begin{cases} x & \text{if } 0 \leq x \leq 1 \\ x - 1 & \text{if } 2 < x \leq 3. \end{cases}$$
    Prove that $f\colon D \to \mathbb{R}$ is continuous. Determine $f^{-1}\colon f(D) \to \mathbb{R}$ and prove that $f^{-1}\colon f(D) \to \mathbb{R}$ is not continuous. Does this contradict Theorem 3.10?

7. Let K be a nonempty, compact set of real numbers and suppose that the function $f\colon K \to \mathbb{R}$ is continuous. Show that its image $f(K)$ is compact.

8. Let the function $f\colon \mathbb{R} \to \mathbb{R}$ be continuous and suppose that its image $f(\mathbb{R})$ is bounded. Prove that there is a solution of the equation
    $$f(x) = x, \qquad x \text{ in } \mathbb{R}.$$
    Now choose a number a with $f(a) > a$ and define the sequence $\{a_n\}$ recursively by defining $a_1 = a$ and $a_{n+1} = f(a_n)$ if n is a natural number for which a_n is defined. If $f\colon \mathbb{R} \to \mathbb{R}$ is strictly increasing, show that $\{a_n\}$ converges to a solution of the above equation. This method for approximating the solution is called an *iterative method*.

3.5 An Equivalent Criterion for Continuity; Uniform Continuity

For a function $f\colon D \to \mathbb{R}$ and a point x_0 in its domain D, we have defined $f\colon D \to \mathbb{R}$ to be continuous at x_0 provided that whenever a sequence $\{x_n\}$ in D converges to x_0, the image sequence $\{f(x_n)\}$ converges to $f(x_0)$. With this definition of continuity, we have been able to use the results that we proved for sequences to establish properties of continuous functions. In particular, we used the Bolzano-Weierstrass Theorem to prove the Extreme Value Theorem, and the Nested Interval Theorem to prove the Intermediate Value Theorem.

There is an equivalent way of defining continuity that gives us a different perspective from which to view this concept. From this alternative perspective, certain properties of continuous functions can be seen more clearly.

THEOREM 3.13 For a function $f: D \to \mathbb{R}$ and a point x_0 in its domain D, the following two assertions are equivalent:

   (i) The function $f: D \to \mathbb{R}$ is continuous at x_0.

   (ii) For each positive number ϵ there is a positive number δ such that

$$|f(x) - f(x_0)| < \epsilon \quad \text{for all points } x \text{ in } D \text{ such that } |x - x_0| < \delta. \qquad (3.9)$$

FIGURE 3.4

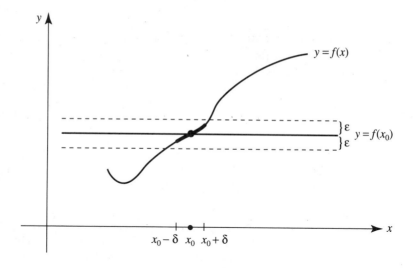

Proof First of all, suppose that $f: D \to \mathbb{R}$ is continuous at x_0. We will argue by contradiction to verify criterion (ii). Suppose that (ii) does not hold. Then there is some $\epsilon_0 > 0$ such that for $\epsilon = \epsilon_0$ there is no $\delta > 0$ for which (3.9) holds. Let n be a natural number. Then (3.9) does not hold for $\epsilon = \epsilon_0$ and $\delta = 1/n$. This means precisely that there is a point x in D such that $|x - x_0| < 1/n$ but $|f(x) - f(x_0)| \geq \epsilon_0$. Choose such a point and label it x_n. This defines a sequence $\{x_n\}$ in D that converges to x_0. But by the continuity of $f: D \to \mathbb{R}$ at x_0, $\{f(x_n)\}$ converges to $f(x_0)$. This clearly contradicts the assertion that $|f(x_n) - f(x_0)| \geq \epsilon_0$ for every natural number n. Thus (ii) holds.

Now suppose that (ii) holds. We will show that $f: D \to \mathbb{R}$ is continuous at x_0. Indeed, let $\{x_n\}$ be a sequence in D that converges to x_0. To show that $\{f(x_n)\}$ converges to $f(x_0)$, we let $\epsilon > 0$ and seek a natural number N such that

$$|f(x_n) - f(x_0)| < \epsilon \quad \text{for all integers } n \geq N. \qquad (3.10)$$

But (ii) asserts that we may select $\delta > 0$ such that (3.9) holds. Moreover, since $\{x_n\}$ converges to x_0, we can choose a natural number N such that

$$|x_n - x_0| < \delta \quad \text{for all integers } n \geq N. \tag{3.11}$$

Clearly (3.9) and (3.11) imply (3.10).   ∎

Observe the geometric meaning of the "ϵ–δ" criterion in the preceding theorem. It asserts that if one chooses a symmetric band of width 2ϵ about the line $y = f(x_0)$, then no matter how small this width is, one can find a corresponding symmetric open interval about x_0 such that the graph of the function, restricted to this interval, lies within the chosen band.

EXAMPLE 3.6   Define $f(x) = x^3$ for all x in $\mathbb{R}$. We have already proven that the function $f: \mathbb{R} \to \mathbb{R}$ is continuous. However, let us verify the "ϵ–δ" criterion of the preceding theorem at the point $x_0 = 2$. Let $\epsilon > 0$. We must find a $\delta > 0$ such that

$$|x^3 - 8| < \epsilon \quad \text{if} \quad |x - 2| < \delta.$$

But observe that the Difference in Powers formula and the Triangle Inequality imply that

$$|x^3 - 8| = |(x - 2)(x^2 + 2x + 4)|$$
$$\leq |x - 2|[|x|^2 + 2|x| + 4] \quad \text{for all } x \text{ in } \mathbb{R}.$$

However,
$$|x|^2 + 2|x| + 4 \leq 19 \quad \text{for} \quad 1 < x < 3$$

so that
$$|x^3 - 8| \leq 19|x - 2| \quad \text{if} \quad 1 < x < 3. \tag{3.12}$$

Define $\delta = \min\{1, \epsilon/19\}$. If $|x - 2| < \delta$, then x belongs to the interval $(1, 3)$ and $19|x - 2| < \epsilon$, so from (3.12) we see that $|x^3 - 8| < \epsilon$.   □

In the preceding example it is clear that for each number x_0, the choice of $\delta > 0$ that responds to an $\epsilon > 0$ challenge depends both on ϵ and on the point x_0. Frequently, when $f: D \to \mathbb{R}$ is continuous it happens that the choice of $\delta > 0$ depends only on $\epsilon > 0$ and is independent of the choice of point in D. At first glance, this may seem to be a distinction that is too fine. However, we will see when we study integration that this distinction is significant.

DEFINITION   *A function $f: D \to \mathbb{R}$ is said to be uniformly continuous provided that for each positive number ϵ there is a positive number δ such that*

$$|f(u) - f(v)| < \epsilon \quad \text{for all points } u \text{ and } v \text{ in } D \text{ such that } |u - v| < \delta. \tag{3.13}$$

It is clear that the function $f: D \to \mathbb{R}$ is uniformly continuous if and only if $f: D \to \mathbb{R}$ is continuous and that, moreover, for a point x_0 in D, if $\epsilon > 0$ is prescribed, the choice of δ in (3.9) that responds to the ϵ challenge does not depend on the particular point x_0 in D.

EXAMPLE 3.7   Define $f(x) = x^3$ for x in $[0, 20]$. Then the function $f : [0, 20] \to \mathbb{R}$ is uniformly continuous. To see this, observe that for all u and v in $[0, 20]$,

$$|f(u) - f(v)| = |u^2 + uv + v^2||u - v| \le 1200|u - v|.$$

Hence, for $\epsilon > 0$, if we define $\delta = \epsilon/1200$, then (3.13) holds.   □

EXAMPLE 3.8   Define $f(x) = 1/x$ for x in $(0, 1)$. The function $f : (0, 1) \to \mathbb{R}$ is continuous. However, it is not uniformly continuous. To verify this, we must find some $\epsilon_0 > 0$ so that for no choice of $\delta > 0$ is it true that

$$|1/u - 1/v| < \epsilon \text{ for all points } u \text{ and } v \text{ in } (0, 1) \text{ such that } |u - v| < \delta.$$

Indeed, set $\epsilon_0 = 1$. Then, given $\delta > 0$, we may find points u and v in the interval $(0, 1)$ with $|u - v| < \delta$ but $|1/u - 1/v| \ge 1$. For instance, choose u to be any point in the interval $(0, 1)$ such that $0 < u < \delta$, then let $v = u/2$. Then $|u - v| = u/2 < \delta$, but $|f(u) - f(v)| = 1/u > 1$. Thus, $f : \mathbb{R} \to \mathbb{R}$ is continuous at x_0.   □

FIGURE 3.5

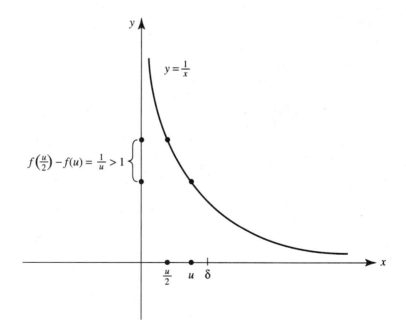

THEOREM 3.14   Suppose that the function $f : [a, b] \to \mathbb{R}$ is continuous. Then $f : [a, b] \to \mathbb{R}$ is uniformly continuous.

Proof   We will argue by contradiction. Suppose that $f:[a,b] \to \mathbb{R}$ is not uniformly continuous. Then there is some $\epsilon_0 > 0$ such that for no $\delta > 0$ is it true that

$$|f(u) - f(v)| < \epsilon_0 \quad \text{for all points } u \text{ and } v \text{ in } [a,b] \text{ such that } |u - v| < \delta.$$

Let n be a natural number. Then there are points u and v in $[a,b]$ such that $|u - v| < 1/n$ but $|f(u) - f(v)| \geq \epsilon_0$. Choose two such points and label them u_n and v_n.

This defines two sequences $\{u_n\}$ and $\{v_n\}$ in $[a,b]$. The Bolzano-Weierstrass Theorem can now be invoked to choose a subsequence $\{u_{n_k}\}$ of $\{u_n\}$ that converges to a point u in $[a,b]$. But for each natural number k, $|u_{n_k} - v_{n_k}| < 1/n_k \leq 1/k$, so the subsequence $\{v_{n_k}\}$ also converges to u. The continuity of $f:[a,b] \to \mathbb{R}$ at u implies that both $\{f(u_{n_k})\}$ and $\{f(v_{n_k})\}$ converge to $f(u)$. Thus, their difference $\{f(u_{n_k}) - f(v_{n_k})\}$ converges to 0. This contradicts the property that for each natural number k, $|f(u_{n_k}) - f(v_{n_k})| \geq \epsilon_0$. It follows that $f:[a,b] \to \mathbb{R}$ is uniformly continuous. ∎

An examination of the above proof shows that the only property of the domain of the function $f:[a,b] \to \mathbb{R}$ that was used was the compactness of $[a,b]$. Hence the theorem is true for a continuous function $f: K \to \mathbb{R}$ provided that its domain K is compact. We leave the proof as an exercise.

EXERCISES

1. Define $f(x) = x^2$ for all x in $\mathbb{R}$. Verify the "ϵ-δ" criterion for continuity at $x = 2$ and at $x = 50$.

2. Define $f(x) = \sqrt{x}$ for all $x \geq 0$. Verify the "ϵ-δ" criterion for continuity at $x = 4$ and at $x = 9$.

3. Define $f(x) = x^3$ for all x in $\mathbb{R}$. Verify the "ϵ-δ" criterion for continuity at each point x_0.

4. Define

$$f(x) = \begin{cases} x & \text{if } x < 0 \\ x+1 & \text{if } x \geq 0. \end{cases}$$

Use the "ϵ-δ" criterion for continuity to show that $f: \mathbb{R} \to \mathbb{R}$ is not continuous at 0.

5. Define $g(x) = 6x + 7$ for all x in $\mathbb{R}$. Prove that the function $g: \mathbb{R} \to \mathbb{R}$ is uniformly continuous.

6. Define $h(x) = 1/(1 + x^2)$ for all x in $\mathbb{R}$. Prove that the function $h: \mathbb{R} \to \mathbb{R}$ is uniformly continuous.

7. Define $f(x) = x/(x - 1)$ for $x \geq 2$. Prove that the function $f:[2, \infty) \to \mathbb{R}$ is uniformly continuous.

8. Define $f(x) = 1/x$ for $1/100 \leq x \leq 1$. Prove that the function $f:[1/100, 1] \to \mathbb{R}$ is uniformly continuous.

9. Define $h(x) = \sqrt{x + 1} - \sqrt{x}$ for $x \geq 0$. Prove that the function $h:[0, \infty) \to \mathbb{R}$ is uniformly continuous.

10. Define $f(x) = x^3$ for all x in $\mathbb{R}$. Prove that the function $f: \mathbb{R} \to \mathbb{R}$ is not uniformly continuous.

11. For an open interval $I = (a, b)$, find a continuous function $f: I \to \mathbb{R}$ that is not uniformly continuous.

12. Prove that the sum of uniformly continuous functions is uniformly continuous. Is the product of uniformly continuous functions uniformly continuous?

13.   A function $f: D \rightarrow \mathbb{R}$ is called a *Lipschitz function* if there is some $c \geq 0$ such that

$$|f(u) - f(v)| \leq c|u - v| \quad \text{for all points } u \text{ and } v \text{ in } D.$$

   Prove that if $f: D \rightarrow \mathbb{R}$ is a Lipschitz function, then it is uniformly continuous.
14.   Define $f(x) = \sqrt{x}$ for $0 \leq x \leq 1$. Prove that the function $f: [0, 1] \rightarrow \mathbb{R}$ is uniformly continuous, but that it is not a Lipschitz function.
15.   Define the function $h: [1, 2] \rightarrow \mathbb{R}$ as follows: $h(x) = 0$ if the point x in $[1, 2]$ is irrational; $h(x) = 1/n$ if the point x in $[1, 2]$ is rational and $x = m/n$, where m and n are natural numbers having no common positive integer factor other than 1.
   (a)   Prove that $h: [1, 2] \rightarrow \mathbb{R}$ fails to be continuous at each rational number in $[1, 2]$.
   (b)   Prove that if $\epsilon > 0$, then the set $\{x \text{ in } [1, 2] \mid h(x) > \epsilon\}$ has only a finite number of points.
   (c)   Use (b) to prove that $h: [1, 2] \rightarrow \mathbb{R}$ is continuous at each irrational number in $[1, 2]$.
16.   Suppose that the function $f: (a, b) \rightarrow \mathbb{R}$ is uniformly continuous. Prove that $f: (a, b) \rightarrow \mathbb{R}$ is bounded.
17.   Suppose that the functions $g: (a, b) \rightarrow \mathbb{R}$ and $h: (a, b) \rightarrow \mathbb{R}$ are uniformly continuous. Prove that $gh: (a, b) \rightarrow \mathbb{R}$ is also uniformly continuous.
18.   A continuous function $f: (a, b) \rightarrow \mathbb{R}$ is said to be *continuously extendable* to $[a, b]$ if there is a continuous function whose domain is $[a, b]$ and whose restriction to (a, b) is $f: (a, b) \rightarrow \mathbb{R}$. Prove that $f: (a, b) \rightarrow \mathbb{R}$ is continuously extendable to $[a, b]$ if and only if $f: (a, b) \rightarrow \mathbb{R}$ is uniformly continuous.
19.   Suppose that $f: (a, b) \rightarrow \mathbb{R}$ is continuous and monotone. Prove that $f: (a, b) \rightarrow \mathbb{R}$ is uniformly continuous if and only if its image $f(a, b)$ is bounded.
20.   Rewrite the proof of Theorem 3.14, with the interval $[a, b]$ replaced by a compact set K.

3.6   Limits

In the preceding sections of this chapter we have studied the properties of continuous functions. We now turn to the study of the behavior of functions near points that are not necessarily in the domain of the given function.

DEFINITION   *For a set D of real numbers, the number x_0 is called a limit point of D provided that there is a sequence of points in $D \setminus \{x_0\}$ that converges to x_0.*

EXAMPLE 3.9   For numbers a and b such that $a < b$, both a and b are limit points of the open interval (a, b), although neither point belongs to (a, b). To see that a is a limit point of (a, b), observe that $\{a + (b - a)/2n\}$ is a sequence in (a, b), distinct from a, that converges to a. Also, every point x_0 in (a, b) is also a limit point of (a, b), because for such a point the sequence $\{x_0 + (b - x_0)/2n\}$ is a sequence in (a, b), distinct from x_0, that converges to x_0. □

EXAMPLE 3.10 Every real number is a limit point of $\mathbb{Q}$, the set of rational numbers. Indeed, let x_0 be any real number. Then, by the density of the rational numbers (Theorem 1.11), for each natural number n we may select a rational number q_n in the interval $(x_0, x_0 + 1/n)$. Then $\{q_n\}$ is a sequence of rational numbers, distinct from x_0, that converges to x_0. A similar argument shows that every real number is also a limit point of the set of irrational numbers. $\square$

DEFINITION *Given a function $f: D \to \mathbb{R}$ and a limit point x_0 of its domain D, for a number ℓ, we write*

$$\lim_{x \to x_0} f(x) = \ell \tag{3.14}$$

provided that whenever $\{x_n\}$ is a sequence in $D\backslash\{x_0\}$ that converges to x_0,

$$\lim_{n \to \infty} f(x_n) = \ell.$$

We read (3.14) as "The limit of $f(x)$ as x approaches x_0, with x in D, equals ℓ."

For a function $f: D \to \mathbb{R}$ and point x_0 that is a limit point of its domain D, if there is a number ℓ such that $\lim_{x \to x_0} f(x) = \ell$, we write "$\lim_{x \to x_0} f(x)$ exists," and if there is no such number ℓ we write "$\lim_{x \to x_0} f(x)$ does not exist."

Comparing the definition of *limit* with the definition of *continuity* of a function at a point in its domain, it is not difficult (see Exercise 9) to see that if the number x_0 is a limit point of the set of numbers D and also belongs to D, then a function $f: D \to \mathbb{R}$ is continuous at x_0 if and only if

$$\lim_{x \to x_0} f(x) = f(x_0).$$

Therefore, since we have already provided many examples of continuous functions, we have already computed many limits.

EXAMPLE 3.11 We have proven that the quotient of polynomials is continuous at points where the denominator is nonzero, that the square root function is continuous, and that composition of continuous functions is continuous. From this it follows that

$$\lim_{x \to 2} \sqrt{\frac{3x + 3}{x^3 - 4}} = \frac{3}{2}. \qquad \square$$

EXAMPLE 3.12

$$\lim_{x \to 1} \frac{x^2 - 1}{x - 1} = 2. \qquad (3.15)$$

To verify this, we let the sequence $\{x_n\}$ converge to 1, with $x_n \neq 1$ for all n. Then, by the Difference of Squares Formula, $[x_n^2 - 1]/[x_n - 1] = x_n + 1$ for all n. By the sum and product properties of convergent sequences,

$$\lim_{n \to \infty} \frac{x_n^2 - 1}{x_n - 1} = \lim_{n \to \infty} [x_n + 1] = 2,$$

and this proves (3.15). $\qquad \qquad \square$

EXAMPLE 3.13

$$\lim_{x \to 8} \frac{x - 8}{x^{1/3} - 2} = 12. \qquad (3.16)$$

To verify this, we let the sequence $\{x_n\}$ converge to 8, with $x_n \neq 8$ for all n. Then, by the Difference of Cubes Formula, for each n,

$$x - 8 = (x^{1/3})^3 - 2^3 = (x^{1/3} - 2)(x^{2/3} + 2x^{1/3} + 4),$$

so that by the continuity of the nth root functions,

$$\lim_{n \to \infty} \frac{x_n - 8}{x_n^{1/3} - 2} = \lim_{n \to \infty} [x_n^{2/3} + 2x_n^{1/3} + 4] = 12. \qquad \square$$

For a function $f : D \to \mathbb{R}$ and a subset U of its domain D having x_0 as a limit point, we define

$$\lim_{x \to x_0, x \in U} f(x) = \ell$$

to mean that whenever $\{x_n\}$ is a sequence in $U \setminus \{x_0\}$ that converges to x_0, then $\{f(x_n)\}$ converges to ℓ. If the point x_0 is a limit point of the set $\{x$ in $D \mid x > x_0\}$ and also of the set $\{x$ in $D \mid x < x_0\}$, then

$$\lim_{x \to x_0} f(x) = \ell \quad \text{if and only if} \quad \lim_{x \to x_0, x > x_0} f(x) = \lim_{x \to x_0, x < x_0} f(x) = \ell.$$

We leave the proof of this equivalence as an exercise.

EXAMPLE 3.14   We will show that

$$\lim_{x \to 0, x>0} \frac{|x|}{x} = 1 \quad \text{and} \quad \lim_{x \to 0, x<0} \frac{|x|}{x} = -1 \quad \text{but that} \quad \lim_{x \to 0, x \neq 0} \frac{|x|}{x} \quad \text{does not exist.}$$

Observe that if $x \neq 0$, then

$$\frac{|x|}{x} = \begin{cases} 1 & \text{if } x > 0 \\ -1 & \text{if } x < 0. \end{cases}$$

To verify that $\lim_{x \to 0, x>0} |x|/x = 1$, just observe that if $\{x_n\}$ is a sequence of positive numbers that converges to 0, then $\{x_n/|x_n|\}$ is a sequence with constant value 1, so $\lim_{n \to \infty} x_n/|x_n| = 1$. Similarly, if $\{x_n\}$ is a sequence of negative numbers that converges to 0, then $\{x_n/|x_n|\}$ is a sequence with constant value -1, so $\lim_{n \to \infty} x_n/|x_n| = -1$. Finally, $\lim_{x \to 0} |x|/x$ does not exist, since $\lim_{x \to 0, x<0} f(x) \neq \lim_{x \to 0, x>0} f(x)$.   □

EXAMPLE 3.15   Define the function $f: \mathbb{R} \to \mathbb{R}$ by

$$f(x) = \begin{cases} 1 & \text{if } x \text{ is rational} \\ 0 & \text{if } x \text{ is irrational.} \end{cases}$$

This function is called *Dirichlet's function*. There is no point x_0 in $\mathbb{R}$ at which $\lim_{x \to x_0} f(x)$ exists. This follows from Example 3.3, in which we showed that there is no point at which the Dirichlet function is continuous.   □

The following theorem is an analogue, and also a consequence, of the sum, product, and quotient properties of convergent sequences. A completely similar result was established for continuous functions in Section 3.1.

THEOREM 3.15   For functions $f: D \to \mathbb{R}$ and $g: D \to \mathbb{R}$, and a limit point x_0 of their domains D, suppose that

$$\lim_{x \to x_0} f(x) = A \quad \text{and} \quad \lim_{x \to x_0} g(x) = B.$$

Then
$$\lim_{x \to x_0} [f(x) + g(x)] = A + B, \tag{3.17}$$

$$\lim_{x \to x_0} [f(x)g(x)] = AB, \tag{3.18}$$

and, if $B \neq 0$ and $g(x) \neq 0$ for all x in D,

$$\lim_{x \to x_0} \frac{f(x)}{g(x)} = \frac{A}{B}. \tag{3.19}$$

Proof Let $\{x_n\}$ be a sequence in $D\backslash\{x_0\}$ that converges to x_0. From the definition of limit, it follows that

$$\lim_{n\to\infty} f(x_n) = A \quad \text{and} \quad \lim_{n\to\infty} g(x_n) = B.$$

The sum property of convergent sequences implies that

$$\lim_{n\to\infty} [f(x_n) + g(x_n)] = A + B, \tag{3.20}$$

and the product property of convergent sequences implies that

$$\lim_{n\to\infty} [f(x_n)g(x_n)] = AB. \tag{3.21}$$

If $g(x) \neq 0$ for all x in D, the quotient property of convergent sequences implies that

$$\lim_{n\to\infty} \frac{f(x_n)}{g(x_n)} = \frac{A}{B}. \tag{3.22}$$

From the definition of limit, (3.17), (3.18), and (3.19) follow from (3.20), (3.21), and (3.22), respectively. ∎

We have the following composition property for limits.

THEOREM 3.16 For functions $f: D \to \mathbb{R}$ and $g: U \to \mathbb{R}$, suppose that x_0 is a limit point of D such that

$$\lim_{x\to x_0} f(x) = y_0, \tag{3.23}$$

and that y_0 is a limit point of U such that

$$\lim_{y\to y_0} g(y) = \ell. \tag{3.24}$$

Moreover, suppose that

$$f(D\backslash\{x_0\}) \quad \text{is contained in} \quad U\backslash\{y_0\}. \tag{3.25}$$

Then
$$\lim_{x\to x_0} (g \circ f)(x) = \ell.$$

Proof Let $\{x_n\}$ be a sequence in $D\backslash\{x_0\}$ that converges to x_0. From (3.23) it follows that $\{f(x_n)\}$ converges to y_0. Set $y_n = f(x_n)$ for each natural number n. Then the sequence $\{y_n\}$ converges to y_0, and assumption (3.25) implies that $\{y_n\}$ is a sequence in $U\backslash\{y_0\}$. From (3.24) it follows that $\{g(y_n)\}$ converges to ℓ. Thus,

$$\lim_{n\to\infty} (g \circ f)(x_n) = \ell. \qquad ∎$$

EXAMPLE 3.16   Suppose that the function $f: \mathbb{R} \to \mathbb{R}$ has the property that

$$\lim_{x \to 0} \frac{f(x) - f(0)}{x} = \ell.$$

From the composition property of limits it follows that if k is any natural number, then

$$\lim_{x \to 0} \frac{f(x^k) - f(0)}{x^k} = \ell.$$

Moreover, for any $c \neq 0$, the composition property also implies that

$$\lim_{x \to 0} \frac{f(cx) - f(0)}{cx} = \ell,$$

and so $\displaystyle\lim_{x \to 0} \frac{f(cx) - f(0)}{x} = c \lim_{x \to 0} \frac{f(cx) - f(0)}{cx} = c\ell.$ □

EXERCISES

1. Find the following limits or determine that they do not exist:

   (a) $\lim_{x \to 0} |x|$

   (b) $\lim_{x \to 0, x > 0} \dfrac{x + \sqrt{x}}{2 + \sqrt{x}}$

   (c) $\lim_{x \to 0} \dfrac{|x|^2}{x}$

   (d) $\lim_{x \to 0} \dfrac{1}{x}$

 2. Prove that

   (a) $\lim_{x \to 1} \dfrac{x^4 - 1}{x - 1} = 4$

   (b) $\lim_{x \to 1} \dfrac{\sqrt{x} - 1}{x - 1} = \dfrac{1}{2}$

3. Define the function $f: \mathbb{R} \to \mathbb{R}$ by $f(x) = x$ if $x \neq 0$, and $f(0) = 4$. Show that $\lim_{x \to 0} f(x) = 0$.

4. Find the following limits or determine that they do not exist:

   (a) $\lim_{x \to 0} \dfrac{1 + 1/x}{1 + 1/x^2}$

   (b) $\lim_{x \to 0} \dfrac{1 + 1/x^2}{1 + 1/x}$

   (c) $\lim_{x \to 1} \dfrac{1 + 1/(x - 1)}{2 + 1/(x - 1)^2}$

5. For functions $f: D \to \mathbb{R}$ and $g: D \to \mathbb{R}$, with x_0 a limit point of D, suppose that $\lim_{x \to x_0} [f(x) + g(x)]$ exists. Can any conclusion be drawn about $\lim_{x \to x_0} f(x)$?

6. Let D be the set of real numbers consisting of the single number x_0. Show that the set D has no limit points. Also show that the set $\mathbb{N}$ of natural numbers has no limit points.

7. Let D be a nonempty subset of $\mathbb{R}$ that is bounded above. Is the supremum of D a limit point of D?

8. Explain why, in the definition of $\lim_{x \to x_0} f(x)$, it is necessary to require that x_0 be a limit point of D.

9. (a) A point x_0 in D is said to be an *isolated point* of D provided that there is an $r > 0$ such that the only point of D in the interval $(x_0 - r, x_0 + r)$ is x_0 itself. Prove that a point x_0 in D is either an isolated point or a limit point of D.

   (b) Suppose that x_0 is an isolated point of D. Prove that every function $f: D \to \mathbb{R}$ is continuous at x_0.

(c)   Prove that if the point x_0 in D is a limit point of D, then a function $f: D \to \mathbb{R}$ is continuous at x_0 if and only if $\lim_{x \to x_0} f(x) = f(x_0)$.

10.   Suppose the function $f: \mathbb{R} \to \mathbb{R}$ has the property that there is some $M > 0$ such that

$$|f(x)| \le M|x|^2 \quad \text{for all } x \text{ in } \mathbb{R}.$$

Prove that

$$\lim_{x \to 0} f(x) = 0 \quad \text{and} \quad \lim_{x \to 0} \frac{f(x)}{x} = 0.$$

11.   For each number x, define $f(x)$ to be the largest integer that is less than or equal to x. Graph the function $f: \mathbb{R} \to \mathbb{R}$. Given a number x_0, analyze the following limits:

(a) $\lim_{x \to x_0, x < x_0} f(x)$ (b) $\lim_{x \to x_0, x > x_0} f(x)$

12.   Let k be a natural number. Prove that

$$\lim_{x \to 1} \frac{x^k - 1}{x - 1} = k.$$

13.   (A general Squeezing Principle.) Let the number x_0 be a limit point of the set D and suppose that the functions $f: D \to \mathbb{R}$, $g: D \to \mathbb{R}$, and $h: D \to \mathbb{R}$ have the property that

$$f(x) \le g(x) \le h(x) \quad \text{for all } x \text{ in } D.$$

If $\lim_{x \to x_0} f(x) = \lim_{x \to x_0} h(x) = \ell$, prove that $\lim_{x \to x_0} g(x) = \ell$.

14.   (A general Monotone Convergence Principle.) Let a and b be numbers with $a < b$ and set $I = (a, b)$. Suppose that the function $f: I \to \mathbb{R}$ is bounded, and is monotone increasing in the sense that if u and v are in I and $u < v$, then $f(u) \le f(v)$. Prove that $\lim_{x \to a} f(x)$ exists and that $\lim_{x \to b} f(x)$ exists.

4 Differentiation

4.1 The Algebra of Derivatives

The simplest type of function $f: \mathbb{R} \to \mathbb{R}$ is one whose graph is a line. For such a function, the ratio

$$\frac{f(x_1) - f(x_2)}{x_1 - x_2},$$

where $x_1 \neq x_2$, does not depend on the choice of points x_1 and x_2. We denote this ratio by m and call m the *slope* of the graph of $f: \mathbb{R} \to \mathbb{R}$. So a function $f: \mathbb{R} \to \mathbb{R}$ whose graph is a line is completely determined by prescribing its functional value at one point, say at x_0, and then prescribing its slope m; it is then defined by the formula

$$f(x) = f(x_0) + m(x - x_0) \quad \text{for all } x \text{ in } \mathbb{R}. \tag{4.1}$$

For a function whose graph is not a line, it makes no sense to speak of "the slope of the graph." However, many functions have the property that at certain points on their graph, the graph can be approximated, in a sense that we will soon make precise, by a tangent line. One then defines the slope of the graph at that point to be the slope of the tangent line. The slope will vary from point to point, and when we can determine the

68

slope at each point we have very useful information for analyzing the function. This is the basic geometric idea behind differentiation.

To make the above precise, we need to define *tangent line*. For a function $f: I \to \mathbb{R}$, where I is an open interval containing the point x_0, observe that for a point x in I, with $x \neq x_0$, the slope of the line joining the points $(x_0, f(x_0))$ and $(x, f(x))$ is

$$\frac{f(x) - f(x_0)}{x - x_0}.$$

FIGURE 4.1

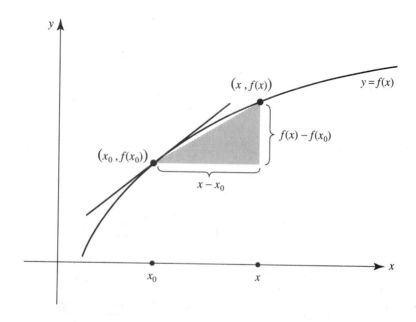

It is reasonable to expect that if there is a tangent line to the graph of $f: I \to \mathbb{R}$ at $(x_0, f(x_0))$, which has a slope m_0, then one should have

$$\lim_{x \to x_0} \frac{f(x) - f(x_0)}{x - x_0} = m_0.$$

DEFINITION *Let I be an open interval containing the point x_0. Then the function $f: I \to \mathbb{R}$ is said to be differentiable at x_0 if*

$$\lim_{x \to x_0} \frac{f(x) - f(x_0)}{x - x_0} \tag{4.2}$$

exists, in which case we denote this limit by $f'(x_0)$ and call it the derivative of $f: I \to \mathbb{R}$ at x_0; that is

$$f'(x_0) \equiv \lim_{x \to x_0} \frac{f(x) - f(x_0)}{x - x_0}. \tag{4.3}$$

If the function $f: I \to \mathbb{R}$ is differentiable at every point in I, we say that $f: I \to \mathbb{R}$ is differentiable and call the function $f': I \to \mathbb{R}$ the derivative of $f: I \to \mathbb{R}$.

For a function $f: I \to \mathbb{R}$ that is differentiable at x_0, we call the line determined by the equation

$$y = f(x_0) + f'(x_0)(x - x_0) \quad \text{for all } x \text{ in } \mathbb{R}$$

the *tangent line to the graph of* $f: I \to \mathbb{R}$ *at the point* $(x_0, f(x_0))$.

Observe that if I is an open interval containing the point x_0 and the function $f: I \to \mathbb{R}$ is continuous at x_0, then no matter what number m is chosen, the line determined by the graph of

$$g(x) = f(x_0) + m(x - x_0) \quad \text{for all } x \text{ in } \mathbb{R}$$

contains the point $(x_0, f(x_0))$ and is a "good approximation to $f: I \to \mathbb{R}$ near x_0" in the sense that

$$\lim_{x \to x_0} [f(x) - g(x)] = \lim_{x \to x_0} [f(x) - f(x_0) - m(x - x_0)] = 0.$$

Does there exist a line—that is, a choice of m—that has the much better approximation property

$$\lim_{x \to x_0} \frac{f(x) - g(x)}{x - x_0} = 0?$$

Since

$$\frac{f(x) - g(x)}{x - x_0} = \frac{f(x) - f(x_0)}{x - x_0} - m \quad \text{if } x \neq x_0 \text{ is in } I,$$

it is clear that the preceding approximation property holds if and only if the function $f: I \to \mathbb{R}$ is differentiable at x_0 and one chooses $m = f'(x_0)$.

We will devote this chapter to the study of differentiation. In Chapters 6 and 7 we will study integration. Once we have understood differentiation and integration, we will prove a version of formula (4.1) for differentiable functions whose graphs are not lines; it is called a Fundamental Theorem of Calculus.*

Observe that since $\lim_{x \to x_0} [x - x_0] = 0$, we cannot use the quotient formula for limits in the determination of differentiability. To overcome this obstacle, in this and the next section we will develop techniques for evaluating limits of the type (4.2), which are referred to as *differentiation rules*. Before turning to these, we will consider some specific examples.

---

*For a differentiable function $f: \mathbb{R} \to \mathbb{R}$ whose derivative is continuous, formula (4.1) becomes

$$f(x) = f(x_0) + \int_{x_0}^{x} f'(t)\, dt \quad \text{for all } x \text{ in } \mathbb{R}.$$

The symbols and the formula will be explained in Chapters 6 and 7.

EXAMPLE 4.1 Define $f(x) = mx + b$ for all x in $\mathbb{R}$. Then $f: \mathbb{R} \to \mathbb{R}$ is differentiable and

$$f'(x) = m \quad \text{for all } x \text{ in } \mathbb{R}.$$

This is clear since for each x_0 in $\mathbb{R}$,

$$\lim_{x \to x_0} \frac{f(x) - f(x_0)}{x - x_0} = \lim_{x \to x_0} \frac{m(x - x_0)}{x - x_0} = m. \qquad \square$$

EXAMPLE 4.2 Consider the simplest function whose graph is not a line. Define $f(x) = x^2$ for all x in $\mathbb{R}$. Then $f: \mathbb{R} \to \mathbb{R}$ is differentiable and

$$f'(x) = 2x \quad \text{for all } x \text{ in } \mathbb{R}.$$

Indeed, for each x_0 in $\mathbb{R}$,

$$\frac{f(x) - f(x_0)}{x - x_0} = \frac{x^2 - x_0^2}{x - x_0} = x + x_0 \quad \text{if } x \neq x_0,$$

and so

$$\lim_{x \to x_0} \frac{f(x) - f(x_0)}{x - x_0} = \lim_{x \to x_0} [x + x_0] = 2x_0. \qquad \square$$

More generally, we have:

PROPOSITION 4.1 For a natural number n, define $f(x) = x^n$ for all x in $\mathbb{R}$. Then the function $f: \mathbb{R} \to \mathbb{R}$ is differentiable and

$$f'(x) = nx^{n-1} \quad \text{for all } x \text{ in } \mathbb{R}.$$

Proof Fix a number x_0. Observe that by the Difference of Powers Formula,

$$x^n - x_0^n = (x - x_0)(x^{n-1} + x^{n-2}x_0 + \cdots + xx_0^{n-2} + x_0^{n-1}) \quad \text{for all } x \text{ in } \mathbb{R},$$

and hence

$$\frac{f(x) - f(x_0)}{x - x_0} = x^{n-1} + x^{n-2}x_0 + \cdots + xx_0^{n-2} + x_0^{n-1} \quad \text{if} \quad x \neq x_0.$$

Thus, by the sum and product properties of limits,

$$\lim_{x \to x_0} \frac{f(x) - f(x_0)}{x - x_0} = nx_0^{n-1}. \qquad \blacksquare$$

EXAMPLE 4.3   Define $f(x) = |x|$ for all x in $\mathbb{R}$. Then $f: \mathbb{R} \to \mathbb{R}$ is not differentiable at $x = 0$. To see this, observe that

$$\lim_{x \to 0, x > 0} \frac{f(x) - f(0)}{x - 0} = \lim_{x \to 0, x > 0} \frac{|x|}{x} = 1$$

while $$\lim_{x \to 0, x < 0} \frac{f(x) - f(0)}{x - 0} = \lim_{x \to 0, x < 0} \frac{|x|}{x} = -1.$$

Thus $\lim_{x \to 0}[f(x) - f(0)]/[x - 0]$ does not exist. It is easy to see that if $x \neq 0$, then $f: \mathbb{R} \to \mathbb{R}$ is differentiable at x, and $f'(x) = 1$ if $x > 0$, while $f'(x) = -1$ if $x < 0$.   □

Let us now turn to some general results. We will use the sum, product, and quotient properties of limits to determine formulas for the derivative of the sum, product, and quotient of differentiable functions. Before doing so, we will prove that differentiability implies continuity.

PROPOSITION 4.2   Let I be an open interval containing the point x_0, and suppose that the function $f: I \to \mathbb{R}$ is differentiable at x_0. Then $f: I \to \mathbb{R}$ is continuous at x_0.

Proof   Since

$$\lim_{x \to x_0} \frac{f(x) - f(x_0)}{x - x_0} = f'(x_0) \quad \text{and} \quad \lim_{x \to x_0} [x - x_0] = 0,$$

it follows from the product property of limits that

$$\lim_{x \to x_0} [f(x) - f(x_0)] = \lim_{x \to x_0} \left[\frac{f(x) - f(x_0)}{x - x_0} \cdot (x - x_0) \right] = f'(x_0) \cdot 0 = 0.$$

Thus $\lim_{x \to x_0} f(x) = f(x_0)$, which means that $f: I \to \mathbb{R}$ is continuous at x_0.   ∎

As Example (4.3) shows, it is not true that continuity implies differentiability.

THEOREM 4.3   Let I be an open interval containing the point x_0, and suppose that the functions $f: I \to \mathbb{R}$ and $g: I \to \mathbb{R}$ are differentiable at x_0. Then

(i) $f + g: I \to \mathbb{R}$ is differentiable at x_0 and

$$(f + g)'(x_0) = f'(x_0) + g'(x_0),$$

(ii) $fg: I \to \mathbb{R}$ is differentiable at x_0 and

$$(fg)'(x_0) = f(x_0)g'(x_0) + f'(x_0)g(x_0),$$

and

(iii) if $g(x) \neq 0$ for all x in I, then $f/g: I \to \mathbb{R}$ is differentiable at x_0 and

$$(f/g)'(x_0) = \frac{g(x_0)f'(x_0) - f(x_0)g'(x_0)}{\left(g(x_0)\right)^2}.$$

Proof of (i) For x in I, with $x \neq x_0$,

$$\frac{(f+g)(x) - (f+g)(x_0)}{x - x_0} = \frac{f(x) - f(x_0)}{x - x_0} + \frac{g(x) - g(x_0)}{x - x_0}.$$

Hence, by the definition of derivative and the sum property of limits,

$$\lim_{x \to x_0} \left[\frac{(f+g)(x) - (f+g)(x_0)}{x - x_0} \right] = f'(x_0) + g'(x_0).$$

Proof of (ii) For x in I, with $x \neq x_0$,

$$\frac{(fg)(x) - (fg)(x_0)}{x - x_0} = \frac{f(x)g(x) - f(x_0)g(x_0)}{x - x_0}$$

$$= \frac{f(x)g(x) - f(x)g(x_0) + f(x)g(x_0) - f(x_0)g(x_0)}{x - x_0}$$

$$= f(x)\left[\frac{g(x) - g(x_0)}{x - x_0} \right] + g(x_0)\left[\frac{f(x) - f(x_0)}{x - x_0} \right].$$

Since differentiability implies continuity, $\lim_{x \to x_0} f(x) = f(x_0)$. Consequently, using the definition of derivative and the addition and product properties for limits,

$$\lim_{x \to x_0} \left[\frac{(fg)(x) - (fg)(x_0)}{x - x_0} \right] = f(x_0)g'(x_0) + g(x_0)f'(x_0).$$

Proof of (iii) For x in I, with $x \neq x_0$,

$$\frac{(f/g)(x) - (f/g)(x_0)}{x - x_0}$$

$$= \frac{f(x)/g(x) - f(x_0)/g(x_0)}{x - x_0}$$

$$= \frac{1}{g(x)g(x_0)}\left[\frac{f(x)g(x_0) - f(x_0)g(x)}{x - x_0} \right]$$

$$= \frac{1}{g(x)g(x_0)}\left[\frac{f(x)g(x_0) - f(x_0)g(x_0) + f(x_0)g(x_0) - f(x_0)g(x)}{x - x_0} \right]$$

$$= \frac{1}{g(x)g(x_0)}\left[g(x_0)\left\{ \frac{f(x) - f(x_0)}{x - x_0} \right\} - f(x_0)\left\{ \frac{g(x) - g(x_0)}{x - x_0} \right\} \right].$$

Since differentiability implies continuity, $\lim_{x \to x_0} g(x) = g(x_0)$. Hence we may use the definition of derivative together with the sum, product, and quotient properties of limits to conclude from the preceding identity that

$$\lim_{x \to x_0} \left[\frac{(f/g)(x) - (f/g)(x_0)}{x - x_0} \right] = \frac{g(x_0)f'(x_0) - f(x_0)g'(x_0)}{(g(x_0))^2}. \qquad \blacksquare$$

PROPOSITION 4.4

For an integer n, define $\mathcal{O} = \mathbb{R}$ if $n \geq 0$ and $\mathcal{O} = \{x \text{ in } \mathbb{R} \mid x \neq 0\}$ if $n < 0$. Then define

$$f(x) = x^n \quad \text{for all } x \text{ in } \mathcal{O}.$$

The function $f: \mathcal{O} \to \mathbb{R}$ is differentiable and

$$f'(x) = nx^{n-1} \quad \text{for all } x \text{ in } \mathcal{O}.$$

Proof The case in which $n > 0$ is precisely Proposition 4.1, so we need only consider the case $n < 0$. But if $n < 0$, then

$$f(x) = \frac{1}{x^{-n}} \quad \text{for all } x \text{ in } \mathcal{O},$$

where $-n$ is a natural number. Then from Proposition 4.1 and the quotient formula for derivatives, it follows that $f: \mathcal{O} \to \mathbb{R}$ is differentiable and

$$f'(x) = \frac{x^{-n} \cdot 0 - (-n)x^{-n-1} \cdot 1}{(x^{-n})^2}$$

$$= nx^{2n-n-1}$$

$$= nx^{n-1} \quad \text{for } x \text{ in } \mathcal{O}. \qquad \blacksquare$$

COROLLARY 4.5

For polynomials $p: \mathbb{R} \to \mathbb{R}$ and $q: \mathbb{R} \to \mathbb{R}$, define $\mathcal{O} = \{x \text{ in } \mathbb{R} \mid q(x) \neq 0\}$. Then the quotient $p/q: \mathcal{O} \to \mathbb{R}$ is differentiable.

Proof From Proposition 4.1 and parts (i) and (ii) of Theorem 4.3 it follows that both $p: \mathcal{O} \to \mathbb{R}$ and $q: \mathcal{O} \to \mathbb{R}$ are differentiable. Then part (iii) of Theorem 4.3 implies that $p/q: \mathcal{O} \to \mathbb{R}$ is differentiable. $\qquad \blacksquare$

EXERCISES

1. Use the definition of derivative to compute the derivative of the following functions at $x = 1$:
   (a) $f(x) = \sqrt{x+1}$ for all $x > 0$.
   (b) $f(x) = x^3 + 2x$ for all x in $\mathbb{R}$.
   (c) $f(x) = 1/(1+x^2)$ for all x in $\mathbb{R}$.

2. Define $f(x) = x^3 + 2x + 1$ for all x in $\mathbb{R}$. Find the equation of the tangent line to the graph of $f: \mathbb{R} \to \mathbb{R}$ at the point $(2, 13)$.

3. For m_1 and m_2 distinct real numbers, define

$$f(x) = \begin{cases} m_1 x + 4 & \text{if } x \leq 0 \\ m_2 x + 4 & \text{if } x \geq 0. \end{cases}$$

   Prove that the function $f: \mathbb{R} \to \mathbb{R}$ is continuous but not differentiable at $x = 0$.

4. Evaluate the following limits or determine that they do not exist:
   (a) $\lim_{x \to 0} \dfrac{x^2}{x}$
   (b) $\lim_{x \to 1} \dfrac{x^2 - 1}{\sqrt{x} - 1}$
   (c) $\lim_{x \to 0} \dfrac{x - 1}{\sqrt{x} - 1}$
   (d) $\lim_{x \to 2} \dfrac{x^4 - 16}{x - 2}$

5. For a natural number $n \geq 2$, define
$$f(x) = \begin{cases} 0 & \text{if } x \leq 0 \\ x^n & \text{if } x > 0. \end{cases}$$
    Prove that the function $f: \mathbb{R} \to \mathbb{R}$ is differentiable.

6. Suppose that the function $f: \mathbb{R} \to \mathbb{R}$ has the property that
$$-x^2 \leq f(x) \leq x^2 \quad \text{for all } x \text{ in } \mathbb{R}.$$
    Prove that $f: \mathbb{R} \to \mathbb{R}$ is differentiable at $x = 0$ and that $f'(0) = 0$.

7. Define
$$g(x) = \begin{cases} x^2 & \text{if } x \text{ is rational} \\ -x^2 & \text{if } x \text{ is irrational}. \end{cases}$$
    Prove that the function $g: \mathbb{R} \to \mathbb{R}$ is differentiable at $x = 0$.

8. Determine the differentiability of each of the following functions at $x = 0$:
    (a) $f(x) = x|x|$ for all x in $\mathbb{R}$.
    (b) $g(x) = \sqrt{|x|^3}$ for all x in $\mathbb{R}$.

9. For real numbers a and b, define
$$g(x) = \begin{cases} 3x^2 & \text{if } x \leq 1 \\ a + bx & \text{if } x > 1. \end{cases}$$
    For what values of a and b is the function $g: \mathbb{R} \to \mathbb{R}$ differentiable at $x = 1$?

10. Define
$$f(x) = |x^3(1 - x)| \quad \text{for all } x \text{ in } \mathbb{R}.$$
    At what points is the function $f: \mathbb{R} \to \mathbb{R}$ differentiable?

11. For a natural number n, the Geometric Sum Formula asserts that
$$1 + x + \cdots + x^n = \frac{1 - x^{n+1}}{1 - x} \quad \text{if } x \neq 1.$$
    By differentiating, find a formula for
$$1 + x + 2x^2 + \cdots + nx^n,$$
    and then for $\qquad\qquad 1^2 + 2^2x + \cdots + n^2x^{n-1}.$

12. Suppose that the function $g: \mathbb{R} \to \mathbb{R}$ is differentiable at $x = 0$. Also, suppose that for each natural number n, $g(1/n) = 0$. Prove that $g(0) = 0$ and $g'(0) = 0$.

13. Suppose that the function $f: \mathbb{R} \to \mathbb{R}$ is differentiable at x_0. Analyze the limit
$$\lim_{h \to 0} \left[\frac{f(x_0 + h) - f(x_0 - h)}{h} \right].$$

14. Suppose that the function $f: \mathbb{R} \to \mathbb{R}$ is differentiable at x_0. Prove that
$$\lim_{x \to x_0} \frac{xf(x_0) - x_0 f(x)}{x - x_0} = f(x_0) - x_0 f'(x_0).$$

15. Let the function $g: \mathbb{R} \to \mathbb{R}$ be differentiable. Under what conditions is the function $|g|: \mathbb{R} \to \mathbb{R}$ differentiable at $x = 0$?

16. Let the function $f: \mathbb{R} \to \mathbb{R}$ be differentiable at $x = 0$. Prove that
$$\lim_{x \to 0} \frac{f(x^2) - f(0)}{x} = 0.$$

17. Define $p(x) = 1 - x + x^3$ for all x in $\mathbb{R}$. Find $p'(1)$. Then write $p(x)$ as the sum of powers of $(x - 1)$ and observe that the coefficient of $(x - 1)$ is $p'(1)$.

18. Let the function $h: \mathbb{R} \to \mathbb{R}$ be bounded. Define the function $f: \mathbb{R} \to \mathbb{R}$ by

$$f(x) = 1 + x + x^2 h(x) \quad \text{for all } x \text{ in } \mathbb{R}.$$

Prove that $f(0) = 1$ and $f'(0) = 1$.

4.2 Differentiating Inverses and Compositions

Theorem 3.1 asserts that if I is an interval and the function $f: I \to \mathbb{R}$ is strictly monotone, then its inverse is continuous. It is natural to consider the question of the differentiability of the inverse function at the point $y_0 = f(x_0)$ if $f: I \to \mathbb{R}$ is differentiable at x_0. The following example is instructive.

EXAMPLE 4.4 Define $f(x) = x^3$ for all x in $\mathbb{R}$. We have shown that $f: \mathbb{R} \to \mathbb{R}$ is differentiable, strictly increasing, that $f(\mathbb{R}) = \mathbb{R}$, and that its inverse $f^{-1}: \mathbb{R} \to \mathbb{R}$ is continuous. However, its inverse is not differentiable at $x = 0$. Indeed, if $x \neq 0$, then

$$\frac{f^{-1}(x) - f^{-1}(0)}{x - 0} = \frac{x^{1/3}}{x} = \frac{1}{x^{2/3}},$$

so that

$$\lim_{x \to 0} \frac{f^{-1}(x) - f^{-1}(0)}{x - 0}$$

does not exist. $\qquad\square$

Thus the inverse of a differentiable function need not be differentiable. In the above example, the nondifferentiability of the inverse occurred at a point $f(x_0)$ where $f'(x_0) = 0$. The next theorem proves that it is only at such points that the inverse of a differentiable function can fail to be differentiable.

THEOREM 4.6 Let I be an open interval containing the point x_0 and let the function $f: I \to \mathbb{R}$ be strictly monotone and continuous. Suppose that $f: I \to \mathbb{R}$ is differentiable at x_0 and that $f'(x_0) \neq 0$. Define $J = f(I)$. Then the inverse $f^{-1}: J \to \mathbb{R}$ is differentiable at the point $y_0 = f(x_0)$ and

$$(f^{-1})'(y_0) = \frac{1}{f'(x_0)}.$$

Proof   It follows from the Intermediate Value Theorem that J is an open interval containing the point $y_0 = f(x_0)$. For a point y in J, with $y \neq y_0$, since

$$y = f(f^{-1}(y)) \quad \text{and} \quad y_0 = f(f^{-1}(y_0)),$$

we have

$$\frac{f^{-1}(y) - f^{-1}(y_0)}{y - y_0} = 1 \bigg/ \frac{y - y_0}{f^{-1}(y) - f^{-1}(y_0)} = 1 \bigg/ \frac{f(f^{-1}(y)) - f(f^{-1}(y_0))}{f^{-1}(y) - f^{-1}(y_0)}.$$

(4.4)

Since the inverse function is continuous,

$$\lim_{y \to y_0} f^{-1}(y) = f^{-1}(y_0) = x_0,$$

and, by the definition of a derivative,

$$\lim_{x \to x_0} \frac{f(x) - f(x_0)}{x - x_0} = f'(x_0).$$

Thus, using the composition theorem for limits (Theorem 3.16), it follows that

$$\lim_{y \to y_0} \frac{f(f^{-1}(y)) - f(f^{-1}(y_0))}{f^{-1}(y) - f^{-1}(y_0)} = f'(x_0).$$

(4.5)

From (4.4), (4.5), and the quotient formula for limits, it follows that

$$\lim_{y \to y_0} \frac{f^{-1}(y) - f^{-1}(y_0)}{y - y_0} = \frac{1}{f'(x_0)}. \qquad \blacksquare$$

COROLLARY 4.7   Let I be an open interval and suppose that the function $f: I \to \mathbb{R}$ is strictly monotone and differentiable with $f'(x) \neq 0$ for all x in I. Define $J = f(I)$. Then the inverse function $f^{-1}: J \to \mathbb{R}$ is differentiable and

$$(f^{-1})'(x) = \frac{1}{f'(f^{-1}(x))} \qquad \text{for all } x \text{ in } J.$$

Proof   Since differentiability implies continuity, the function $f: I \to \mathbb{R}$ is continuous. Hence we may apply the previous theorem at x in J, where we have $x = f(f^{-1}(x))$ and $f^{-1}(x)$ plays the role of x_0 in the preceding theorem. $\qquad \blacksquare$

PROPOSITION 4.8   For a natural number n, define $g(x) = x^{1/n}$ for all $x > 0$. Then the function $g: (0, \infty) \to \mathbb{R}$ is differentiable and

$$g'(x) = \frac{1}{n} x^{1/n - 1} \qquad \text{for all } x > 0.$$

Proof If $f: (0, \infty) \to \mathbb{R}$ is defined by $f(x) = x^n$ for $x > 0$, then, by definition, $g: (0, \infty) \to \mathbb{R}$ is the inverse of $f: (0, \infty) \to \mathbb{R}$. According to Proposition 4.1, $f'(x) = nx^{n-1}$ if $x > 0$. Using Corollary 4.7, we conclude that

$$g'(x) = \frac{1}{f'(g(x))} = \frac{1}{n\left(x^{1/n}\right)^{n-1}} = \frac{1}{n}x^{1/n-1} \quad \text{if } x > 0. \qquad \blacksquare$$

We have shown that the composition of continuous functions is continuous. The composition of differentiable functions is differentiable, and there is a formula for the derivative of the composition. This is the content of the following theorem.

THEOREM 4.9 **The Chain Rule** Let I be an open interval containing the point x_0 and suppose that the function $f: I \to \mathbb{R}$ is differentiable at x_0. Let J be an open interval such that $f(I) \subseteq J$, and suppose that $g: J \to \mathbb{R}$ is differentiable at $f(x_0)$. Then the composition $g \circ f: I \to \mathbb{R}$ is differentiable at x_0, and

$$(g \circ f)'(x_0) = g'(f(x_0))f'(x_0). \tag{4.6}$$

Proof Define $y_0 = f(x_0)$. For each x in I with $x \neq x_0$, if we let $y = f(x)$, we have

$$\frac{(g \circ f)(x) - (g \circ f)(x_0)}{x - x_0} = \frac{g(y) - g(y_0)}{y - y_0} \cdot \frac{f(x) - f(x_0)}{x - x_0}, \tag{4.7}$$

provided that $f(x) \neq f(x_0)$. If there is an open interval containing x_0 in which $f(x) \neq f(x_0)$ if $x \neq x_0$, then the result follows by taking limits in the above identity and using the composition and product properties of limits. To account for the possibility that there is no such interval, we introduce an auxiliary function $h: J \to \mathbb{R}$ by defining

$$h(y) = \begin{cases} [g(y) - g(y_0)]/[y - y_0] & \text{for } y \text{ in } J \text{ with } y \neq y_0 \\ g'(y_0) & \text{if } y = y_0. \end{cases}$$

Observe that

$$g(y) - g(y_0) = h(y)[y - y_0] \quad \text{for all } y \text{ in } J,$$

so the preceding identity (4.7) can be rewritten as

$$\frac{(g \circ f)(x) - (g \circ f)(x_0)}{x - x_0} = h(f(x))\left[\frac{f(x) - f(x_0)}{x - x_0}\right] \quad \text{for } x \neq x_0 \text{ in } I. \tag{4.8}$$

From the very definition of $g'(y_0)$ it follows that $h: J \to \mathbb{R}$ is continuous at y_0. Furthermore, the differentiability of $f: I \to \mathbb{R}$ at x_0 implies the continuity of $f: I \to \mathbb{R}$ at x_0, and hence, since the composition of continuous functions is continuous, $h \circ f: I \to \mathbb{R}$ is also continuous at x_0. From this, using the product theorem for limits and the identity (4.8), we see that

$$\lim_{x \to x_0} \frac{g(f(x)) - g(f(x_0))}{x - x_0} = h(f(x_0))f'(x_0) = g'(f(x_0))f'(x_0). \qquad \blacksquare$$

<table>
<tr><td>PROPOSITION
4.10</td><td>For a rational number r, define $h(x) = x^r$ for $x > 0$. Then the function $h: (0, \infty) \to \mathbb{R}$ is differentiable and</td></tr>
</table>

$$h'(x) = rx^{r-1} \quad \text{for } x > 0.$$

Proof   Since r is a rational number, we can choose integers m and n with $m > 0$ such that $r = m/n$. For $x > 0$, define $g(x) = x^n$ and $f(x) = x^{1/m}$, so that $h(x) = g(f(x))$. According to Proposition 4.4, the function $g: (0, \infty) \to \mathbb{R}$ is differentiable and $g'(x) = nx^{n-1}$ if $x > 0$. On the other hand, according to Proposition 4.8, the function $f: (0, \infty) \to \mathbb{R}$ is differentiable and $f'(x) = (1/m)x^{1/m-1}$ if $x > 0$. From the Chain Rule, it follows that

$$h'(x) = g'(f(x))f'(x)$$
$$= n(x^{1/m})^{n-1}\frac{1}{m}x^{1/m-1}$$
$$= rx^{r-1} \quad \text{if } x > 0. \qquad \blacksquare$$

So far, in the present chapter, all of the results have been concerned with the evaluation of limits of the form

$$\lim_{x \to x_0} \frac{h(x)}{x - x_0}, \qquad (4.9)$$

where I is an interval containing the point x_0 and the function $h: I \to \mathbb{R}$ has the property that $\lim_{x \to x_0} h(x) = 0$. The reason, of course, that we need these particular results is that since $\lim_{x \to x_0} (x - x_0) = 0$, we cannot use the quotient formula for limits in the analysis of the limit (4.9). We have the same difficulty in evaluating any limit of the form

$$\lim_{x \to x_0} \frac{h(x)}{g(x)} \qquad (4.10)$$

if $\lim_{x \to x_0} g(x) = 0$. If $\lim_{x \to x_0} h(x) \neq 0$, the limit (4.10) does not exist. The remaining case, when

$$\lim_{x \to x_0} g(x) = 0 \quad \text{and} \quad \lim_{x \to x_0} h(x) = 0,$$

is often called the *indeterminate case*. We have, however, the following simple but useful result, which is the first of various formulas for computing the limit of quotients known as L'Hôpital's Rules.

<table>
<tr><td>THEOREM 4.11</td><td>Let I be an open interval containing the point x_0. Suppose that the functions $g: I \to \mathbb{R}$ and $h: I \to \mathbb{R}$ are differentiable at the point x_0 and that</td></tr>
</table>

$$g(x_0) = h(x_0) = 0.$$

Assume, moreover, that $g(x) \neq 0$ for x in I with $x \neq x_0$, and that $g'(x_0) \neq 0$. Then

$$\lim_{x \to x_0} \frac{h(x)}{g(x)} = \frac{h'(x_0)}{g'(x_0)}. \qquad (4.11)$$

Proof For a point x in I, with $x \neq x_0$,

$$\frac{h(x)}{g(x)} = \frac{h(x) - h(x_0)}{g(x) - g(x_0)} = \frac{h(x) - h(x_0)}{x - x_0} \Bigg/ \frac{g(x) - g(x_0)}{x - x_0}.$$

Thus (4.11) follows from the very definition of a derivative and the quotient formula for limits. ■

EXAMPLE 4.5 Formula (4.11) implies that

$$\lim_{x \to 0} \frac{4x + x^4}{x - x^3} = 4 \quad \text{and} \quad \lim_{x \to 1} \frac{x^2 - 1}{\sqrt{1 + x^2} - \sqrt{2}} = 2\sqrt{2}. \qquad \square$$

We will consider a more refined version of L'Hôpital's Rule in Section 4.4.

EXERCISES

1. Suppose that the function $f: (0, \infty) \to \mathbb{R}$ is differentiable and let $c > 0$. Now define $g: (0, \infty) \to \mathbb{R}$ by $g(x) = f(cx)$, for $x > 0$. Prove that the function $g: (0, \infty) \to \mathbb{R}$ is also differentiable and $g'(x) = cf'(cx)$, for $x > 0$.

2. Define
$$f(x) = \frac{1}{\sqrt{1 + x^2}} \quad \text{for all } x > 0.$$
Prove that $f: (0, \infty) \to \mathbb{R}$ is differentiable, strictly decreasing, and that $f(0, \infty) = (0, 1)$. Find $(f^{-1})'\left(\sqrt{1/5}\right)$.

3. Let I be an open interval containing the point x_0 and let $f: I \to \mathbb{R}$ be continuous, strictly monotone, and differentiable at x_0. Assume that $f'(x_0) = 0$. Use the Chain Rule to prove that $f^{-1}: f(I) \to \mathbb{R}$ is not differentiable at $f(x_0)$. Thus Theorem 4.6 cannot be improved.

4. If the function $f: \mathbb{R} \to \mathbb{R}$ is differentiable at 0, does the limit $\lim_{x \to 0}[f(x) - f(0)]/x^2$ necessarily exist?

5. Let $f: \mathbb{R} \to \mathbb{R}$ be differentiable and suppose that $h: \mathbb{R} \to \mathbb{R}$ is differentiable, strictly increasing, $h'(x) > 0$ for all x in $\mathbb{R}$, and $h(\mathbb{R}) = \mathbb{R}$. Define $g(x) = f(h^{-1}(x))$ for all x in $\mathbb{R}$. Find $g'(x)$ for x in $\mathbb{R}$.

6. Suppose that the function $f: \mathbb{R} \to \mathbb{R}$ is differentiable at 0. For real numbers $a, b,$ and c, with $c \neq 0$, prove that
$$\lim_{x \to 0} \frac{f(ax) - f(bx)}{cx} = \frac{a - b}{c} f'(0).$$

7. Let I be an open interval and suppose that the function $f: I \to \mathbb{R}$ is differentiable and monotone increasing. Prove that $f'(x) \geq 0$ for all x in I.

8. Suppose that the function $f: \mathbb{R} \to \mathbb{R}$ is differentiable and that there is a bounded sequence $\{x_n\}$, with $x_n \neq x_m$ if $n \neq m$, such that $f(x_n) = 0$ for all natural numbers n. Prove that there is a number x_0 at which $f'(x_0) = 0$. (We will see in the next section that the conclusion holds if $f: \mathbb{R} \to \mathbb{R}$ attains the value 0 at just two distinct points.) (*Hint:* Apply the Bolzano-Weierstrass Theorem.)

9. Suppose that the function $f: \mathbb{R} \to \mathbb{R}$ is differentiable and $\{x_n\}$ is a strictly increasing, bounded sequence with $f(x_n) \leq f(x_{n+1})$, for all n in $\mathbb{N}$. Prove that there is a number x_0 at which $f'(x_0) \geq 0$. (*Hint:* Apply the Monotone Convergence Theorem.)

10.   A function $f: \mathbb{R} \to \mathbb{R}$ is called *even* if

$$f(x) = f(-x) \quad \text{for all } x \text{ in } \mathbb{R},$$

and $f: \mathbb{R} \to \mathbb{R}$ is called *odd* if

$$f(x) = -f(-x) \quad \text{for all } x \text{ in } \mathbb{R}.$$

Prove that if $f: \mathbb{R} \to \mathbb{R}$ is differentiable and odd, $f': \mathbb{R} \to \mathbb{R}$ is even.

4.3   The Lagrange Mean Value Theorem and Its Geometric Consequences

We will now prove one of the most useful and geometrically attractive results in calculus, the Lagrange Mean Value Theorem, or simply the Mean Value Theorem. It asserts that if the function $f: [a, b] \to \mathbb{R}$ is continuous and $f: (a, b) \to \mathbb{R}$ is differentiable, then there is a point x_0 in the open interval (a, b) with the property that the tangent line to the graph at $(x_0, f(x_0))$ is parallel to the line passing through $(a, f(a))$ and $(b, f(b))$.

To prove the Mean Value Theorem, it is convenient first to prove some preliminary results.

LEMMA 4.12   Let I be an open interval containing the point x_0 and suppose that the function $f: I \to \mathbb{R}$ is differentiable at x_0. If the point x_0 is either a maximizer or a minimizer of the function $f: I \to \mathbb{R}$, then $f'(x_0) = 0$.

FIGURE 4.2

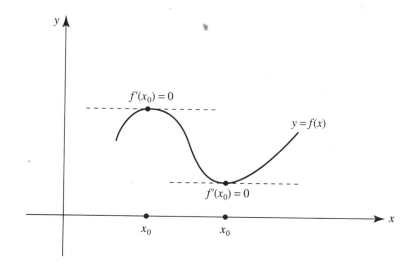

Proof   Observe that by the very definition of derivative,

$$\lim_{x \to x_0, x < x_0} \frac{f(x) - f(x_0)}{x - x_0} = \lim_{x \to x_0, x > x_0} \frac{f(x) - f(x_0)}{x - x_0} = f'(x_0).$$

First suppose that x_0 is a maximizer. Then

$$\frac{f(x) - f(x_0)}{x - x_0} \geq 0 \quad \text{for } x \text{ in } I \text{ with } x < x_0,$$

and hence

$$f'(x_0) = \lim_{x \to x_0, x < x_0} \frac{f(x) - f(x_0)}{x - x_0} \geq 0.$$

On the other hand,

$$\frac{f(x) - f(x_0)}{x - x_0} \leq 0 \quad \text{for } x \text{ in } I \text{ with } x > x_0,$$

and hence

$$f'(x_0) = \lim_{x \to x_0, x > x_0} \frac{f(x) - f(x_0)}{x - x_0} \leq 0.$$

Thus $f'(x_0) = 0$.

In the case when x_0 is a minimizer, the same proof applies, with inequalities reversed. ∎

THEOREM 4.13   **Rolle's Theorem**   Suppose that the function $f:[a, b] \to \mathbb{R}$ is continuous and $f:(a, b) \to \mathbb{R}$ is differentiable. Assume, moreover, that

$$f(a) = f(b) = 0.$$

Then there is a point x_0 in the open interval (a, b) at which

$$f'(x_0) = 0.$$

FIGURE 4.3

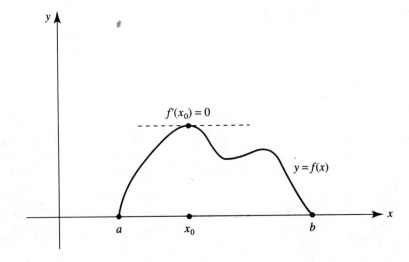

Proof   Since $f \colon [a, b] \to \mathbb{R}$ is continuous, according to the Extreme Value Theorem, it attains both a minimum value and a maximum value on $[a, b]$. Since $f(a) = f(b) = 0$, if both the maximizers and the minimizers occur at the endpoints, then the function $f \colon [a, b] \to \mathbb{R}$ is identically equal to 0, so $f'(x) = 0$ at every point x in (a, b). Otherwise, the function has either a maximizer or a minimizer at some point x_0 in the open interval $I = (a, b)$ and hence, by the preceding lemma, at this point $f'(x_0) = 0$.   ∎

Rolle's Theorem is a special case of the Lagrange Mean Value Theorem, but in fact, the general result follows from Rolle's Theorem by some algebraic manipulations.

THEOREM 4.14   **The Lagrange Mean Value Theorem**   Suppose that the function $f \colon [a, b] \to \mathbb{R}$ is continuous and $f \colon (a, b) \to \mathbb{R}$ is differentiable. Then there is a point x_0 in the open interval (a, b) at which

$$f'(x_0) = \frac{f(b) - f(a)}{b - a}.$$

FIGURE 4.4

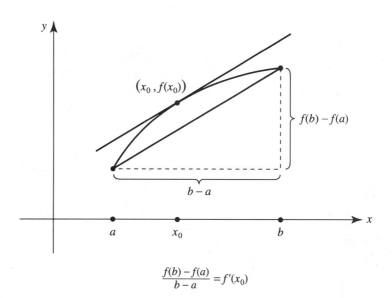

$$\frac{f(b) - f(a)}{b - a} = f'(x_0)$$

Proof   The line passing through the points $(a, f(a))$ and $(b, f(b))$ has slope $[f(b) - f(a)]/[b - a]$, so the equation of the line passing through these points is

$$y = g(x) = f(a) + \left[\frac{f(b) - f(a)}{b - a} \right] (x - a).$$

Define the auxiliary function $d \colon [a, b] \to \mathbb{R}$ by $d(x) = f(x) - g(x)$ for all x in $[a, b]$. Then clearly $d(a) = d(b) = 0$. Moreover, from the addition theorems for continuous and differentiable functions, it follows that $d \colon [a, b] \to \mathbb{R}$ is continuous and $d \colon (a, b) \to \mathbb{R}$ is differentiable. We apply Rolle's Theorem to select a point x_0 in (a, b) at which $d'(x_0) = 0$. But

$$d'(x) = f'(x) - \frac{f(b) - f(a)}{b - a} \quad \text{for} \quad a < x < b,$$

so that
$$f'(x_0) = \frac{f(b) - f(a)}{b - a}.$$ ∎

The preceding Mean Value Theorem is one of the most important results in calculus. Observe that its proof depends merely on the definition of the derivative and on the Extreme Value Theorem.

As a general principle, if we have information about the derivative of a function that we wish to use in order to analyze the function, we should first try to apply the Mean Value Theorem. The remainder of this section consists of various applications of this strategy.

A function $f: D \to \mathbb{R}$ is said to be *constant* provided that there is some number c such that $f(x) = c$ for all x in D.

LEMMA 4.15   Let I be an open interval and suppose that the function $f: I \to \mathbb{R}$ is differentiable. Then $f: I \to \mathbb{R}$ is constant if and only if

$$f'(x) = 0 \quad \text{for all } x \text{ in } I.$$

Proof   It is clear that if $f: I \to \mathbb{R}$ is constant, then $f'(x) = 0$ for all x in I. To prove the converse, let u and v be points in I with $u < v$. Since differentiability implies continuity, the function $f: [u, v] \to \mathbb{R}$ is continuous and, of course, $f: (u, v) \to \mathbb{R}$ is differentiable. According to the Mean Value Theorem, there is a point x_0 in (u, v) such that

$$f'(x_0) = \frac{f(v) - f(u)}{v - u}.$$

But $f'(x_0) = 0$, and thus $f(u) = f(v)$. Consequently, the function $f: I \to \mathbb{R}$ is constant. ∎

Two functions $g: I \to \mathbb{R}$ and $h: I \to \mathbb{R}$ are said to *differ by a constant* if there is some number c such that

$$g(x) = h(x) + c \quad \text{for all } x \text{ in } I.$$

Of course, two functions $g: I \to \mathbb{R}$ and $h: I \to \mathbb{R}$ are equal provided that $g(x) = h(x)$ for all x in I. Sometimes we say that equal functions are *identically equal*, in order to emphasize that the functions have the same value at all points of their domain. For this reason, we label the following result the *Identity Criterion*.

PROPOSITION 4.16   **The Identity Criterion**   Let I be an open interval and let the functions $g: I \to \mathbb{R}$ and $h: I \to \mathbb{R}$ be differentiable. Then these functions differ by a constant if and only if

$$g'(x) = h'(x) \quad \text{for all } x \text{ in } I. \tag{4.12}$$

In particular, these functions are identically equal if and only if (4.12) holds and there is some point x_0 in I at which

$$g(x_0) = h(x_0).$$

Proof Define $f = g - h: I \to \mathbb{R}$. According to the differentiation rule for sums, $f: I \to \mathbb{R}$ is differentiable and

$$f'(x) = g'(x) - h'(x) \quad \text{for all } x \text{ in } I.$$

Also, observe that $f: I \to \mathbb{R}$ is constant if and only if the functions $g: I \to \mathbb{R}$ and $h: I \to \mathbb{R}$ differ by a constant. The result now follows from the preceding lemma. ∎

COROLLARY 4.17 Let I be an open interval and the function $f: I \to \mathbb{R}$ be differentiable. Suppose that $f'(x) > 0$ for all x in I. Then $f: I \to \mathbb{R}$ is strictly increasing.

Proof Let u and v be points in I with $u < v$. Then we may apply the Mean Value Theorem to $f: [u, v] \to \mathbb{R}$ and choose a point x_0 in (u, v) at which

$$f'(x_0) = \frac{f(v) - f(u)}{v - u}.$$

Since $f'(x_0) > 0$ and $v - u > 0$, it follows that $f(v) > f(u)$. ∎

By replacing $f: I \to \mathbb{R}$ with $-f: I \to \mathbb{R}$, the above corollary implies that if $f: I \to \mathbb{R}$ has a negative derivative at all x in I, then $f: I \to \mathbb{R}$ is strictly decreasing.

The above results give a method for finding intervals on which a differentiable function $f: I \to \mathbb{R}$ is strictly monotonic. The effectiveness of the method depends on being able to find those points at which $f'(x) = 0$. In fact, unless the function $f: I \to \mathbb{R}$ is quite simple, it is usually very difficult to find these points.

DEFINITION *A point x_0 in the domain D of a function $f: D \to \mathbb{R}$ is said to be a local maximizer for $f: D \to \mathbb{R}$ provided that there is some $\delta > 0$ such that*

$$f(x) \le f(x_0) \quad \text{for all } x \text{ in } D \text{ such that } |x - x_0| < \delta.$$

We call x_0 a local minimizer for $f: D \to \mathbb{R}$ provided that there is some $\delta > 0$ such that

$$f(x) \ge f(x_0) \quad \text{for all } x \text{ in } D \text{ such that } |x - x_0| < \delta.$$

Lemma 4.12 implies that if I is an open interval containing the point x_0 and $f: I \to \mathbb{R}$ is differentiable at x_0, then for x_0 to be either a local minimizer or a local maximizer for $f: I \to \mathbb{R}$, it is necessary that

$$f'(x_0) = 0.$$

However, knowing that $f'(x_0) = 0$ does not guarantee that x_0 is either a local maximizer or a local minimizer. For instance, if $f(x) = x^3$ for all x in $\mathbb{R}$, then $f'(0) = 0$, but the point 0 is neither a local maximizer nor a local minimizer. In order to establish criteria that are sufficient for the existence of local maximizers and local minimizers, it is necessary to introduce higher derivatives.

For a differentiable function $f: I \to \mathbb{R}$ that has as its domain an open interval I, we say that $f: I \to \mathbb{R}$ has *one derivative* if $f: I \to \mathbb{R}$ is differentiable, and define $f^{(1)}(x) = f'(x)$ for all x in I. If the function $f': I \to \mathbb{R}$ itself has a derivative, we say that $f: I \to \mathbb{R}$ has *two derivatives*, or has a *second derivative*, and denote the derivative of $f': I \to \mathbb{R}$ by $f'': I \to \mathbb{R}$ or by $f^{(2)}: I \to \mathbb{R}$. Now let k be a natural number for which we have defined what it means for $f: I \to \mathbb{R}$ to *have k derivatives* and have defined $f^{(k)}: I \to \mathbb{R}$. Then $f: I \to \mathbb{R}$ is said to *have k + 1 derivatives* if $f^{(k)}: I \to \mathbb{R}$ is differentiable, and we define $f^{(k+1)}: I \to \mathbb{R}$ to be the derivative of $f^{(k)}: I \to \mathbb{R}$. In this context, is it useful to denote $f(x)$ by $f^{(0)}(x)$.

In general, if a function has k derivatives, it does not necessarily have $k + 1$ derivatives. For instance, the function $f: \mathbb{R} \to \mathbb{R}$ defined by $f(x) = |x|x$ for all x in $\mathbb{R}$ is differentiable, but does not have a second derivative.

THEOREM 4.18   Let I be an open interval containing the point x_0 and suppose that the function $f: I \to \mathbb{R}$ has a second derivative. Suppose that

$$f'(x_0) = 0.$$

If $f''(x_0) > 0$, then x_0 is a local minimizer of $f: I \to \mathbb{R}$.
If $f''(x_0) < 0$, then x_0 is a local maximizer of $f: I \to \mathbb{R}$.

Proof   First suppose that $f''(x_0) > 0$. Since

$$f''(x_0) = \lim_{x \to x_0} \frac{f'(x) - f'(x_0)}{x - x_0} > 0,$$

it follows (see Exercise 16) that there is a $\delta > 0$ such that the open interval $(x_0 - \delta, x_0 + \delta)$ is contained in I and

$$\frac{f'(x) - f'(x_0)}{x - x_0} > 0 \quad \text{if} \quad 0 < |x - x_0| < \delta. \tag{4.13}$$

But $f'(x_0) = 0$, so (4.13) amounts to the assertion that if $|x - x_0| < \delta$, then

$$f'(x) > 0 \quad \text{if} \quad x > x_0 \qquad \text{and} \qquad f'(x) < 0 \quad \text{if} \quad x < x_0.$$

Using these two inequalities and the Mean Value Theorem, it follows that

$$f(x) > f(x_0) \quad \text{if} \quad 0 < |x - x_0| < \delta.$$

A similar argument applies when $f''(x_0) < 0$.   ∎

The preceding theorem provides no information about $f(x_0)$ as a local extreme point if both $f'(x_0) = 0$ and $f''(x_0) = 0$. As we see from examining functions of the form $f(x) = cx^n$ for all x in $\mathbb{R}$ at $x_0 = 0$, if $f'(x_0) = 0$ and $f''(x_0) = 0$, then x_0 may be a local maximizer or a local minimizer or neither.

The geometric consequences of the Mean Value Theorem that we have presented so far certainly conform to one's geometric intuition. However, it is always necessary to be careful. In Section 9.5 we will describe a function $f: \mathbb{R} \to \mathbb{R}$ that is continuous but has the following two properties:

(i) There is no point at which $f: \mathbb{R} \to \mathbb{R}$ is differentiable.

(ii) There is no interval I such that $f: I \to \mathbb{R}$ is monotonic.

It is the existence of such functions that makes it absolutely necessary to root geometrical arguments in firm analytical ground. A less startling, but still somewhat surprising, example is the following function $f: \mathbb{R} \to \mathbb{R}$ that has $f'(0) > 0$ but for which there is no open interval I containing 0 on which $f: I \to \mathbb{R}$ is increasing:

EXAMPLE 4.6   Define

$$f(x) = \begin{cases} x - x^2 & \text{if } x \text{ is rational} \\ x + x^2 & \text{if } x \text{ is irrational.} \end{cases}$$

Observe that

$$\left| \frac{f(x) - f(0)}{x - 0} - 1 \right| = |x| \text{ if } x \neq 0,$$

and so

$$f'(0) = \lim_{x \to 0} \frac{f(x) - f(0)}{x - 0} = 1.$$

On the other hand, if I is any open interval containing the point 0, and u is any positive rational number in I, then there is a positive irrational number v that is less than u whereas $f(u) > f(v)$. For instance, choose α to be any positive irrational number such that $\alpha < \min\{u, u^2\}$, and observe that $u - \alpha > u - u^2$, so that if $v = u - \alpha$, then v is irrational and $f(v) = u - \alpha + (u - \alpha)^2 > u - u^2 = f(u)$. Thus, $f: I \to \mathbb{R}$ is not increasing. □

In the above example, the function $f: \mathbb{R} \to \mathbb{R}$, although differentiable at $x = 0$, failed even to be continuous at each $x \neq 0$. However, this is not the source of the difficulty. If we work a little harder, we can construct a function $f: \mathbb{R} \to \mathbb{R}$ that is differentiable at every x in $\mathbb{R}$, has $f'(0) > 0$, and yet fails to be increasing on any open interval containing 0. So why does our intuition fail? It fails because it overestimates the consequences of the assumption that $f'(0) > 0$. Even if $f: \mathbb{R} \to \mathbb{R}$ is differentiable at every x in $\mathbb{R}$, the assumption that $f'(0) > 0$ does not imply that there is an open interval containing 0 at each point of which $f'(x) > 0$. The crucial observation is that if $f: \mathbb{R} \to \mathbb{R}$ is differentiable, it need not be the case that $f': \mathbb{R} \to \mathbb{R}$ is continuous, so if $f'(0) > 0$, we cannot conclude that there is a $\delta > 0$ such that $f'(x) > 0$ for all x in $(-\delta, \delta)$.

EXERCISES

1. Sketch the graphs of the following functions. Find the intervals on which they are increasing or decreasing.
   (a) $f: \mathbb{R} \to \mathbb{R}$ defined by $f(x) = x^3 + ax^2 + bx + c$ for all x in $\mathbb{R}$.
   (b) $h: (0, \infty) \to \mathbb{R}$ defined by $h(x) = a + b/x$ for $x > 0$, where $a > 0, b > 0$.
2. For real numbers $a, b, c,$ and d, define $\mathcal{O} = \{x \mid cx + d \neq 0\}$. Then define

$$f(x) = \frac{ax + b}{cx + d} \quad \text{for all } x \text{ in } \mathcal{O}.$$

   Show that if the function $f: \mathcal{O} \to \mathbb{R}$ is not constant, then it fails to have any local maximizers or minimizers. Sketch the graph.
3. For $c > 0$, prove that the following equation does not have two solutions:

$$x^3 - 3x + c = 0, \quad 0 < x < 1.$$

4. Prove that the following equation has exactly one solution:

$$x^5 + 5x + 1 = 0, \qquad -1 < x < 0.$$

5. Prove that the following equation has exactly two solutions:

$$x^4 + 2x^2 - 6x + 2 = 0, \qquad x \text{ in } \mathbb{R}.$$

6. For any numbers a and b and an even natural number n, show that the following equation has at most two solutions:

$$x^n + ax + b = 0, \qquad x \text{ in } \mathbb{R}.$$

   Is this true if n is odd?

7. For numbers a and b, prove that the following equation has exactly three solutions if and only if $4a^3 + 27b^2 < 0$:

$$x^3 + ax + b = 0, \qquad x \text{ in } \mathbb{R}.$$

8. Let D be the set of nonzero real numbers. Suppose that the functions $g: D \to \mathbb{R}$ and $h: D \to \mathbb{R}$ are differentiable and that

$$g'(x) = h'(x) \quad \text{for all } x \text{ in } D.$$

   Do the functions $g: D \to \mathbb{R}$ and $h: D \to \mathbb{R}$ differ by a constant? (*Hint:* Is D an interval?)

9. Let n be a natural number. Suppose that the function $f: \mathbb{R} \to \mathbb{R}$ is differentiable and that the following equation has at most $n - 1$ solutions:

$$f'(x) = 0, \qquad x \text{ in } \mathbb{R}.$$

   Prove that the following equation has at most n solutions:

$$f(x) = 0, \qquad x \text{ in } \mathbb{R}.$$

10. Use an induction argument together with the preceding exercise to prove that if $p: \mathbb{R} \to \mathbb{R}$ is a polynomial of degree n, then there are at most n solutions of the equation

$$p(x) = 0, \qquad x \text{ in } \mathbb{R}.$$

11. Suppose that the function $f: \mathbb{R} \to \mathbb{R}$ is differentiable and

$$\begin{cases} f'(x) = x + x^3 + 2 & \text{for all } x \text{ in } \mathbb{R} \\ f(0) = 5. \end{cases}$$

   What is the function $f: \mathbb{R} \to \mathbb{R}$?

12. Suppose that the function $g: (-1, 1) \to \mathbb{R}$ is differentiable and

$$\begin{cases} g'(x) = x/\sqrt{1 - x^2} & \text{for } -1 < x < 1 \\ g(0) = 25. \end{cases}$$

   What is the function $g: \mathbb{R} \to \mathbb{R}$?

13. Let $g: \mathbb{R} \to \mathbb{R}$ and $f: \mathbb{R} \to \mathbb{R}$ be differentiable functions, and suppose that

$$g(x)f'(x) = f(x)g'(x) \quad \text{for all } x \text{ in } \mathbb{R}.$$

If $g(x) \neq 0$ for all x in $\mathbb{R}$, show that there is some c in $\mathbb{R}$ such that $f(x) = cg(x)$ for all x in $\mathbb{R}$.

14. Suppose that $f: \mathbb{R} \to \mathbb{R}$ and $g: \mathbb{R} \to \mathbb{R}$ are each differentiable, and that

$$\begin{cases} f'(x) = g(x) & \text{and} \quad g'(x) = -f(x) \quad \text{for all } x \text{ in } \mathbb{R} \\ f(0) = 0 & \text{and} \quad g(0) = 1. \end{cases}$$

Prove that

$$[f(x)]^2 + [g(x)]^2 = 1 \quad \text{for all } x \text{ in } \mathbb{R}.$$

(*Hint:* Show that $h(x) = [f(x)]^2 + [g(x)]^2$, for all x in $\mathbb{R}$, defines a constant function.)

Final **15.** Let I be an open interval. Suppose that the function $f: I \to \mathbb{R}$ is continuous and that at the point x_0 in I, $f(x_0) > 0$. Prove that there is a $\delta > 0$ such that $f(x) > 0$ if $|x - x_0| < \delta$.

Final **16.** Let I be an open interval containing the point x_0 and suppose that the function $g: I \to \mathbb{R}$ is differentiable. Define

$$h(x) = \begin{cases} [g(x) - g(x_0)]/[x - x_0] & \text{if } x \neq x_0 \\ g'(x_0) & \text{if } x = x_0. \end{cases}$$

Show that $h: I \to \mathbb{R}$ is continuous. If $g'(x_0) > 0$, use the preceding exercise to show that there is a $\delta > 0$ such that $[g(x) - g(x_0)]/[x - x_0] > 0$ if $0 < |x - x_0| < \delta$.

17. Suppose that the function $f: \mathbb{R} \to \mathbb{R}$ is differentiable, that $f': \mathbb{R} \to \mathbb{R}$ is continuous at 0, and that $f'(0) > 0$. Prove that there is an open interval I containing 0 such that $f: I \to \mathbb{R}$ is strictly monotonic.

18. Let the function $f: \mathbb{R} \to \mathbb{R}$ have the property that there is a positive number c such that $|f(u) - f(v)| \leq c(u - v)^2$ for all u, v in $\mathbb{R}$. Prove that the function $f: \mathbb{R} \to \mathbb{R}$ is constant.

19. Suppose that $f: \mathbb{R} \to \mathbb{R}$ is differentiable and that there is a positive number c such that

$$f'(x) \geq c \quad \text{for all } x \text{ in } \mathbb{R}.$$

Prove that

$$f(x) \geq f(0) + cx \quad \text{if} \quad x \geq 0 \quad \text{and} \quad f(x) \leq f(0) + cx \quad \text{if} \quad x \leq 0.$$

Use these inequalities to prove that $f(\mathbb{R}) = \mathbb{R}$.

20. Let the function $f: \mathbb{R} \to \mathbb{R}$ have two derivatives and suppose that

$$f(x) \leq 0 \quad \text{and} \quad f''(x) \geq 0 \quad \text{for all } x \text{ in } \mathbb{R}.$$

Prove that $f: \mathbb{R} \to \mathbb{R}$ is constant. (*Hint:* Observe that $f': \mathbb{R} \to \mathbb{R}$ is increasing.)

21. Let the function $f: \mathbb{R} \to \mathbb{R}$ have two derivatives with $f(0) = 0$ and

$$f'(x) \leq f(x) \quad \text{for all } x \text{ in } \mathbb{R}.$$

Is $f(x) = 0$ for all x in $\mathbb{R}$?

4.4   The Cauchy Mean Value Theorem and Its Analytic Consequences

The following is a useful extension of the Lagrange Mean Value Theorem.

THEOREM 4.19   **The Cauchy Mean Value Theorem**   Suppose that the functions $f: [a, b] \to \mathbb{R}$ and $g: [a, b] \to \mathbb{R}$ are continuous, and that $f: (a, b) \to \mathbb{R}$ and $g: (a, b) \to \mathbb{R}$ are differentiable. Moreover, assume that

$$g'(x) \neq 0 \quad \text{for all } x \text{ in } (a, b).$$

Then there is a point x_0 in the open interval (a, b) at which

$$\frac{f(b) - f(a)}{g(b) - g(a)} = \frac{f'(x_0)}{g'(x_0)}. \tag{4.14}$$

Proof   Observe that since $g'(x) \neq 0$ for $a < x < b$, it follows from the Lagrange Mean Value Theorem that $g(b) - g(a) \neq 0$. Let us define an auxiliary function $\psi: [a, b] \to \mathbb{R}$ by

$$\psi(x) = f(x) - f(a) - \left[\frac{f(b) - f(a)}{g(b) - g(a)} \right] [g(x) - g(a)] \quad \text{for} \quad a \leq x \leq b.$$

The addition properties of continuous and differentiable functions imply that $\psi: [a, b] \to \mathbb{R}$ is continuous and $\psi: (a, b) \to \mathbb{R}$ is differentiable. Moreover, we check to see that

$$\psi(a) = \psi(b) = 0.$$

According to Rolle's Theorem, there is a point x_0 in the open interval (a, b) at which $\psi'(x_0) = 0$. But

$$\psi'(x_0) = f'(x_0) - \left[\frac{f(b) - f(a)}{g(b) - g(a)} \right] g'(x_0),$$

and hence we obtain (4.14).   ∎

Observe that if $g(x) = x$ for $a \leq x \leq b$, then the Cauchy Mean Value Theorem reduces to the Lagrange Mean Value Theorem. Also observe that if we were to apply the Lagrange Mean Value Theorem first to $f: [a, b] \to \mathbb{R}$ and then to $g: [a, b] \to \mathbb{R}$, then instead of (4.14) we would have

$$\frac{f(b) - f(a)}{g(b) - g(a)} = \frac{f'(x_1)}{g'(x_2)}$$

for some points x_1 and x_2 in (a, b). The whole point of Theorem 4.19 is that we can select $x_1 = x_2$. The following is another one of L'Hôpital's Rules.

THEOREM 4.20   Let x_0 be an endpoint of an open interval I. Suppose that the functions $f: I \to \mathbb{R}$ and $g: I \to \mathbb{R}$ are differentiable and

$$\lim_{x \to x_0} f(x) = 0 = \lim_{x \to x_0} g(x). \qquad (4.15)$$

Moreover, suppose that $g'(x) \neq 0$ for all x in I and

$$\lim_{x \to x_0} \frac{f'(x)}{g'(x)} = \ell. \qquad (4.16)$$

Then

$$\lim_{x \to x_0} \frac{f(x)}{g(x)} = \ell. \qquad (4.17)$$

Proof   We will suppose that $I = (x_0, b)$, with $b > x_0$. Extend the functions $f: I \to \mathbb{R}$ and $g: I \to \mathbb{R}$ to $f: [x_0, b) \to \mathbb{R}$ and $g: [x_0, b) \to \mathbb{R}$ by defining $f(x_0) = g(x_0) = 0$. Then (4.15) implies that each of these extensions is continuous at x_0. Therefore, since differentiability implies continuity, both $f: [x_0, b) \to \mathbb{R}$ and $g: [x_0, b) \to \mathbb{R}$ are continuous. Let x be in I. According to the Cauchy Mean Value Theorem, applied to $f: [x_0, x] \to \mathbb{R}$ and $g: [x_0, x] \to \mathbb{R}$, we can select a point $c = c(x)$ in the interval (x_0, x) at which

$$\frac{f(x)}{g(x)} = \frac{f(x) - f(x_0)}{g(x) - g(x_0)} = \frac{f'(c(x))}{g'(c(x))}. \qquad (4.18)$$

Since $\lim_{x \to x_0} c(x) = x_0$, (4.17) follows from (4.18) and (4.16).   ∎

EXAMPLE 4.7   As a simple illustration of Theorem 4.20, we observe that

$$\lim_{x \to 0, x > 0} \frac{x + \sqrt{1 + x} - 1}{x + x^{3/2}} = \frac{3}{2}. \qquad \square$$

We will see many more interesting uses of the above theorem in the context of exponential and trigonometric functions.

THEOREM 4.21   Let I be an open interval and n be a nonnegative integer, and suppose the function $f: I \to \mathbb{R}$ has n derivatives. Suppose also that at the point x_0 in I,

$$f^{(k)}(x_0) = 0 \quad \text{for} \quad 0 \le k \le n - 1.$$

Then for each point $x \neq x_0$ in I, there is a point z strictly between x and x_0 at which

$$f(x) = \frac{f^{(n)}(z)}{n!}(x - x_0)^n. \qquad (4.19)$$

Proof   Define $g(x) = (x - x_0)^n$ for all x in I. Then $g^{(k)}(x_0) = 0$ for $0 \le k \le n - 1$, and $g^{(n)}(x_0) = n!$. Let x be a point in I, with $x \ne x_0$. We may suppose that $x > x_0$. By applying the Cauchy Mean Value Theorem to the functions $f: [x_0, x] \to \mathbb{R}$ and $g: [x_0, x] \to \mathbb{R}$, we may select a point x_1 in (x_0, x) at which

$$\frac{f(x)}{g(x)} = \frac{f(x) - f(x_0)}{g(x) - g(x_0)} = \frac{f'(x_1)}{g'(x_1)}. \qquad (4.20)$$

Now apply the Cauchy Mean Value Theorem to $f': [x_0, x_1] \to \mathbb{R}$ and $g': [x_0, x_1] \to \mathbb{R}$ in order to select x_2 in (x_0, x_1), at which

$$\frac{f'(x_1)}{g'(x_1)} = \frac{f'(x_1) - f'(x_0)}{g'(x_1) - g'(x_0)} = \frac{f''(x_2)}{g''(x_2)}, \qquad (4.21)$$

so that by (4.20),

$$\frac{f(x)}{g(x)} = \frac{f''(x_2)}{g''(x_2)}.$$

Continuing with successively higher derivatives, we obtain a point x_n in (x_0, x) such that

$$\frac{f(x)}{g(x)} = \frac{f^{(n)}(x_n)}{g^{(n)}(x_0)} = \frac{f^{(n)}(x_n)}{n!},$$

and setting $z = x_n$ we obtain (4.19).   ∎

EXERCISES

1. Evaluate the following limits or determine that they do not exist:

    (a) $\lim_{x \to 0, x > 0} \dfrac{2 - 2(1 + x)^{3/2}}{x}$

    (b) $\lim_{x \to 0, x > 0} \dfrac{1 + x}{x}$

    (c) $\lim_{x \to 1} \dfrac{x^3 - 3x^2 + 3x - 1}{(x - 1)^2}$

    (d) $\lim_{x \to 0, x > 0} \dfrac{2x^2 + x^3}{x|x|}$

2. Suppose that the function $f: \mathbb{R} \to \mathbb{R}$ has two derivatives, with $f(0) = f'(0) = 0$ and $|f''(x)| \le 1$ if $|x| \le 1$. Prove that $f(x) \le 1/2$ if $x \le 1$.

3. Let $p: \mathbb{R} \to \mathbb{R}$ be a polynomial of degree no greater than 5. Suppose that at some point x_0 in $\mathbb{R}$,

    $$p(x_0) = p'(x_0) = \cdots = p^{(5)}(x_0) = 0.$$

    Prove that $p(x) = 0$ for all x in $\mathbb{R}$.

4. Define $f(t) = t^2$ for $0 \le t \le 1$ and $g(t) = t^3$ for $0 \le t \le 1$.

    (a) Find the number c with $0 < c < 1$ at which

    $$\frac{f(1) - f(0)}{g(1) - g(0)} = \frac{f'(c)}{g'(c)}.$$

    (b) Show that there does not exist a number c with $0 < c < 1$ at which

    $$\begin{cases} f(1) - f(0) = f'(c)(1 - 0) \\ \text{and} \\ g(1) - g(0) = g'(c)(1 - 0). \end{cases}$$

5. Suppose that the functions $f:[a, b] \to \mathbb{R}$ and $g:[a, b] \to \mathbb{R}$ are continuous, and that $f:(a, b) \to \mathbb{R}$ and $g:(a, b) \to \mathbb{R}$ are differentiable. Also suppose that $|f'(x)| \geq |g'(x)| > 0$ for all x in (a, b). Prove that

$$|f(u) - f(v)| \geq |g(u) - g(v)| \quad \text{for all } u, v \text{ in } [a, b].$$

6. Suppose that the function $f:(-1, 1) \to \mathbb{R}$ has n derivatives, and $f^{(n)}:(-1, 1) \to \mathbb{R}$ is bounded. Assume also that $f(0) = f'(0) = \cdots = f^{(n-1)}(0) = 0$. Prove that there is a positive number M such that

$$|f(x)| \leq M|x|^n \quad \text{for all } x \text{ in } (-1, 1).$$

7. Suppose that the function $f:(-1, 1) \to \mathbb{R}$ has n derivatives. Assume that there is a positive number M such that

$$|f(x)| \leq M|x|^n \quad \text{for all } x \text{ in } (-1, 1).$$

Prove that $f(0) = f'(0) = \cdots = f^{(n-1)}(0) = 0$.

8. Let I be an open interval containing the point x_0 and suppose that the function $f: I \to \mathbb{R}$ has two derivatives. Prove that

$$\lim_{h \to 0} \frac{f(x_0 + h) - 2f(x_0) + f(x_0 - h)}{h^2} = f''(x_0).$$

9. Let I be an open interval and n be a natural number. Suppose that both $f: I \to \mathbb{R}$ and $g: I \to \mathbb{R}$ have n derivatives. Prove that $fg: I \to \mathbb{R}$ has n derivatives, and we have the following formula, called *Leibnitz's formula*:

$$(fg)^{(n)}(x) = \sum_{k=0}^{n} \binom{n}{k} f^{(k)}(x) g^{(n-k)}(x) \quad \text{for all } x \text{ in } I.$$

Write the formula out explicitly for $n = 2$ and $n = 3$.

4.5 A Fundamental Differential Equation

For a function $f: I \to \mathbb{R}$ defined on an open interval I, consider the following question:

Does there exist a differentiable function $F: I \to \mathbb{R}$ such that

$$F'(x) = f(x) \quad \text{for all } x \text{ in } I, \tag{4.22}$$

and if there is such a function $F: I \to \mathbb{R}$, is it unique?

A *differential equation* is an equation in which we prescribe some conditions that the derivative or derivatives of a function must satisfy, and from this we wish to find the function. Equation (4.22) is the prototypical differential equation. Differential equations occur throughout mathematics and science. Many of the basic laws of physics are stated as differential equations. As we shall see in Chapter 6, equation (4.22) is the crucial link between differential and integral calculus.

It follows from the first part of the Identity Criterion (Proposition 4.16) that if there is a particular function $F: I \to \mathbb{R}$ that satisfies (4.22), then all of the other functions that satisfy (4.22) are obtained by adding a constant to that particular function. However, it is not at all clear that there are any functions that satisfy (4.22). Consider the following examples.

EXAMPLE 4.8

(i) A solution of the differential equation

$$F'(x) = x^7 - 3x + 1 \quad \text{for all } x \text{ in } \mathbb{R}$$

is given by $F(x) = \dfrac{x^8}{8} - \dfrac{3}{2}x^2 + x$ for all x in $\mathbb{R}$.

(ii) A solution of the differential equation

$$F'(x) = \frac{x}{\sqrt{1 - x^2}} \quad \text{for} - 1 < x < 1$$

is given by $F(x) = -\sqrt{1 - x^2}$ for $-1 < x < 1$.

(iii) A solution of the differential equation

$$F'(x) = \frac{1}{1 + x^4} \quad \text{for all } x \text{ in } \mathbb{R}$$

cannot be determined on the basis of our present results.   □

In (i) and (ii) above, using the differentiation formulas that we have proven, a solution of the given differential equation was determined by inspection; in (iii), the reader will not be able to find a solution. A more complete analysis of (4.22) will require the development of a new concept, the integral, which we will address in Chapters 6 and 7. For now, we prove a result, due to Darboux, that asserts that if I is an open interval and $f: I \to \mathbb{R}$ fails to have the Intermediate Value Property, then there does not exist a solution of the differential equation (4.22).

THEOREM 4.22   **Darboux's Theorem**   Let I be an open interval and suppose that the function $F: I \to \mathbb{R}$ is differentiable. Then the image of the derivative $F': I \to \mathbb{R}$ is an interval; that is, if u and v are points in I and c is strictly between $F'(u)$ and $F'(v)$, then there is a point x_0 in I at which $F'(x_0) = c$.

Proof   Let u, v, and c be as in the statement of the theorem and we suppose that $u < v$. It is necessary to show that c is in the image of $F': I \to \mathbb{R}$. In order to do this, we define an auxiliary function $h: I \to \mathbb{R}$ by

$$h(x) = F(x) - cx \quad \text{for all } x \text{ in } I.$$

Since $h'(x) = F'(x) - c$, the strategy will be to show that the function $h: (u, v) \to \mathbb{R}$ has a maximizer or minimizer x_0. At such a point, by Lemma 4.12, $h'(x_0) = 0$, and so $F'(x_0) = c$.

Since differentiability implies continuity, the function $h: I \to \mathbb{R}$ is continuous. In particular, $h: [u, v] \to \mathbb{R}$ is continuous, and so, according to the Extreme Value Theorem, the function $h: [u, v] \to \mathbb{R}$ attains both maximum and minimum values.

Case 1: $F'(u) < F'(v)$. There is a point x_0 in $[u, v]$ that is a minimizer for the function $h: [u, v] \to \mathbb{R}$. But $h'(u) = F'(u) - c < 0$, so u is not the minimizer, and $h'(v) = F'(v) - c > 0$, so v is not the minimizer. Thus x_0 belongs to the open interval (u, v), and so it is a minimizer for $h: (u, v) \to \mathbb{R}$.

Case 2: $F'(u) > F'(v)$. We argue in the same way to show that if x_0 is a maximizer of $h: [u, v] \to \mathbb{R}$, then x_0 is in the open interval (u, v), so it is a maximizer for $h: (u, v) \to \mathbb{R}$.   ∎

EXAMPLE 4.9   Define the function $f: \mathbb{R} \to \mathbb{R}$ by

$$f(x) = \begin{cases} 1 & \text{if } x \geq 0 \\ 0 & \text{if } x < 0. \end{cases}$$

Then the image $f(\mathbb{R})$ consists of two points, so the image is certainly not an interval. It follows from Darboux's theorem that there does not exist a differentiable function $F: \mathbb{R} \to \mathbb{R}$ such that

$$F'(x) = f(x) \quad \text{for all } x \text{ in } \mathbb{R}.$$ □

EXERCISES

1. Let $F: \mathbb{R} \to \mathbb{R}$ be a differentiable function such that $F(1) = 3$ and $F'(x) = 2x + x^3$ for all x in $\mathbb{R}$. Find $F(-1)$.

2. Suppose that the function $h: \mathbb{R} \to \mathbb{R}$ has a second derivative and that $h''(x) = 0$ for all x in $\mathbb{R}$. Prove that there are numbers m and b such that

$$h(x) = mx + b \quad \text{for all } x \text{ in } \mathbb{R}.$$

3. Find a function $F: \mathbb{R} \to \mathbb{R}$ having a second derivative such that

$$\begin{cases} F''(x) = -x & \text{for all } x \text{ in } \mathbb{R} \\ F(0) = 0 \quad \text{and} \quad F'(0) = 1. \end{cases}$$

    Prove that there is only one such function $F: \mathbb{R} \to \mathbb{R}$.

4. Find a differentiable function $F: \mathbb{R} \to \mathbb{R}$ such that $F(2) = 4$ and

$$F'(x) = \begin{cases} x & \text{if } x \leq 0 \\ x^2 & \text{if } x > 0. \end{cases}$$

5. Suppose that the function $F: \mathbb{R} \to \mathbb{R}$ is differentiable and that for every number x, $F'(x)$ is rational. Prove that the graph of $F: \mathbb{R} \to \mathbb{R}$ is a line having a rational slope.

6. Let I be an open interval containing the points a and b with $a < b$. Suppose that the function $f: I \to \mathbb{R}$ is differentiable and that $f'(a) > 0$. Show that the point a cannot be a maximizer for the function $f: [a, b] \to \mathbb{R}$.

7. Let the function $f: \mathbb{R} \to \mathbb{R}$ be differentiable with $f'(x) \neq 0$ for each x in $\mathbb{R}$. Prove that $f: \mathbb{R} \to \mathbb{R}$ is strictly monotonic.

8. Show that there does not exist a differentiable function $F: \mathbb{R} \to \mathbb{R}$ with $F'(x) = 0$ if $x < 0$ and $F'(x) = 1$ if $x \geq 0$, by arguing that such a function would necessarily be constant on $(-\infty, 0)$ and of the form $F(x) = A + Bx$ on $(0, \infty)$, and then deriving a contradiction.

4.6 The Notation of Leibnitz

So far, given an open interval I and a differentiable function $f: I \to \mathbb{R}$, we have denoted the function's derivative by

$$f': I \to \mathbb{R},$$

so that $f'(x)$ is the derivative of $f: I \to \mathbb{R}$ at x in I. This notation has been completely adequate. However, as we introduce new classes of functions and when we study integration, certain formulas and algorithmic techniques become easier to remember in an alternate notation, due to Leibnitz.

For a differentiable function $f: I \to \mathbb{R}$, we will denote $f'(x)$ by

$$\frac{d}{dx}(f(x)) \quad \text{or} \quad \frac{df}{dx}.$$

If points on the graph of $f: I \to \mathbb{R}$ are denoted by (x, y), we will also denote $f'(x)$ by

$$\frac{dy}{dx} \quad \text{or} \quad y'.$$

The great advantage of the Leibnitzian symbolism is that, when it is properly interpreted, we can treat the symbols df, dy, dx, and so on as if they represented members of $\mathbb{R}$ and carry out various algebraic operations, and the resulting formulas will have meaning. We give two examples.

First, for any two real nonzero numbers,

$$\frac{a}{b} = 1 \bigg/ \frac{b}{a}.$$

A corresponding inversion formula for the Leibnitz symbols is

$$\frac{dx}{dy} = 1 \bigg/ \frac{dy}{dx}. \tag{4.23}$$

What significance can be attached to (4.23)? Well, suppose that $f: I \to \mathbb{R}$ is differentiable, with $f'(x) > 0$ for all x in I, and we set $y = f(x)$ for x in I. According to Theorem 4.6, letting $J = f(I)$, the inverse function $f^{-1}: J \to \mathbb{R}$ is differentiable and

$$(f^{-1})'(f(x)) = \frac{1}{f'(x)} \quad \text{for all } x \text{ in } I. \tag{4.24}$$

If we now let
$$x = f^{-1}(y) \quad \text{for all } y \text{ in } J,$$
then, according to the symbolism introduced above,

$$\frac{dx}{dy} = (f^{-1})'(y) = (f^{-1})'(f(x)),$$

and so, since
$$\frac{dy}{dx} = f'(x),$$

we see that (4.23) may be interpreted as a compact rewriting of (4.24).

As a second example, note that for numbers $a, b \neq 0$, and $c \neq 0$,

$$\frac{a}{b} = \frac{a}{c} \cdot \frac{c}{b}.$$

A corresponding cancellation formula for the Leibnitz symbols is

$$\frac{df}{dx} = \frac{df}{du} \cdot \frac{du}{dx}. \tag{4.25}$$

Again we seek a suitable interpretation of (4.25). The following is reasonable: Suppose that the functions $f \colon \mathbb{R} \to \mathbb{R}$ and $u \colon \mathbb{R} \to \mathbb{R}$ are differentiable. Consider the composition $h = f \circ u \colon \mathbb{R} \to \mathbb{R}$. According to the Chain Rule, $h \colon \mathbb{R} \to \mathbb{R}$ is differentiable and

$$h'(x) = f'(u(x))u'(x) \quad \text{for all } x \text{ in } \mathbb{R}. \tag{4.26}$$

If we substitute

$$\frac{df}{dx} \quad \text{for} \quad \frac{d}{dx}[f(u(x))], \qquad \frac{df}{du} \quad \text{for} \quad f'(u(x)), \quad \text{and} \quad \frac{du}{dx} \quad \text{for} \quad u'(x),$$

$$\tag{4.27}$$

then (4.26) becomes (4.25).

The reader should be careful to observe that in this section *we have not proven anything*. We have simply indicated how (4.23) can reasonably be interpreted as a compact form of (4.24) and (4.25) as a compact symbolic rewriting of (4.26). In fact, not only have we not proven anything, we have used the symbol d/dt ambiguously in (4.25). In spite of this, the symbolism of Leibnitz is extremely useful. We just have to be quite careful to interpret in a precise manner any formulas we are using, then justify this precise interpretation using proven results.

One final notational convention: When $f \colon I \to \mathbb{R}$ has a second derivative, we denote $f''(x)$ by

$$\frac{d^2}{dx^2}(f(x)), \qquad \frac{d^2 f}{dx^2}, \qquad \frac{d^2 y}{dx^2}, \qquad \text{and} \quad y''.$$

EXERCISES

1. Give a reasonable interpretation of the formula
$$\frac{d}{dx}(f + g) = \frac{df}{dx} + \frac{dg}{dx}.$$

2. Is there any way we can justify inequalities and the Leibnitz symbols? For instance, under what conditions does
$$\frac{df}{dx} \geq \frac{dg}{dx} \quad \text{imply} \quad f \geq g?$$

3. Give a reasonable interpretation of the formula
$$\frac{df}{dr} = \frac{df}{du} \cdot \frac{du}{ds} \cdot \frac{ds}{dr}.$$

4. Give a reasonable interpretation of the formula
$$\frac{ds}{ds} = 1.$$

5

The Elementary Functions as Solutions of Differential Equations

5.1   The Natural Logarithm and Exponential Functions

Given a rational number r, we seek a differentiable function $F: (0, \infty) \to \mathbb{R}$ such that

$$F'(x) = x^r \quad \text{for all } x > 0.$$

We immediately see that if $r \neq -1$ and c is any real number, then the function $F: (0, \infty) \to \mathbb{R}$ defined by

$$F(x) = \frac{x^{r+1}}{r+1} + c \quad \text{for all } x > 0$$

is a solution of the above differential equation, and, by the Identity Criterion (Proposition 4.16), all the solutions are of this form. The exceptional case, $r = -1$, is more interesting. The exceptional problem is to find a differentiable function $F: (0, \infty) \to \mathbb{R}$ such that

$$F'(x) = \frac{1}{x} \quad \text{for all } x > 0.$$

Based on the results that we have so far established, we cannot determine whether there is such a function.

In order to extend our stock of differentiable functions, let us provisionally *assume* that there is a differentiable function $F: (0, \infty) \to \mathbb{R}$ such that

$$\begin{cases} F'(x) = 1/x & \text{for all } x > 0 \\ F(1) = 0. \end{cases} \tag{5.1}$$

In Chapter 7 we will prove that there is indeed such a function. It follows from the Identity Criterion that there can be at most one such function.

THEOREM 5.1   Let the function $F: (0, \infty) \to \mathbb{R}$ satisfy the differential equation (5.1). Then

(i) $F(ab) = F(a) + F(b)$ for all $a, b > 0$.

(ii) $F(a^r) = rF(a)$ if $a > 0$ and r is rational.

(iii) For each real number c there is a unique positive number x such that $F(x) = c$.

Proof of (i)   Fix $a > 0$ and define $g(x) = F(ax) - F(x) - F(a)$ for all $x > 0$. According to the Chain Rule, the function $g: (0, \infty) \to \mathbb{R}$ is differentiable and

$$g'(x) = aF'(ax) - F'(x) = \frac{a}{ax} - \frac{1}{x} = 0 \quad \text{for all } x > 0.$$

The Identity Criterion implies that $g: (0, \infty) \to \mathbb{R}$ is constant. But $g(1) = -F(1) = 0$, so $g(x) = 0$ for all $x > 0$. This proves (i).

Proof of (ii)   Define $h(x) = F(x^r) - rF(x)$ for all $x > 0$. Again using the Chain Rule, we see that the function $h: (0, \infty) \to \mathbb{R}$ is differentiable and that

$$h'(x) = rx^{r-1}F'(x^r) - rF'(x) = \frac{rx^{r-1}}{x^r} - \frac{r}{x} = 0 \quad \text{for all } x > 0.$$

Since $h(1) = 0$, it follows from the Identity Criterion that $h(x) = 0$ for all $x > 0$. Thus (ii) is proven.

Proof of (iii)   Since $F'(x) = 1/x > 0$ for all $x > 0$, the function $F: (0, \infty) \to \mathbb{R}$ is strictly increasing. Also observe, using (i), that

$$0 = F(1) = F\left(x \cdot \frac{1}{x}\right) = F(x) + F\left(\frac{1}{x}\right) \quad \text{for all } x > 0,$$

so that $F(1/x) = -F(x)$ for all $x > 0$. Thus we may assume $c > 0$, and it suffices to show that there is a solution of the equation

$$F(x) = c, \quad x > 1. \tag{5.2}$$

Since differentiability implies continuity, the function $F: (0, \infty) \to \mathbb{R}$ is continuous. Consequently, since $F(1) = 0 < c$, according to the Intermediate Value Theorem, to show that equation (5.2) has a solution it will suffice to show that there is a number $x_0 > 1$ such that $F(x_0) > c$. However, $F(2) > F(1) = 0$, and (ii) implies that $F(2^n) = nF(2)$ for every natural number n. According to the Archimedean Property, we can choose a natural number n such that $nF(2) > c$, and so, letting $x_0 = 2^n$, we have $F(x_0) > c$. ∎

The function $F: (0, \infty) \to \mathbb{R}$ that satisfies the differential equation (5.1) occurs so frequently in science that it has a special name—it is called the *natural logarithm*—and $F(x)$ is denoted by $\ln x$ for $x > 0$.

From the definition of the natural logarithm and the Chain Rule, it follows that *if I is an open interval and the function $h: I \to \mathbb{R}$ is differentiable and is such that $h(x) > 0$ for all x in I, then*

$$\frac{d}{dx}(\ln h(x)) = \frac{h'(x)}{h(x)} \qquad \text{for all } x \text{ in } I. \tag{5.3}$$

Observe that part (iii) of the preceding theorem implies that the function $\ln: (0, \infty) \to \mathbb{R}$ has an inverse function that is defined on all of $\mathbb{R}$. Denote the inverse function by $g: \mathbb{R} \to \mathbb{R}$. Then

$$\begin{cases} g(\ln x) = x & \text{for all } x > 0 \\ \qquad \text{and} \\ \ln g(x) = x & \text{for all } x \text{ in } \mathbb{R}. \end{cases}$$

Moreover, according to Corollary 4.7, the inverse function $g: \mathbb{R} \to \mathbb{R}$ is differentiable. Since

$$\ln g(x) = x \qquad \text{for all } x \text{ in } \mathbb{R},$$

it follows from the Chain Rule that

$$\frac{g'(x)}{g(x)} = 1 \qquad \text{for all } x \text{ in } \mathbb{R}.$$

Thus $g: \mathbb{R} \to \mathbb{R}$ is a differentiable function that has the property that

$$\begin{cases} g'(x) = g(x) & \text{for all } x \text{ in } \mathbb{R} \\ g(0) = 1. \end{cases} \tag{5.4}$$

Since the function $\ln: (0, \infty) \to \mathbb{R}$ is strictly increasing and its image is all of $\mathbb{R}$, there is a unique solution of the equation

$$\ln x = 1, \qquad x > 0. \tag{5.5}$$

DEFINITION *The unique solution of equation (5.5) is denoted by e.*

Recall that if a is a positive number and b is a rational number, we have defined a^b. In particular, since $e > 0$, for each rational number x the number e^x is defined.

PROPOSITION 5.2 Let the function $g: \mathbb{R} \to \mathbb{R}$ and the number e be as defined above. Then

$$g(x) = e^x \qquad \text{for all rational numbers } x. \tag{5.6}$$

Proof   Let x be a rational number. Since both $g(x)$ and e^x are positive and the function $\ln: (0, \infty) \to \mathbb{R}$ is strictly increasing,

$$g(x) = e^x \quad \text{if and only if} \quad \ln g(x) = \ln e^x.$$

But, by the very definition of the inverse, $\ln g(x) = x$. On the other hand, part (ii) of Theorem 5.1 and the definition of e imply that $\ln e^x = x \ln e = x$. ∎

Observe that at present, formula (5.6) has no meaning if the number x is irrational, since we have not defined the symbol a^x if x is irrational. For instance, we have not defined the symbol $3^{\sqrt{2}}$. However, since the left-hand side of formula (5.6) is defined for any number x, rational or irrational, we now have a natural way to define *irrational powers of positive numbers*.

DEFINITION   *For an irrational number b, we define $e^b \equiv g(b)$, where $g: \mathbb{R} \to \mathbb{R}$ is the inverse of the natural logarithm. More generally, for any positive number a, we define $a^b \equiv g(b \ln a)$.*

This definition, together with Proposition 5.2, implies that

$$a^b = g(b \ln a) = e^{b \ln a} \quad \text{for all } a > 0 \text{ and all } b. \tag{5.7}$$

It is not difficult to check that with this extended definition of exponentiation the familiar rules for exponents are still valid (see Exercise 1). Formula (5.4) and the Chain Rule imply that *if I is an open interval and the function $h: I \to \mathbb{R}$ is differentiable, then*

$$\frac{d}{dx}\left[e^{h(x)}\right] = e^{h(x)} h'(x) \quad \text{for all } x \text{ in } I. \tag{5.8}$$

We now have two new classes of differentiable functions.

PROPOSITION 5.3   Let $a > 0$. Then

$$\frac{d}{dx}[a^x] = a^x \ln a \text{ for all } x \text{ in } \mathbb{R}. \tag{5.9}$$

Proof   Using formula (5.8), we have

$$\frac{d}{dx}[a^x] = \frac{d}{dx}[e^{x \ln a}] = a^x \ln a \quad \text{for all } x \text{ in } \mathbb{R}. \quad ∎$$

PROPOSITION 5.4   Let r be any number. Then

$$\frac{d}{dx}[x^r] = rx^{r-1} \quad \text{for all } x > 0. \tag{5.10}$$

Proof   Again using formula (5.8), we have

$$\frac{d}{dx}[x^r] = \frac{d}{dx}[e^{r \ln x}]$$

$$= [e^{r \ln x}]\frac{d}{dx}(r \ln x)$$

$$= x^r \left(\frac{r}{x}\right)$$

$$= rx^{r-1} \quad \text{for all } x > 0. \qquad \blacksquare$$

PROPOSITION 5.5   Let c and k be any real numbers. Then the differential equation

$$\begin{cases} F'(x) = kF(x) & \text{for all } x \text{ in } \mathbb{R} \\ F(0) = c \end{cases} \qquad (5.11)$$

has exactly one solution. It is given by the formula

$$F(x) = ce^{kx} \text{ for all } x \text{ in } \mathbb{R}. \qquad (5.12)$$

Proof   From the differentiation formula (5.8), we see that (5.12) defines a solution of (5.11). It remains to prove uniqueness. Let the function $F: \mathbb{R} \to \mathbb{R}$ be a solution of (5.11). Define

$$g(x) = \frac{F(x)}{e^{kx}} \quad \text{for all } x \text{ in } \mathbb{R}.$$

Using the quotient rule for derivatives, we have

$$g'(x) = \frac{ke^{kx} F(x) - ke^{kx} F(x)}{(e^{kx})^2} = 0$$

for all x. The Identity Criterion implies that the function $g: \mathbb{R} \to \mathbb{R}$ is constant. Since $g(0) = F(0) = c$, $g(x) = c$ for all x; that is, $F(x) = ce^{kx}$ for all x. Thus, there is exactly one solution of (5.11). $\qquad \blacksquare$

In Section 2.2, we showed that the sequence $\{(1 + 1/n)^n\}$ was monotone increasing and bounded above by 3. In fact,

$$\lim_{n \to \infty} \left[(1 + 1/n)^n\right] = e. \qquad (5.13)$$

To see this, observe that from the very definition of the derivative of the natural logarithm at $x = 1$ we have

$$\lim_{n \to \infty} \left[\frac{\ln(1 + 1/n) - \ln 1}{1/n}\right] = \lim_{n \to \infty} [n \ln(1 + 1/n)] = 1.$$

Therefore, since the exponential function is continuous at $x = 1$,

$$\lim_{n \to \infty} (1 + 1/n)^n = \lim_{n \to \infty} e^{n \ln(1 + 1/n)} = e^1.$$

EXERCISES

1. Let $a > 0$. Prove that for any numbers x_1 and x_2,
   (a) $a^{x_1} \cdot a^{x_2} = a^{x_1 + x_2}$
   (b) $(a^{x_1})^{x_2} = a^{x_1 x_2}$

2. For $a > 0$, show that

   $$\lim_{n \to \infty} n[a^{1/n} - 1] = \ln a.$$

3. Let $0 < a \le b$. Prove that

   $$\frac{b-a}{b} \le \ln\left[\frac{b}{a}\right] \le \frac{b-a}{a}.$$

4. Let $a > 0$. Prove that there is a number k such that

   $$a^x = e^{kx} \quad \text{for all } x \text{ in } \mathbb{R}.$$

5. Use the Mean Value Theorem to show that $e^x > 1 + x$ if $x \ne 0$. Then show that the following equation has exactly one solution:

   $$2e^x = (1+x)^2, \quad x \text{ in } \mathbb{R}.$$

6. Show that there is a number c in $(1, e)$ such that

   $$1 = \ln e - \ln 1 = \frac{1}{c}(e - 1).$$

   From this, conclude that $e > 2$.

7. Use the preceding exercise to prove that the following equation has exactly one solution:

   $$xe^x = 2, \quad 0 < x < 1.$$

8. For a fixed number a, how many solutions does the following equation have?

   $$x \ln x = a, \quad x > 0.$$

9. Suppose that $h: \mathbb{R} \to \mathbb{R}$ is a differentiable function having the property that

   $$h(a + b) = h(a)h(b) \quad \text{for all } a \text{ and } b \text{ in } \mathbb{R},$$

   and that the function is not identically equal to 0.
   (a) Using the definition of derivative, prove that

   $$h'(x) = h'(0)h(x) \quad \text{for all } x \text{ in } \mathbb{R}.$$

   (b) Show that if $k = h'(0)$, then $h(x) = e^{kx}$ for all x in $\mathbb{R}$.

10. Let a be a limit point of the set U. Use the continuity of the natural logarithm and the exponential function to show that

    $$\lim_{x \to a} f(x) = \ell \quad \text{if and only if} \quad \lim_{x \to a} e^{f(x)} = e^\ell.$$

    Moreover, if $\ell > 0$ and $f(x) > 0$ for all x in U, show that

    $$\lim_{x \to a} f(x) = \ell \quad \text{if and only if} \quad \lim_{x \to a} \ln f(x) = \ln \ell.$$

11. By using the preceding exercise, or by other means, analyze the following limits:
    (a) $\lim_{x \to 0}(1 + x)^{1/x}$
    (b) $\lim_{x \to 1} \dfrac{\ln x}{x - 1}$
    (c) $\lim_{n \to \infty} n[e^{b/n} - 1]$
    (d) $\lim_{x \to 0} \dfrac{a^x - b^x}{x}$ for $a, b > 0$

12. The *hyperbolic cosine* of x, which is denoted by $\cosh x$, and the *hyperbolic sine* of x, which is denoted by $\sinh x$, are defined by

$$\cosh x \equiv \frac{e^x + e^{-x}}{2} \quad \text{and} \quad \sinh x \equiv \frac{e^x - e^{-x}}{2} \quad \text{for all } x \text{ in } \mathbb{R}.$$

Given numbers a, α, and β, find a solution of the equation

$$\begin{cases} f''(x) - a^2 f(x) = 0 & \text{for all } x \text{ in } \mathbb{R} \\ f(0) = \alpha \quad \text{and} \quad f'(0) = \beta \end{cases}$$

that is of the form

$$f(x) = c_1 \cosh ax + c_2 \sinh ax \quad \text{for all } x \text{ in } \mathbb{R}.$$

5.2 The Trigonometric Functions

A function $f \colon \mathbb{R} \to \mathbb{R}$ is called *periodic*, with *period* $T > 0$, if

$$f(x + T) = f(x) \quad \text{for all } x \text{ in } \mathbb{R}.$$

So far, with the exception of constant functions, we have not encountered any periodic functions. Since periodic phenomena occur in nature (planets, pendulums, and so on) and since the basic functions of trigonometry are periodic, we need to analyze such functions.

In the same way in which the properties of the logarithm and the exponential functions were deduced from a single differential equation, we will now define and analyze the sine and cosine functions with a single differential equation as our starting point. In this section we will study functions $f \colon \mathbb{R} \to \mathbb{R}$ that have the property that

$$f''(x) + f(x) = 0 \quad \text{for all } x \text{ in } \mathbb{R}. \tag{5.14}$$

LEMMA 5.6 Suppose that the function $f \colon \mathbb{R} \to \mathbb{R}$ is a solution of the differential equation

$$\begin{cases} f''(x) + f(x) = 0 & \text{for all } x \text{ in } \mathbb{R} \\ f(0) = 0 \quad \text{and} \quad f'(0) = 0. \end{cases} \tag{5.15}$$

Then $f(x) = 0$ for all x in $\mathbb{R}$.

Proof   Define $g(x) = [f(x)]^2 + [f'(x)]^2$ for all x in $\mathbb{R}$. Observe that

$$\begin{aligned}
g'(x) &= 2f(x)f'(x) + 2f'(x)f''(x) \\
&= 2f'(x)[f(x) + f''(x)] \\
&= 0 \quad \text{for all } x \text{ in } \mathbb{R}.
\end{aligned}$$

Thus, by the Identity Criterion, the function $g: \mathbb{R} \to \mathbb{R}$ is constant, and since $g(0) = 0$, $g(x) = 0$ for all x in $\mathbb{R}$. But observe that

$$0 \leq [f(x)]^2 \leq g(x) \quad \text{for all } x \text{ in } \mathbb{R},$$

so $f(x) = 0$ for all x in $\mathbb{R}$. ∎

For fixed numbers α and β, consider the differential equation

$$\begin{cases} f''(x) + f(x) = 0 & \text{for all } x \text{ in } \mathbb{R} \\ f(0) = \alpha \quad \text{and} \quad f'(0) = \beta. \end{cases} \tag{5.16}$$

This equation can have at most one solution, since if there were two distinct functions that were solutions of (5.16), we see that their difference would be a solution of (5.15) that is not identically zero, which would contradict Lemma 5.6.

We provisionally *assume* that in the case $\alpha = 1$ and $\beta = 0$, there is a solution of (5.16). In Chapter 9, we will prove that there is such a function. We denote this solution by $C: \mathbb{R} \to \mathbb{R}$. Thus, by definition,

$$\begin{cases} C''(x) + C(x) = 0 & \text{for all } x \text{ in } \mathbb{R} \\ C(0) = 1 \quad \text{and} \quad C'(0) = 0. \end{cases} \tag{5.17}$$

The function $C: \mathbb{R} \to \mathbb{R}$ is *even*; that is,

$$C(-x) = C(x) \quad \text{for all } x \text{ in } \mathbb{R}.$$

This follows from the observation that if we define $f(x) = C(-x)$ for all x in $\mathbb{R}$, then $f: \mathbb{R} \to \mathbb{R}$ is seen to be a solution of the differential equation (5.17), and since there is only one solution, $f(x) = C(x)$ for all x in $\mathbb{R}$.

We define a companion function $S: \mathbb{R} \to \mathbb{R}$ by

$$S(x) = -C'(x) \quad \text{for all } x \text{ in } \mathbb{R}.$$

Thus $S(0) = 0$, since $C'(0) = 0$. Moreover, since $S'(x) = -C''(x) = C(x)$ and $C(0) = 1$, it follows that $S'(0) = 1$. Finally, if we differentiate the first line of (5.17) we see that $C'''(x) + C'(x) = 0$ for all x in $\mathbb{R}$, and hence $S''(x) + S(x) = 0$ for all x in $\mathbb{R}$. Thus

$$\begin{cases} S''(x) + S(x) = 0 & \text{for all } x \text{ in } \mathbb{R} \\ S(0) = 0 \quad \text{and} \quad S'(0) = 1. \end{cases} \tag{5.18}$$

The function $S: \mathbb{R} \to \mathbb{R}$ is *odd*; that is,

$$S(-x) = -S(x) \quad \text{for all } x \text{ in } \mathbb{R}.$$

This follows from the observation that if we define $f(x) = -S(-x)$ for all x in $\mathbb{R}$, then the function $f: \mathbb{R} \to \mathbb{R}$ is seen to be a solution of the differential equation (5.18), and since there is only one solution, $f(x) = S(x)$ for all x in $\mathbb{R}$. For future reference, it is useful to record the formulas

$$S'(x) = C(x) \quad \text{and} \quad C'(x) = -S(x) \quad \text{for all } x \text{ in } \mathbb{R}. \tag{5.19}$$

THEOREM 5.7   For all a and b,

$$[S(a)]^2 + [C(a)]^2 = 1, \tag{5.20}$$

$$S(a + b) = S(a)C(b) + C(a)S(b), \tag{5.21}$$

$$C(a + b) = C(a)C(b) - S(a)S(b). \tag{5.22}$$

Proof   In order to prove (5.20), define $g(x) = [S(x)]^2 + [C(x)]^2 - 1$ for all x in $\mathbb{R}$. Observe that

$$g'(x) = 2S(x)S'(x) + 2C(x)C'(x)$$
$$= 2C(x)[S(x) + S''(x)] = 0 \quad \text{for all } x \text{ in } \mathbb{R}.$$

Thus, by the Identity Criterion, the function $g: \mathbb{R} \to \mathbb{R}$ is constant, and since $g(0) = 0$, it follows that $g(x) = 0$ for all x in $\mathbb{R}$. This proves (5.20).

In order to prove (5.21), fix a real number b and define

$$f(x) = S(x + b) - [S(x)C(b) + C(x)S(b)] \quad \text{for all } x \text{ in } \mathbb{R}.$$

Then $f(0) = 0$ and $f'(0) = 0$. Moreover, for all x in $\mathbb{R}$, $f''(x) + f(x) = 0$, since

$$S''(x + b) + S(x + b) = 0, \quad S''(x) + S(x) = 0, \quad \text{and} \quad C''(x) + C(x) = 0.$$

Thus the function $f: \mathbb{R} \to \mathbb{R}$ is a solution of (5.15), and so, according to Lemma 5.6, $f(x) = 0$ for all x in $\mathbb{R}$. This proves (5.21).

Finally, differentiating the above function $f: \mathbb{R} \to \mathbb{R}$, we have

$$0 = f'(x) = C(x + b) - [C(x)C(b) - S(x)S(b)] \quad \text{for all } x \text{ in } \mathbb{R},$$

so (5.22) is proven.   ∎

The above theorem is a statement of the classical trigonometric identities. We call (5.20) the Pythagorean Identity. Observe that as a consequence of the Pythagorean Identity,

$$|S(x)| \leq 1 \quad \text{and} \quad |C(x)| \leq 1 \quad \text{for all } x \text{ in } \mathbb{R}. \tag{5.23}$$

We will now show that the functions $S: \mathbb{R} \to \mathbb{R}$ and $C: \mathbb{R} \to \mathbb{R}$ are periodic. The strategy is to show that there is a smallest positive number p at which $C(p) = 0$, and then to use the addition formulas to prove that these functions have period $T = 4p$.

LEMMA 5.8   There is a positive number x at which $C(x) = 0$.

Proof From the Mean Value Theorem, it follows that we may select a number z strictly between 0 and 2 such that $S(2) - S(0) = 2C(z)$. Since $S(0) = 0$ and $|S(2)| \leq 1$, we see that $|2C(z)| \leq 1$. Thus, using the identities (5.22) and (5.20), we have

$$C(2z) = [C(z)]^2 - [S(z)]^2 = 2[C(z)]^2 - 1 \leq 0.$$

Hence $C(0) > 0$ and $C(2z) \leq 0$, and so, by the Intermediate Value Theorem, there is a number x between 0 and $2z$ at which $C(x) = 0$. ∎

THEOREM 5.9 There is a smallest positive number at which $C(x) = 0$.

Proof For any continuous function $g: \mathbb{R} \to \mathbb{R}$ for which $g(0) > 0$ and there is a positive number x at which $g(x) = 0$, there is a smallest positive number x_0 at which $g(x_0) = 0$ (see Exercise 16). The preceding lemma asserts that at some positive number x, $C(x) = 0$. On the other hand, $C(0) = 1$. ∎

THEOREM 5.10 Let p be the smallest positive number at which $C(x) = 0$. Then the functions $C: \mathbb{R} \to \mathbb{R}$ and $S: \mathbb{R} \to \mathbb{R}$ both have period $4p$.

Proof Since $S'(x) = C(x) > 0$ if $0 < x < p$, the function $S: [0, p] \to \mathbb{R}$ is strictly increasing. Hence, since $S(0) = 0$, $S(p) > 0$. Since $C(p) = 0$, the Pythagorean Identity implies that $S(p) = 1$. Thus $C(p) = 0$ and $S(p) = 1$, and so, using the addition formulas (5.21) and (5.22),

$$S(x + p) = C(x) \quad \text{and} \quad C(x + p) = -S(x) \quad \text{for all } x \text{ in } \mathbb{R}. \tag{5.24}$$

Substituting $x + p$ for x in (5.24), we obtain

$$S(x + 2p) = -S(x) \quad \text{and} \quad C(x + 2p) = -C(x) \quad \text{for all } x \text{ in } \mathbb{R}, \tag{5.25}$$

and now, substituting $x + 2p$ for x in (5.25), we see that the functions $S: \mathbb{R} \to \mathbb{R}$ and $C: \mathbb{R} \to \mathbb{R}$ have period $4p$. ∎

As we have already mentioned, none of the functions that we have seen until now have been periodic, except, of course, constant functions.

We define the number π to be $2p$, where p is the smallest positive number at which $C(p) = 0$. Hence $S: \mathbb{R} \to \mathbb{R}$ and $C: \mathbb{R} \to \mathbb{R}$ have period 2π. Of course, we need to show that this definition of π is in accordance with the usual definition of π as the area of a circle of unit radius. Specifically, we must show that the first positive zero of the solution of the differential equation (5.17) occurs at p, where p is half the area of a circle of unit radius. To do this, we first need to discuss integration, and so we postpone a justification of our use of the symbol π until Chapter 7. However, from now on we will denote $S(x)$ by $\sin x$ and denote $C(x)$ by $\cos x$, for all x in $\mathbb{R}$. The function $S: \mathbb{R} \to \mathbb{R}$ is called the *sine* function; the function $C: \mathbb{R} \to \mathbb{R}$ is called the *cosine* function.

The cosine function was defined to be the unique solution of the differential equation (5.17). In fact, the cosine and sine functions play a central role in the theory of general differential equations. One indication of this is the following.

THEOREM 5.11 Let α and β be any numbers. Then there is exactly one solution of the differential equation

$$\begin{cases} f''(x) + f(x) = 0 & \text{for all } x \text{ in } \mathbb{R} \\ f(0) = \alpha \quad \text{and} \quad f'(0) = \beta. \end{cases} \tag{5.26}$$

This solution is defined by

$$f(x) = \alpha \cos x + \beta \sin x \quad \text{for all } x \text{ in } \mathbb{R}. \tag{5.27}$$

Proof The differential equation (5.26) can have at most one solution, since if there were two distinct solutions, their difference would be a solution of the differential equation (5.15) that is not identically zero, which would contradict Lemma 5.6. From (5.17) and (5.18), it follows that formula (5.27) defines a solution of the differential equation (5.26). ∎

We conclude this section with a discussion of the tangent function. We begin with two observations about the cosine. First, note that the second identity in (5.25) may be rewritten as

$$\cos(x + \pi) = -\cos x \quad \text{for all } x \text{ in } \mathbb{R}.$$

Second, by definition, $\cos \pi/2 = 0$ and $\cos x > 0$ if $0 \leq x < \pi/2$. It follows that $\cos x > 0$ if $-\pi/2 < x < \pi/2$, and that

$$\cos x = 0 \quad \text{if and only if} \quad x = \pi/2 + n\pi \quad \text{for some integer } n.$$

Define $D = \{x \text{ in } \mathbb{R} \mid x \neq \pi/2 + n\pi, n \text{ an integer}\}$. The *tangent* function, with domain D, is defined by

$$\tan x = \frac{\sin x}{\cos x} \quad \text{for all } x \text{ in } D.$$

Thus the tangent, being the quotient of differentiable functions, is differentiable, and from the quotient formula for derivatives, together with (5.19), it follows that

$$\frac{d}{dx}[\tan(x)] = \frac{1}{\cos^2 x} \quad \text{if} \quad x \neq \frac{\pi}{2} + n\pi, \quad n \text{ an integer}. \tag{5.28}$$

THEOREM 5.12 The function $\tan: (-\pi/2, \pi/2) \to \mathbb{R}$ is strictly increasing, is odd, and has as its image all of $\mathbb{R}$.

Proof Since

$$\frac{d}{dx}[\tan x] = \cos^{-2} x > 0 \quad \text{for} \quad -\frac{\pi}{2} < x < \frac{\pi}{2},$$

the function $\tan: (-\pi/2, \pi/2) \to \mathbb{R}$ is strictly increasing. The oddness of the sine and the evenness of the cosine imply that the tangent is odd.

It remains to be proven that the range is all of $\mathbb{R}$. Since the tangent is odd and $\tan 0 = 0$, it will suffice to show that given $c > 0$ there is a solution of the equation

$$\tan x = c, \quad 0 < x < \frac{\pi}{2}. \tag{5.29}$$

According to the Intermediate Value Theorem, since $\tan 0 = 0$, in order to prove that there is a solution of (5.29) it suffices to find a point x in the interval $(-\pi/2, \pi/2)$ at which $\tan x > c$. However, since the sine is increasing on the interval $[0, \pi/2]$,

$$\tan x = \frac{\sin x}{\cos x} \geq \frac{\sin \pi/4}{\cos x} \quad \text{if} \quad \frac{\pi}{4} \leq x < \frac{\pi}{2}.$$

Moreover, since the cosine is continuous and positive on the interval $(0, \pi/2)$ and $\cos \pi/2 = 0$, we can choose a point x in the interval $(\pi/4, \pi/2)$ at which $\cos x < (\sin \pi/4)/c$. At this point, $\tan x > c$.   ∎

---

1. Derive formulas for $\cos(a - b)$ and $\sin(a - b)$ in terms of $\sin a$, $\sin b$, $\cos a$, and $\cos b$.
2. Find a formula for $\sin 3a$ in terms of $\sin a$ and $\cos a$. Use this to calculate $\sin \pi/3$ and $\cos \pi/3$. Also calculate $\sin \pi/6$ and $\cos \pi/4$.
3. For numbers a and b such that $|a| < 1$, prove that the following equation, which is called *Kepler's equation*, has exactly one solution:

$$x = a \sin x + b, \qquad x \text{ in } \mathbb{R}.$$

4. Prove that the following equation has exactly one solution:

$$e^{2x} + \cos x + x = 0, \qquad x \text{ in } \mathbb{R}.$$

5. For numbers a and b, define

$$f(x) = \sin x + ax + b \quad \text{for all } x \text{ in } \mathbb{R}.$$

For what values of a is the function $f: \mathbb{R} \to \mathbb{R}$ increasing?
6. Find the maximum and minimum points of the set $\{\sin x + \cos x \mid x \text{ in } \mathbb{R}\}$.
7. Using the definition of derivative, prove that

$$\lim_{x \to 0} \frac{\sin x}{x} = 1 \quad \text{and} \quad \lim_{x \to 0} \frac{\cos x - 1}{x} = 0.$$

8. Let k be a fixed number. Suppose that the function $f: \mathbb{R} \to \mathbb{R}$ is a solution of the differential equation

$$\begin{cases} f''(x) + k^2 f(x) = 0 & \text{for all } x \text{ in } \mathbb{R} \\ f(0) = 0 \quad \text{and} \quad f'(0) = 0. \end{cases}$$

Prove that $f(x) = 0$ for all x in $\mathbb{R}$.
9. Let a, b, and k be fixed numbers. Use the preceding exercise to show that the following differential equation has at most one solution:

$$\begin{cases} f''(x) + k^2 f(x) = 0 & \text{for all } x \text{ in } \mathbb{R} \\ f(0) = a \quad \text{and} \quad f'(0) = b. \end{cases}$$

Then verify that if $k \neq 0$, the solution is defined by

$$f(x) = a \cos kx + b \sin kx \quad \text{for all } x \text{ in } \mathbb{R}.$$

10. Let a and b be numbers such that $a^2 + b^2 = 1$. Prove that there exists exactly one number θ in the interval $[0, 2\pi)$ such that

$$\begin{cases} \cos \theta = a \\ \sin \theta = b. \end{cases}$$

11. For positive numbers M and T, and a number θ_0 in the interval $[0, 2\pi)$, define

$$g(x) = M \sin(Tx + \theta_0) \quad \text{for all } x \text{ in } \mathbb{R}.$$

Graph the function $g \colon \mathbb{R} \to \mathbb{R}$.

12. Let c_1 and c_2 be numbers such that $c_1^2 + c_2^2 = 1$. Define

$$h(x) = c_1 \cos x + c_2 \sin x \quad \text{for all } x \text{ in } \mathbb{R}.$$

Use Exercise 10 and the Addition Formula for the cosine to show that there is a number θ_0 such that

$$h(x) = \cos(x + \theta_0) \quad \text{for all } x \text{ in } \mathbb{R}.$$

13. Define

$$f(x) = \begin{cases} x^2 \sin(1/x) + x & \text{if } x \neq 0 \\ 0 & \text{if } x = 0. \end{cases}$$

Prove that the function $f \colon \mathbb{R} \to \mathbb{R}$ is differentiable and that $f'(0) = 1$. Also prove that there is no neighborhood I of 0 such that the function $f \colon I \to \mathbb{R}$ is increasing.

14. Does the function $f \colon \mathbb{R} \to \mathbb{R}$ defined in the previous exercise have a continuous derivative? Justify your answer.

15. By using Theorem 4.20 (perhaps repeatedly), verify that:

(a) $\displaystyle \lim_{x \to 0} \frac{x - \sin x}{x^3} = \frac{1}{6}$.

(b) $\displaystyle \lim_{x \to 0} \frac{\cos x - 1 + x^2}{x^2} = \frac{1}{2}$.

(c) $\displaystyle \lim_{x \to 0} \frac{x^3 \sin 1/x}{\sin x} = 0$.

16. Suppose that the function $g \colon \mathbb{R} \to \mathbb{R}$ is continuous, $g(0) > 0$, and at some positive number x_0, $g(x_0) = 0$. Prove that there is a smallest positive number p at which $g(x) = 0$. (*Hint:* Define $p = \inf \{x \text{ in } \mathbb{R} \mid x > 0, g(x) = 0\}$ and prove that $p > 0$ and $g(p) = 0$.)

5.3 The Inverse Trigonometric Functions

The sine, cosine, and tangent functions are all periodic, so none of them has an inverse. However, if we restrict these functions to appropriate intervals, the restrictions will have inverses.

Since $\sin \colon [-\pi/2, \pi/2] \to \mathbb{R}$ is a strictly increasing continuous function with $\sin -\pi/2 = -1$ and $\sin \pi/2 = 1$, it follows from the Intermediate Value Theorem that for each number x in $[-1, 1]$, there is a unique solution to the equation

$$\sin z = x, \qquad z \text{ in } \left[-\frac{\pi}{2}, \frac{\pi}{2}\right].$$

We denote this solution by arcsin x, and so we have defined the *arcsine* function, denoted by arcsin: $[-1, 1] \to \mathbb{R}$, as the inverse of sin: $\left[-\frac{\pi}{2}, \frac{\pi}{2}\right] \to \mathbb{R}$.

Since

$$\frac{d}{dx}[\sin x] = \cos x \neq 0 \quad \text{if} \quad -\frac{\pi}{2} < x < \frac{\pi}{2},$$

it follows from Corollary 4.7 that the arcsine function is differentiable and that

$$\frac{d}{dx}[\arcsin x] = \frac{1}{\cos(\arcsin x)} \quad \text{for} \quad -1 < x < 1.$$

However, $\arcsin x$ is in $(-\pi/2, \pi/2)$, so $\cos(\arcsin x) > 0$. Consequently, using the Pythagorean Identity, we have

$$\cos(\arcsin x) = [1 - \sin^2(\arcsin x)]^{1/2} = \sqrt{1 - x^2}.$$

Thus, $$\frac{d}{dx}[\arcsin x] = \frac{1}{\sqrt{1 - x^2}} \quad \text{if} \quad -1 < x < 1. \tag{5.30}$$

We now turn to the *arccosine* function. Indeed, since $\cos: [0, \pi] \to \mathbb{R}$ is a strictly decreasing continuous function with $\cos 0 = 1$ and $\cos \pi = -1$, it follows from the Intermediate Value Theorem that for each x in $[-1, 1]$ there is a unique solution to the equation

$$\cos z = x, \qquad z \text{ in } [0, \pi]. \tag{5.31}$$

We denote this solution by $\arccos x$, and therefore we have defined the function $\arccos: [-1, 1] \to \mathbb{R}$, which is the inverse of $\cos: [0, \pi] \to \mathbb{R}$. Since

$$\frac{d}{dx}[\cos x] = -\sin x \neq 0 \quad \text{if} \quad 0 < x < \pi,$$

it follows from Corollary 4.7 that

$$\frac{d}{dx}[\arccos x] = -\frac{1}{\sin(\arccos x)} \quad \text{if} \quad -1 < x < 1.$$

However, $\arccos x$ belongs to the interval $(0, \pi)$ when x is in $(-1, 1)$, so $\sin(\arccos x) > 0$. Consequently, using the Pythagorean Identity, we see that

$$\sin(\arccos x) = [1 - \cos^2(\arccos x)]^{1/2} = \sqrt{1 - x^2}.$$

Thus, $$\frac{d}{dx}[\arccos x] = -\frac{1}{\sqrt{1 - x^2}} \quad \text{if} \quad -1 < x < 1. \tag{5.32}$$

Finally, we consider the *arctangent* function. According to Theorem 5.12, the function $\tan: (-\pi/2, \pi/2) \to \mathbb{R}$ is a strictly increasing function whose image is all of $\mathbb{R}$. It follows that for each number x the equation

$$\tan z = x, \qquad z \text{ in } \left(-\frac{\pi}{2}, \frac{\pi}{2}\right)$$

has a unique solution. We denote this solution by $\arctan x$, and so we have defined $\arctan: \mathbb{R} \to \mathbb{R}$, the inverse of $\tan: (-\pi/2, \pi/2) \to \mathbb{R}$.

From formula (5.28) and Corollary 4.7, we conclude that

$$\frac{d}{dx}[\arctan x] = \cos^2(\arctan x) \quad \text{for all } x \text{ in } \mathbb{R},$$

from which, setting $\alpha = \arctan x$ and using the Pythagorean Identity, it follows that

$$\frac{d}{dx}[\arctan x] = \frac{1}{1+x^2} \quad \text{for all } x \text{ in } \mathbb{R}. \tag{5.33}$$

EXERCISES

1. Prove that $\arcsin x + \arccos x = \pi/2$ if $-1 \le x \le 1$.

2. Find the unique solution of the differential equation
$$\begin{cases} F'(x) = x/\sqrt{1-x^4}, & -1 < x < 1 \\ F(0) = 1. \end{cases}$$

3. Suppose that $f: \mathbb{R} \to \mathbb{R}$ and $g: \mathbb{R} \to \mathbb{R}$ are periodic functions of period T. Under what conditions is the sum $f + g: \mathbb{R} \to \mathbb{R}$ also periodic? Under what conditions is the composition $f \circ g: \mathbb{R} \to \mathbb{R}$ periodic?

4. Define $h(x) = 4\sin(x/2)$ for all x in $\mathbb{R}$. By restricting the function $h: \mathbb{R} \to \mathbb{R}$ to a suitable interval $[a, b]$ such that $h: [a, b] \to \mathbb{R}$ is strictly increasing and $h([a, b]) = [-4, 4]$, find the inverse of $h: [a, b] \to \mathbb{R}$ and calculate its derivative on the interval $(-4, 4)$.

5. Let I be an open interval and suppose that
$$p(x) = ax^2 + bx + c > 0 \quad \text{for all } x \text{ in } I.$$

Find a solution of the differential equation
$$F'(x) = \frac{1}{p(x)} \quad \text{for all } x \text{ in } I.$$

(*Hint:* Complete the square.)

6. Prove that
$$\arctan v - \arctan u < v - u \quad \text{if} \quad u < v.$$

6

Integration

6.1 Motivation for the Definition

For certain functions $f:[a, b] \to \mathbb{R}$, we will define a real number called the *integral* of $f:[a, b] \to \mathbb{R}$ and denoted by $\int_a^b f$. The integral is one of the cornerstones on which mathematical analysis is built. The significance of the integral depends on the context in which it is being considered. For example, the following interpretation of the integral is appropriate in a geometric context:

- For a function $f:[a, b] \to \mathbb{R}$ having the property that $f(x) \geq 0$ for all x in $[a, b]$, the integral $\int_a^b f$ is the area under the graph of $f:[a, b] \to \mathbb{R}$ and above the interval $[a, b]$.

The integral of $f:[a, b] \to \mathbb{R}$ has many other physical interpretations,* and the concept of the integral is central in the theory of differential equations, but the geometric interpretation of it as an area is sufficient to motivate our definition.

---

*The book *Introduction to Calculus and Analysis,* by R. Courant and F. John (Springer-Verlag, 1989), presents many interesting applications of the integral that arise in problems in physics and engineering.

FIGURE 6.1

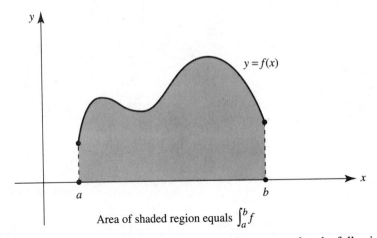

Area of shaded region equals $\int_a^b f$

We will define the notion of the integral in such a manner that the following three properties are satisfied:

(i) If $f(x) = c$ for all x in (a, b), then

$$\int_a^b f = c(b - a).$$

(ii) If $a < c < b$, then

$$\int_a^c f + \int_c^b f = \int_a^b f.$$

(iii) If $f(x) \le g(x)$ for all x in $[a, b]$, then

$$\int_a^b f \le \int_a^b g.$$

If the integral is to have properties (i) and (ii) and the function $f: [a, b] \to \mathbb{R}$ is *piecewise constant*, meaning that there is a natural number n and points $x_0, x_1, \ldots, x_n$ with

$$a = x_0 < x_1 < \cdots < x_{n-1} < x_n = b$$

such that for each index i with $1 \le i \le n$,

$$f(x) = c_i \quad \text{for all } x \text{ in } (x_{i-1}, x_i),$$

then $\qquad \displaystyle\int_a^b f = c_1(x_1 - x_0) + c_2(x_2 - x_1) + \cdots + c_n(x_n - x_{n-1}).$

This formula for the integral of a piecewise constant function, together with the monotonicity property (iii), leads to a natural definition of the integral $\int_a^b f$ for a large class of functions $f: [a, b] \to \mathbb{R}$ that includes functions $f: [a, b] \to \mathbb{R}$ that are either continuous or monotone.

Once we have defined the integral and studied its properties, we will see that—as just one example of its importance—it is necessary to understand integration in order to study differential equations. In fact, although the geometric interpretation of the integral as an area is an attractive motivation for the definition, the integral has much greater significance as an analytical tool for describing the solutions of differential equations.

6.2   The Definition of the Integral and Criteria for Integrability

Let a and b be real numbers with $a < b$. If n is a natural number and

$$a = x_0 < x_1 < \cdots < x_{n-1} < x_n = b,$$

then $P = \{x_0, \ldots, x_n\}$ is called a *partition* of the interval $[a, b]$. For each index i with $0 \leq i \leq n$, we call x_i a *partition point* of P, and if $i \geq 1$ we call the interval $[x_{i-1}, x_i]$ a *subinterval induced by the partition P*. The crudest partition of $[a, b]$ occurs when $n = 1$, so that $x_0 = a$ and $x_1 = b$.

Suppose that the function $f: [a, b] \rightarrow \mathbb{R}$ is bounded. For each index i with $0 \leq i \leq n$, we define

$$\begin{cases} m_i \equiv & \inf\{f(x) \mid x \text{ in } [x_{i-1}, x_i]\} \\ M_i \equiv & \sup\{f(x) \mid x \text{ in } [x_{i-1}, x_i]\}. \end{cases} \tag{6.1}$$

FIGURE 6.2

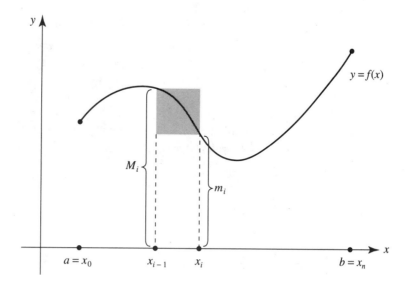

We then define

$$\begin{cases} L(f, P) \equiv & \displaystyle\sum_{i=1}^{n} m_i(x_i - x_{i-1}) \\ U(f, P) \equiv & \displaystyle\sum_{i=1}^{n} M_i(x_i - x_{i-1}). \end{cases} \tag{6.2}$$

We call $U(f, P)$ the *upper Darboux sum for the function* $f:[a, b] \to \mathbb{R}$ *based on the partition* P, and call $L(f, P)$ the *lower Darboux sum for the function* $f:[a, b] \to \mathbb{R}$ *based on the partition* P.

FIGURE 6.3

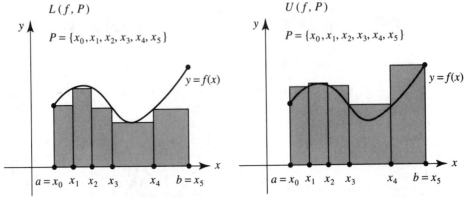

DEFINITION

Suppose that the function $f:[a, b] \to \mathbb{R}$ *is bounded. Then* $f:[a, b] \to \mathbb{R}$ *is said to be integrable provided that there is exactly one number* A *that has the property that*

$$L(f, P) \leq A \leq U(f, P) \quad \text{for every partition } P \text{ of the interval } [a, b]. \quad (6.3)$$

We call A *the integral of the function* $f:[a, b] \to \mathbb{R}$ *and denote it by* $\int_a^b f$.

It is not immediately clear how one can check that a function is integrable. We will soon see that if the function $f:[a, b] \to \mathbb{R}$ is continuous, then it is integrable. However, even when we have determined that $f:[a, b] \to \mathbb{R}$ is integrable, there still remains the problem of determining the value of the integral. Before beginning the general theory, we will consider two examples.

EXAMPLE 6.1 Let the function $f:[a, b] \to \mathbb{R}$ have constant value c. Then $f: [a, b] \to \mathbb{R}$ is integrable and

$$\int_a^b f = c(b - a).$$

Indeed, this follows immediately from the definition and the observation that if P is any partition of $[a, b]$, then $L(f, P) = U(f, P) = c(b - a)$. □

EXAMPLE 6.2 Consider the Dirichlet function $f:[0, 1] \to \mathbb{R}$ defined by

$$f(x) = \begin{cases} 0 & \text{if the point } x \text{ in } [0, 1] \text{ is rational} \\ 1 & \text{if the point } x \text{ in } [0, 1] \text{ is irrational.} \end{cases}$$

Let $P = \{x_0, \ldots, x_1\}$ be a partition of $[0, 1]$. Since the rationals and the irrationals are dense in $\mathbb{R}$, it follows that for each index i with $1 \leq i \leq n$, if m_i and M_i are as defined by (6.1), then $m_i = 0$ and $M_i = 1$. Hence $L(f, P) = 0$ and $U(f, P) = 1$. It follows that *any* number A in the interval $[0, 1]$ satisfies criterion (6.3). Therefore, the function $f: [0, 1] \rightarrow \mathbb{R}$ is not integrable.   □

If one interprets the integral in terms of area, these examples are not surprising. The first is the formula for the area of a rectangle. The second reflects the fact that there is no obvious way to assign an area to a region bounded by a very wild graph.

LEMMA 6.1   Suppose that the function $f: [a, b] \rightarrow \mathbb{R}$ is bounded and the numbers m and M have the property that

$$m \leq f(x) \leq M \quad \text{for all } x \text{ in } [a, b].$$

Then if P is a partition of the interval $[a, b]$,

$$m(b - a) \leq L(f, P) \leq U(f, P) \leq M(b - a).$$

Proof   Let $P = \{x_0, \ldots, x_n\}$. For each index i with $1 \leq i \leq n$, from the very definition of supremum and infimum it follows that

$$m \leq m_i = \inf\{f(x) \mid x \text{ in } [x_{i-1}, x_i]\} \leq \sup\{f(x) \mid x \text{ in } [x_{i-1}, x_1]\} \leq M_i \leq M.$$

Multiply this inequality by $x_i - x_{i-1}$ and sum the resulting n inequalities to obtain

$$m(b - a) = \sum_{i=1}^{n} m(x_i - x_{i-1}) \leq L(f, P) \leq U(f, P)$$

$$\leq \sum_{i=1}^{n} M(x_i - x_{i-1}) = M(b - a). \qquad \blacksquare$$

Given a partition P of the interval $[a, b]$, another partition P^* of $[a, b]$ is called a *refinement* of P if each partition point of P is also a partition point of P^*. If $P = \{x_0, \ldots, x_n\}$ and P^* is a refinement of P, then for each index i with $1 \leq i \leq n$, P^* induces a partition of the subinterval $[x_{i-1}, x_i]$ that we may denote by P_i. Observe that

$$L(f, P^*) = \sum_{i=1}^{n} L(f, P_i) \quad \text{and} \quad U(f, P^*) = \sum_{i=1}^{n} U(f, P_i).$$

LEMMA 6.2   **The Refinement Lemma**   Suppose that the function $f: [a, b] \rightarrow \mathbb{R}$ is bounded. Let P be a partition of $[a, b]$ and let P^* be a refinement of P. Then

$$L(f, P) \leq L(f, P^*) \leq U(f, P^*) \leq U(f, P).$$

Proof   Let $P = \{x_0, \ldots, x_n\}$. For each index i, let m_i and M_i be as defined by (6.1) and let P_i be the partition of $[x_{i-1}, x_i]$ that is induced by P^*. Then Lemma 6.1, applied to the function $f: [x_{i-1}, x_i] \rightarrow \mathbb{R}$, yields

$$m_i(x_i - x_{i-1}) \le L(f, P_i) \le U(f, P_i) \le M_i(x_i - x_{i-1}).$$

Sum these n inequalities to obtain

$$L(f, P) \le \sum_{i=1}^{n} L(f, P_i) = L(f, P^*) \le U(f, P^*) = \sum_{i=1}^{n} U(f, P_i) \le U(f, P). \quad \blacksquare$$

Given two partitions P_1 and P_2 of the interval $[a, b]$, the partition P^* formed by taking the union of the partition points of P_1 and of P_2 is a *common refinement* of P_1 and P_2, since P^* is a refinement of both P_1 and P_2.

LEMMA 6.3   Suppose that the function $f: [a, b] \to \mathbb{R}$ is bounded. Then for any two partitions P_1 and P_2 of $[a, b]$,

$$L(f, P_1) \le U(f, P_2).$$

Proof   Let P^* be a common refinement of P_1 and P_2. From the Refinement Lemma, it follows that

$$L(f, P_1) \le L(f, P^*) \le U(f, P^*) \le U(f, P_2). \quad \blacksquare$$

This leads us to the following very useful theorem.

THEOREM 6.4   **The Integrability Criterion**   Suppose that the function $f: [a, b] \to \mathbb{R}$ is bounded. Then $f: [a, b] \to \mathbb{R}$ is integrable if and only if for each positive number ϵ there is a partition P of the interval $[a, b]$ such that

$$U(f, P) - L(f, P) < \epsilon.$$

Proof   Denote by $\mathcal{L}$ the collection of all lower Darboux sums for $f: [a, b] \to \mathbb{R}$ and by $\mathcal{U}$ the collection of all upper Darboux sums for $f: [a, b] \to \mathbb{R}$. Then Lemma 6.3 amounts to the assertion that

$$s \le t \quad \text{whenever } s \text{ is in } \mathcal{L} \text{ and } t \text{ is in } \mathcal{U}. \tag{6.4}$$

Moreover, the function $f: [a, b] \to \mathbb{R}$ is defined to be integrable provided that there is exactly one number A with the property that

$$s \le A \le t \quad \text{whenever } s \text{ is in } \mathcal{L} \text{ and } t \text{ is in } \mathcal{U}. \tag{6.5}$$

According to the Dedekind Gap Theorem, which we proved in Section 1.1, the function $f: [a, b] \to \mathbb{R}$ is integrable if and only if for each positive number ϵ there are partitions P_1 and P_2 of the interval $[a, b]$ such that

$$U(f, P_2) - L(f, P_1) < \epsilon. \tag{6.6}$$

This proves the theorem if we can choose $P_1 = P_2$. However, by the Refinement Lemma, if P is a common refinement of P_1 and P_2, then

$$U(f, P) - L(f, P) \le U(f, P_2) - L(f, P_1) < \epsilon.$$ ∎

EXAMPLE 6.3   Define

$$f(x) = \begin{cases} 7 & \text{if } 1 \le x < 2 \\ 10 & \text{if } x = 2 \\ -4 & \text{if } 2 < x \le 3. \end{cases}$$

We will use the Integrability Criterion to prove that the function $f: [1, 3] \to \mathbb{R}$ is integrable. Let $\epsilon > 0$. We must find a partition P of the interval $[1, 3]$ such that $U(f, P) - L(f, P) < \epsilon$.

Observe that the only contribution to the sum $U(f, P) - L(f, P)$ comes from subintervals that contain the point $x = 2$. Define $P = \{1, 2 - \epsilon/30, 2 + \epsilon/30, 3\}$. For $i = 1, 2, 3$, let m_i and M_i be defined by (6.1); we see that $m_1 = M_1, m_3 = M_3, m_2 = -4$, and $M_2 = 10$. Hence

$$U(f, P) - L(f, P) = \frac{14}{15} \epsilon < \epsilon.$$ □

It is not difficult to see that the previous example may be generalized. A function $f: [a, b] \to \mathbb{R}$ is said to be *piecewise constant* if there is a partition $P = \{x_0, \dots, x_n\}$ of $[a, b]$ such that for each index i with $1 \le i \le n$, the function $f: (x_{i-1}, x_i) \to \mathbb{R}$ is constant. A piecewise constant function is integrable (see Exercise 5).

The following example shows that it is possible for $f: [a, b] \to \mathbb{R}$ to have infinitely many discontinuities and still be integrable.

EXAMPLE 6.4   Define

$$f(x) = \begin{cases} 1 & \text{if } x = 1/n \text{ for some natural number } n \\ 0 & \text{if the point } x \text{ in } [0, 1] \text{ is not of the above form.} \end{cases}$$

We will again use the Integrability Criterion to prove that the function $f: [0, 1] \to \mathbb{R}$ is integrable. Let $\epsilon > 0$. Observe that the function $f: [\epsilon/2, 1] \to \mathbb{R}$ is piecewise constant, and is therefore integrable. The Integrability Criterion implies that we may choose a partition P^* of the interval $[\epsilon/2, 1]$ such that $U(f, P^*) - L(f, P^*) < \epsilon/2$. Now let P be the partition of the whole interval $[0, 1]$ obtained by adjoining 0 to P^*. Then

$$U(f, P) = \frac{\epsilon}{2} + U(f, P^*) \quad \text{and} \quad L(f, P) = L(f, P^*).$$

It follows that $U(f, P) - L(f, P) < \epsilon$. □

DEFINITION   *A function $f: D \to \mathbb{R}$ is said to be monotonically increasing provided that*

$$f(x_1) \ge f(x_2) \quad \text{for all points } x_1 \text{ and } x_2 \text{ in } D \text{ such that} \quad x_1 \ge x_2.$$

This function is said to be monotonically decreasing provided that

$$f(x_1) \le f(x_2) \quad \text{for all points } x_1 \text{ and } x_2 \text{ in } D \text{ such that} \quad x_1 \ge x_2.$$

If a function is either monotonically decreasing or monotonically increasing, it is said to be monotone.

For a natural number n, the partition $P = \{x_0, \ldots, x_n\}$ of the interval $[a, b]$ defined by

$$x_i = a + i\frac{(b - a)}{n} \quad \text{for} \quad 0 \leq i \leq n$$

is called the *regular partition of* $[a, b]$ *into n subintervals*. This partition is characterized by the fact that all of the subintervals induced by the partition have the same length, $(b - a)/n$.

THEOREM 6.5 Suppose that the function $f : [a, b] \to \mathbb{R}$ is monotone. Then $f : [a, b] \to \mathbb{R}$ is integrable.

Proof Let us first assume that $f : [a, b] \to \mathbb{R}$ is monotonically increasing. We will apply the Integrability Criterion. Let $\epsilon > 0$. We need to find a partition P of $[a, b]$ such that $U(f, P) - L(f, P) < \epsilon$.

The crucial point is that for each natural number n, if P_n is the regular partition of $[a, b]$ into n subintervals, then we have the explicit formula

$$U(f, P_n) - L(f, P_n) = \left(\frac{b - a}{n}\right)(f(b) - f(a)). \tag{6.7}$$

To verify this formula, observe that for each index i with $1 \leq i \leq n$, since the function $f : [x_{i-1}, x_i] \to \mathbb{R}$ is monotonically increasing,

$$m_i = \inf\{f(x) \mid x \text{ in } [x_{i-1}, x_i]\} = f(x_{i-1}),$$
$$M_i = \sup\{f(x) \mid x \text{ in } [x_{i-1}, x_i]\} = f(x_i),$$

FIGURE 6.4

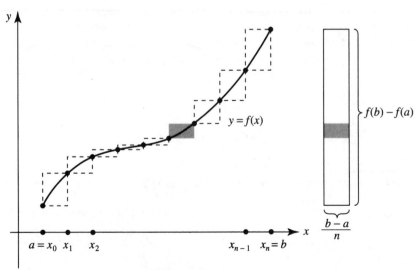

$$U(f, P) - L(f, P) = \frac{[f(b) - f(a)][b - a]}{n}$$

and, by the very definition of a regular partition,

$$x_i - x_{i-1} = \frac{b-a}{n}.$$

Consequently, $U(f, P_n) - L(f, P_n) = \sum_{i=1}^{n}(M_i - m_i)(x_i - x_{i-1})$

$$= \left(\frac{b-a}{n}\right)\sum_{i=1}^{n}(f(x_i) - f(x_{i-1}))$$

$$= \left(\frac{b-a}{n}\right)(f(b) - f(a)),$$

and thus we have the formula (6.7). By the Archimedean Property of $\mathbb{R}$, we can choose a natural number n such that

$$\left(\frac{b-a}{n}\right)(f(b) - f(a)) < \epsilon.$$

If we set $P = P_n$, we have $U(f, P) - L(f, P) < \epsilon$.

This proves the theorem when $f: [a, b] \to \mathbb{R}$ is monotonically increasing. When $f: [a, b] \to \mathbb{R}$ is monotonically decreasing, the proof proceeds as before, except that (6.7) now becomes

$$U(f, P) - L(f, P) = \left(\frac{b-a}{n}\right)(f(a) - f(b)). \qquad \blacksquare$$

EXAMPLE 6.5 According to the previous theorem, if

$$f(x) = e^{x^2} \quad \text{for} \quad 0 \le x \le 1,$$

then since the function $f: [0, 1] \to \mathbb{R}$ is monotonically increasing, it is integrable. □

THEOREM 6.6 Suppose that the function $f: [a, b] \to \mathbb{R}$ is continuous. Then $f: [a, b] \to \mathbb{R}$ is integrable.

Proof Once more, we will apply the Integrability Criterion. Let $\epsilon > 0$. According to Theorem 3.14, the function $f: [a, b] \to \mathbb{R}$ is uniformly continuous. Consequently, since $\epsilon/(b-a) > 0$, we may choose a number $\delta > 0$ such that

$$|f(u) - f(v)| < \frac{\epsilon}{b-a} \quad \text{for all points } u \text{ and } v \text{ in } [a, b] \text{ such that} \quad |u - v| < \delta.$$

$$(6.8)$$

Choose $P = \{x_0, \ldots, x_n\}$ to be a partition of $[a, b]$ with the property that each subinterval $I_i = [x_{i-1}, x_i]$ has length less than δ.

Let $1 \le i \le n$. Since the function $f: I_i \to \mathbb{R}$ is continuous, we may apply the Extreme Value Theorem to choose points u_i and v_i in I_i at which $f: I_i \to \mathbb{R}$ attains maximum and minimum values, respectively. But I_i has length less than δ, so (6.8) implies that

$$M_i - m_i = f(u_i) - f(v_i) < \frac{\epsilon}{b-a}.$$

Consequently,
$$U(f, P) - L(f, P) = \sum_{i=1}^{n}(M_i - m_i)(x_i - x_{i-1})$$
$$< \epsilon/(b - a)\sum_{i=1}^{n}(x_i - x_{i-1})$$
$$= \epsilon.$$
■

There is a slight generalization of the preceding theorem that will turn out to be useful.

COROLLARY 6.7   Suppose that the function $f:[a, b] \to \mathbb{R}$ is bounded and that $f:(a, b) \to \mathbb{R}$ is continuous. Then $f:[a, b] \to \mathbb{R}$ is integrable.

Proof   Again, we will use the Integrability Criterion. Let $\epsilon > 0$. We need to find a partition P of the interval $[a, b]$ such that $U(f, P) - L(f, P) < \epsilon$. Since $f:[a, b] \to \mathbb{R}$ is bounded, we may choose a number $M > 0$ such that

$$-M \le f(x) \le M \quad \text{for all } x \text{ in } [a, b].$$

Define $a_0 = a + \epsilon/8M$ and $b_0 = b - \epsilon/8M$. Since the function $f:[a_0, b_0] \to \mathbb{R}$ is continuous, it follows from the preceding theorem that it is integrable, and so, by the Integrability Theorem, there is a partition P^* of the interval $[a_0, b_0]$ such that $U(f, P^*) - L(f, P^*) < \epsilon/2$. Define P to be the partition of the whole interval $[a, b]$ obtained by adjoining the points a and b to P^*. The contributions to $U(f, P) - L(f, P)$ from the first and the last subinterval induced by P are each at most equal to the length of the subinterval times $2M$. Thus,

$$U(f, P) - L(f, P) \le 2M\frac{\epsilon}{8M} + 2M\frac{\epsilon}{8M} + [U(f, P^*) - L(f, P^*)]$$

$$< 2M\frac{\epsilon}{8M} + 2M\frac{\epsilon}{8M} + \frac{\epsilon}{2} = \epsilon.$$
■

EXAMPLE 6.6   Define

$$f(x) = \begin{cases} \sin(1/x) & \text{if } 0 < x \le 1 \\ 4 & \text{if } x = 0. \end{cases}$$

Then the function $f:[0, 1] \to \mathbb{R}$ is bounded and $f:(0, 1) \to \mathbb{R}$ is continuous. The preceding corollary implies that the function $f:[0, 1] \to \mathbb{R}$ is integrable.   □

For a continuous function $f:[a, b] \to \mathbb{R}$, if we change the functional value at one point, then the new function will not be continuous. In contrast, the property of being integrable is not as sensitive to changes in functional values. It is not difficult to see, for example, that if the function $f:[a, b] \to \mathbb{R}$ is integrable, then by changing its functional values at the endpoints of the interval $[a, b]$ it remains integrable and the value of the integral is unchanged. This observation, together with the preceding theorem, implies that given a bounded, continuous function $f:(a, b) \to \mathbb{R}$, we can define $\int_a^b f$ to be the integral of any extension of the function $f:(a, b) \to \mathbb{R}$ to the interval $[a, b]$.

We will conclude this section with a remark about notation. For an integrable function $f: [a, b] \to \mathbb{R}$, we have denoted the value of the integral by the symbol $\int_a^b f$. The value of the integral is also often denoted by symbols such as $\int_a^b f(x)\,dx$ or $\int_a^b f(t)\,dt$. We will see that this alternate notation, involving Leibnitz symbols, is often quite convenient.

EXERCISES

1. Define $f(x) = x$ for all x in $[0, 1]$. For each natural number n, compute $L(f, P_n)$ and $U(f, P_n)$, where P_n is the regular partition of $[0, 1]$ into n subintervals. Then use the Integrability Criterion to show that the function $f: [0, 1] \to \mathbb{R}$ is integrable. (*Hint:* $\sum_{k=1}^n k = n(n+1)/2$.)

2. Define $f(x) = x^2$ for all x in $[0, 1]$. For each natural number n, compute $L(f, P_n)$ and $U(f, P_n)$, where P_n is the regular partition of $[0, 1]$ into n subintervals. Then use the Integrability Criterion to show that the function $f: [0, 1] \to \mathbb{R}$ is integrable. (*Hint:* $\sum_{k=1}^n k^2 = n(n+1)(2n+1)/6$.)

3. For an interval $[a, b]$ and a positive number δ, show that there is a partition $P = \{x_0, \ldots, x_n\}$ of $[a, b]$ such that each subinterval $[x_{i-1}, x_i]$ has length less than δ.

4. Suppose that the integrable function $f: [a, b] \to \mathbb{R}$ has the property that $f(x) \geq 0$ for all x in $[a, b]$. Prove that $\int_a^b f \geq 0$.

5. Prove that a piecewise constant function is integrable.

6. Define
$$f(x) = \begin{cases} x & \text{if } 2 \leq x \leq 3 \\ 2 & \text{if } 3 < x \leq 4. \end{cases}$$
Prove that the function $f: [2, 4] \to \mathbb{R}$ is integrable.

7. Suppose that the integrable function $f: [a, b] \to \mathbb{R}$ has the property that for each rational number x in the interval $[a, b]$, $f(x) = 0$. Prove that $\int_a^b f = 0$.

8. Suppose that the function $f: [a, b] \to \mathbb{R}$ is bounded and that $f: [a, b] \to \mathbb{R}$ is continuous except at a finite number of points $z_1, \ldots, z_k$ in $[a, b]$. Prove that $f: [a, b] \to \mathbb{R}$ is integrable.

9. For positive numbers m and b, define $f(x) = mx + b$ for all x in $[0, 1]$.
   (a) From elementary area formulas, show that the area under the graph of $f: [0, 1] \to \mathbb{R}$ and above the x axis is $b + m/2$.
   (b) For each natural number n, compute $L(f, P_n)$ and $U(f, P_n)$, where P_n is the regular partition of $[0, 1]$ into n subintervals. Show that
$$L(f, P_n) < b + \frac{m}{2} < U(f, P_n).$$

10. For a point x in the interval $[1, 2]$, define $f(x) = 0$ if x is irrational, and define $f(x) = 1/n$ if x is rational and is expressed as $x = m/n$, for natural numbers m and n having no common positive integer divisor other than 1. Prove that the function $f: [1, 2] \to \mathbb{R}$ is integrable. (*Hint:* First prove that given $\epsilon > 0$ there are only a finite number of points x in the interval $[1, 2]$ at which $f(x) \geq \epsilon$.)

11. Give a geometric interpretation, in terms of areas, of formula (6.7).

12. For a point x in the interval $[0, 1]$, define $f(x) = x$ if x is rational and $f(x) = -x$ if x is irrational. Prove that the function $f: [0, 1] \to \mathbb{R}$ is not integrable.

13. Is the sum of monotone functions also monotone? Is the product of monotone functions also monotone? Justify your answers.

14. Suppose that $f: [a, b] \to \mathbb{R}$ is a bounded function for which there is a partition P of $[a, b]$ with $L(f, P) = U(f, P)$. Prove that $f: [a, b] \to \mathbb{R}$ is constant.

15. Suppose that the function $f:[a, b] \to \mathbb{R}$ is integrable and there is a positive number m such that $f(x) \geq m$ for all x in $[a, b]$. Show that the reciprocal function $1/f:[a, b] \to \mathbb{R}$ is integrable by proving that for each partition P of the interval $[a, b]$,

$$U(1/f, P) - L(1/f, P) \leq \frac{1}{m^2}[U(f, P) - L(f, P)].$$

16. Suppose the continuous function $f:[a, b] \to \mathbb{R}$ has the property that

$$\int_c^d f \leq 0 \quad \text{whenever} \quad a \leq c < d \leq b.$$

Prove that $f(x) \leq 0$ for all x in $[a, b]$. Is this true if we require only integrability of the function?

6.3 The First Fundamental Theorem of Calculus

In the preceding section, we established a number of criteria that guarantee that a function $f:[a, b] \to \mathbb{R}$ is integrable. However, we have not considered the problem of determining the value of the integral. In this section we will turn to this aspect of integration, and we will prove the truly remarkable First Fundamental Theorem of Calculus.

Let us restate the definition of the value of the integral:

Suppose that the function $f:[a, b] \to \mathbb{R}$ is integrable. For a real number A,

$$\int_a^b f = A$$

if and only if

$$L(f, P) \leq A \leq U(f, P) \quad \text{for every partition } P \text{ of the interval } [a, b]. \quad (6.9)$$

EXAMPLE 6.7 Suppose that the function $f:[a, b] \to \mathbb{R}$ has constant value c on the open interval (a, b). We have already seen that $f:[a, b] \to \mathbb{R}$ is integrable. To verify that

$$\int_a^b f = c(b - a),$$

observe that if $P = \{x_0, \ldots, x_n\}$ is any partition of $[a, b]$, each subinterval induced by the partition intersects the interval (a, b), and so, for each index i with $1 \leq i \leq n$, $m_i \leq c \leq M_i$. Consequently, $L(f, P) \leq c(b - a) \leq U(f, P)$, and so, by criterion (6.9), $\int_a^b f = c(b - a)$. $\qquad\square$

In order to directly verify criterion (6.9), it is necessary to evaluate or estimate $L(f, P)$ and $U(f, P)$ for every partition P of $[a, b]$. Even for simple functions, this is usually not so easy. On the other hand, when P is a regular partition of $[a, b]$, the estimation of $L(f, P)$ and $U(f, P)$ sometimes becomes easier. With this in mind, and because it will be useful later, we prove the following result.

PROPOSITION   Suppose that the function $f:[a, b] \to \mathbb{R}$ is bounded. For each natural number n, let P_n
6.8   be a partition of $[a, b]$. Let A be a number having the property that

$$\lim_{n \to \infty} L(f, P_n) = A = \lim_{n \to \infty} U(f, P_n).$$

Then $f:[a, b] \to \mathbb{R}$ is integrable and $\int_a^b = A$.

Proof   By the difference property of convergent sequences,

$$\lim_{n \to \infty} [U(f, P_n) - L(f, P_n)] = A - A = 0,$$

and hence the Integrability Criterion implies that $f:[a, b] \to \mathbb{R}$ is integrable. Observe
that for each natural number n,

$$L(f, P_n) - A \le \int_a^b f - A \le U(f, P_n) - A.$$

It follows from the Squeezing Principle that $\int_a^b f - A = 0$.   ■

EXAMPLE 6.8   We claim that $\int_0^1 x\, dx = 1/2$, and we will verify this claim by applying the preceding proposition. Define $f(x) = x$ for all x in $[0, 1]$. For each natural
number n, let P_n be the regular partition of $[0, 1]$ into n subintervals. The formula
$\sum_{i=1}^m i = m(m + 1)/2$ allows us to explicitly find the Darboux sums. Indeed, since
$f:[0, 1] \to \mathbb{R}$ is increasing, it follows that

$$L(f, P_n) = \sum_{i=1}^n m_i(x_i - x_{i-1})$$

$$= \sum_{i=1}^n f(x_{i-1})\frac{1}{n}$$

$$= \frac{1}{n}\sum_{i=1}^n \left(\frac{i-1}{n}\right)$$

$$= \frac{1}{n^2}\sum_{i=1}^n (i - 1)$$

$$= \frac{1}{n^2} \cdot \frac{n(n-1)}{2}$$

$$= \frac{1}{2} - \frac{1}{2n}.$$

A similar calculation shows that $U(f, P_n) = 1/2 + 1/2n$. Thus,

$$\lim_{n \to \infty} L(f, P_n) = \lim_{n \to \infty} U(f, P_n) = \frac{1}{2},$$

and so $\int_0^1 x\, dx = 1/2$.   □

EXAMPLE 6.9 We will apply Proposition 6.8 to show that $\int_0^1 x^2\, dx = 1/3$. Define $f(x) = x^2$ for all x in $[0, 1]$. For each natural number n, let P_n be the regular partition of $[0, 1]$ into n subintervals. As in the preceding example, there is a formula, namely $\sum_{i=1}^m k^2 = [m(m + 1)(2m + 1)]/6$, that permits calculation of the Darboux sums. Indeed, since $f: [0, 1] \to \mathbb{R}$ is increasing, it follows that

$$L(f, P_n) = \sum_{i=1}^n m_i(x_i - x_{i-1}) = \sum_{i=1}^n f(x_{i-1})\frac{1}{n}$$

$$= \frac{1}{n}\sum_{i=1}^n \left(\frac{i-1}{n}\right)^2 = \frac{1}{n^3}\sum_{i=1}^n (i-1)^2$$

$$= \frac{1}{n^3}\left[\frac{(n-1)n(2n-1)}{6}\right] = \frac{1}{3} - \frac{1}{2n} + \frac{1}{6n^2}.$$

A similar calculation shows that $U(f, P_n) = 1/3 + 1/2n + 1/6n^2$. Thus,

$$\lim_{n\to\infty} L(f, P_n) = \lim_{n\to\infty} U(f, P_n) = \frac{1}{3},$$

and so $\int_0^1 x^2\, dx = 1/3$. □

EXAMPLE 6.10 We wish to evaluate the integral $\int_0^1 \sqrt{x}\, dx$. Define $f(x) = \sqrt{x}$ for all x in $[0, 1]$. Then the function $f: [0, 1] \to \mathbb{R}$ is integrable, since it is monotone. But how can one calculate $\int_0^1 \sqrt{x}\, dx$? For the strategy that succeeded in the previous two examples to succeed here as well, it is necessary to find a formula for the sum

$$1 + \sqrt{2} + \sqrt{3} + \cdots + \sqrt{m}.$$

There is no obvious formula. □

This last example is not atypical. Unless we have very special functions, such as those in Examples 6.8 and 6.9, it is not possible to evaluate $U(f, P)$ or $L(f, P)$, even when P is a regular partition.*

In order to proceed further, a genuinely new idea is needed. The brilliant idea is to replace the problem of calculating the integral with another seemingly different problem, namely the problem of solving the following differential equation:

Given a function $f: [a, b] \to \mathbb{R}$, find a continuous function $F: [a, b] \to \mathbb{R}$ such that $F: (a, b) \to \mathbb{R}$ is differentiable and

$$F'(x) = f(x) \quad \text{for all } x \text{ in } (a, b). \qquad \text{F.D.E.}$$

(F.D.E. denotes the Fundamental Differential Equation.)

Recall that Section 4.5 was devoted to a discussion of the above problem. We saw there that, for example, when $f: \mathbb{R} \to \mathbb{R}$ is a polynomial, there is a simple explicit solution of the F.D.E. Moreover if $\alpha \neq -1$, $0 < a < b$, and $f(x) = x^\alpha$ for all x in $[a, b]$,

---

*There is a rather ingenious trick for evaluating the integral in Example 6.10, which is due to Fermat (see Exercise 11 of Section 6.4). However, the theory of integration could not proceed by requiring ingenious tricks for each example.

the function defined by $F(x) = x^{\alpha+1}/(\alpha + 1)$ for all x in $[a, b]$ is a solution of the F.D.E.

The first relationship between the F.D.E. and integration is provided by the following theorem.

THEOREM 6.9   **The First Fundamental Theorem of Calculus**   Let the function $f: [a, b] \to \mathbb{R}$ be integrable. Suppose that the function $F: [a, b] \to \mathbb{R}$ is continuous, that $F: (a, b) \to \mathbb{R}$ is differentiable, and that

$$F'(x) = f(x) \quad \text{for all } x \text{ in } (a, b).$$

Then
$$\int_a^b f = F(b) - F(a).$$

Proof   According to criterion (6.9), we must show that for each partition P of the interval $[a, b]$,

$$L(f, P) \le F(b) - F(a) \le U(f, P). \tag{6.10}$$

Let $P = \{x_0, \ldots, x_n\}$ be a partition of $[a, b]$. Fix an index i with $1 \le i \le n$. We apply the Lagrange Mean Value Theorem to the function $F: [x_{i-1}, x_i] \to \mathbb{R}$ in order to choose a point c_i in the open interval (x_{i-1}, x_i) at which

$$F(x_i) - F(x_{i-1}) = F'(c_i)(x_i - x_{i-1}),$$

so that, since $F'(c_i) = f(c_i)$,

$$F(x_i) - F(x_{i-1}) = f(c_i)(x_i - x_{i-1}). \tag{6.11}$$

Since the point c_i belongs to the interval $[x_{i-1}, x_i]$,

$$m_i = \inf\{f(x) \,|\, x \text{ in } [x_{i-1}, x_i]\} \le f(c_i) \le \sup\{f(x) \,|\, x \text{ in } [x_{i-1}, x_i]\} = M_i. \tag{6.12}$$

Multiplying this last inequality by $x_i - x_{i-1}$ and substituting (6.11), we obtain

$$m_i(x_i - x_{i-1}) \le F(x_i) - F(x_{i-1}) \le M_i(x_i - x_{i-1}).$$

Finally, adding up these n inequalities gives the required inequality (6.10). ∎

In the following three examples, we will attempt to use the First Fundamental Theorem to evaluate the given integrals.

EXAMPLE 6.11 Let $\alpha > 0$. We will evaluate the integral $\int_0^1 x^\alpha \, dx$. Define $f(x) = x^\alpha$ for all x in $[0, 1]$. The function $f : [0, 1] \to \mathbb{R}$ is continuous, so it is integrable. In order to apply the First Fundamental Theorem of Calculus, we need to find a continuous function $F : [0, 1] \to \mathbb{R}$ such that $F : (0, 1) \to \mathbb{R}$ is differentiable and

$$F'(x) = x^\alpha \quad \text{for all } x \text{ in } (0, 1). \tag{6.13}$$

But the function $F : [0, 1] \to \mathbb{R}$ defined by

$$F(x) = \frac{x^{\alpha+1}}{\alpha + 1} \quad \text{for all } x \text{ in } [0, 1]$$

has these properties. According to the First Fundamental Theorem,

$$\int_0^1 x^\alpha \, dx = F(1) - F(0) = \frac{1}{\alpha + 1}. \qquad \square$$

Compare the preceding example with Examples 6.8, 6.9, and 6.10.

EXAMPLE 6.12 We wish to evaluate $\int_0^1 [1/(1 + x^4)] \, dx$. Define $f(x) = 1/(1 + x^4)$ for all x in $[0, 1]$. Since the function $f : [0, 1] \to \mathbb{R}$ is continuous, it is also integrable. In order to apply the First Fundamental Theorem, we need to find a continuous function $F : [0, 1] \to \mathbb{R}$ such that $F : (0, 1) \to \mathbb{R}$ is differentiable and

$$F'(x) = \frac{1}{1 + x^4} \quad \text{for all } x \text{ in } (0, 1). \tag{6.14}$$

Even if we carefully sift through all of our differentiation results, no solution of (6.14) comes to mind.* Hence we cannot apply the First Fundamental Theorem. $\qquad \square$

EXAMPLE 6.13 Define

$$f(x) = \begin{cases} 1 & \text{if } 2 \le x < 3 \\ 0 & \text{if } 3 \le x \le 6. \end{cases}$$

There is now no possibility of applying the First Fundamental Theorem in the evaluation of $\int_2^6 f$, because, according to Darboux's Theorem, if $F : (2, 6) \to \mathbb{R}$ is differentiable, the function $F' (2, 6) \to \mathbb{R}$ has the Intermediate Value Property. But the function $f : (2, 6) \to \mathbb{R}$ does not have the Intermediate Value Property. However, it is not difficult to see that one can apply Proposition 6.8 to show that $\int_2^6 f = 1$. $\qquad \square$

The above examples illustrate both the power and the limitations of the First Fundamental Theorem. It replaces the problem of calculating $\int_a^b f$ with the problem of solving the F.D.E. Frequently one can solve the F.D.E., and there are cases when one definitely cannot solve the F.D.E.; sometimes it is not clear. There are a number of techniques of integration that consist of taking an integral $\int_a^b f$ and finding another integral $\int_c^d g$ such that $\int_a^b f = \int_c^d g$ and $\int_c^d g$ can be evaluated by the First Fundamental Theorem. We will consider such techniques in Section 7.3.

---

*There is a precise way to assert and prove that it is not possible to find an "elementary function" that is a solution of (6.14). Unfortunately, to do this requires a background in modern abstract algebra that is outside the scope of this book; see the article "Integration in Finite Terms" by Maxwell Rosenlicht in *American Mathematical Monthly*, Nov. 1972.

As we discussed at the end of Section 6.2, for a continuous bounded function $f: (a, b) \to \mathbb{R}$, the symbol $\int_a^b f$ denotes the integral of any extension of $f: (a, b) \to \mathbb{R}$ to the closed interval $[a, b]$.

COROLLARY 6.10 Suppose that the function $F: [a, b] \to \mathbb{R}$ is continuous, that $F: (a, b) \to \mathbb{R}$ is differentiable, and that the derivative $F': (a, b) \to \mathbb{R}$ is both continuous and bounded. Then

$$\int_a^b F'(x)\,dx = F(b) - F(a). \tag{6.15}$$

Proof Define $f(x) = F'(x)$ for all x in (a, b). Since the function $f: (a, b) \to \mathbb{R}$ is both continuous and bounded, any extension of $f: (a, b) \to \mathbb{R}$ to the interval $[a, b]$ defines an integrable function whose integral does not depend on the values $f(a)$ and $f(b)$. The integral of such an extension is what is meant by $\int_a^b F'(x)\,dx$. Formula (6.15) follows directly from the First Fundamental Theorem. ∎

EXERCISES

1. Find the values of the following two integrals:

   (a) $\displaystyle\int_0^1 [x + 1]\,dx$

   (b) $\displaystyle\int_0^1 [4x + 1]\,dx$

   by applying Proposition 6.8 with the sequence of partitions $\{P_n\}$, where for each n, P_n is the regular partition of $[0, 1]$ into n subintervals.

2. Let m and b be positive numbers. Find the value of $\int_0^1 [mx + b]\,dx$ in the following three ways:

   (a) Using elementary geometry, interpreting $\int_0^1 [mx + b]\,dx$ as an area.

   (b) Using Proposition 6.8 where for each natural number n, P_n is a regular partition of $[0, 1]$ into n subintervals.

   (c) Using the First Fundamental Theorem of Calculus.

3. Use the First Fundamental Theorem of Calculus to evaluate each of the following integrals:

   (a) $\displaystyle\int_1^2 [1/x^2 + x + \cos x]\,dx$

   (b) $\displaystyle\int_0^1 x\sqrt{4 - x^2}\,dx$

   (c) $\displaystyle\int_1^3 x\sqrt{10 - x}\,dx$

   (d) $\displaystyle\int_0^\pi \cos^2 x\,dx$

6.4 The Convergence of Darboux Sums and Riemann Sums

For an integrable function $f: [a, b] \to \mathbb{R}$ and a partition P of the interval $[a, b]$, the Refinement Lemma asserts that

$$L(f, P) \leq L(f, P^*) \leq \int_a^b f \leq U(f, P^*) \leq U(f, P)$$

whenever the partition P^* is a refinement of P.

Thus, for an integrable function and a given partition, when we refine the partition the associated Darboux sums become better approximations of the value of the integral. It is reasonable to expect that one can make the Darboux sums arbitrarily close to the integral provided that the associated partitions are sufficiently fine. In this section, we will prove that this is so. We will also study a sum called the Riemann sum, which is closely related to the Darboux sum.

DEFINITION   *For a partition $P = \{x_0, \ldots, x_n\}$ of the interval $[a, b]$, we define the gap of P, which is denoted by $\|P\|$, to be the length of the largest subinterval induced by P, that is,*

$$\|P\| \equiv \max_{1 \leq i \leq n}[x_i - x_{i-1}].$$

Observe that for a partition P and a positive number α, $\|P\| < \alpha$ if and only if each subinterval induced by the partition P has length less than α.

THEOREM 6.11   Suppose that the function $f : [a, b] \to \mathbb{R}$ is bounded. Then $f : [a, b] \to \mathbb{R}$ is integrable if and only if for each positive number ϵ there is a positive number δ such that

$$U(f, P) - L(f, P) < \epsilon \tag{6.16}$$

whenever P is a partition of $[a, b]$ such that $\|P\| < \delta$.

Proof   To show that criterion (6.16) implies the integrability of $f : [a, b] \to \mathbb{R}$, we will use the Integrability Criterion. Let $\epsilon > 0$. According to (6.16), there is a $\delta > 0$ such that $U(f, P) - L(f, P) < \epsilon$ whenever P is a partition of $[a, b]$ such that $\|P\| < \delta$. Thus, if we choose any partition P with $\|P\| < \delta$ the Integrability Criterion is satisfied.

We will now prove the converse. Suppose that $f : [a, b] \to \mathbb{R}$ is integrable. Let $\epsilon > 0$. According to the Integrability Criterion, we may choose a partition $P^* = \{x_0^*, \ldots, x_n^*\}$ of $[a, b]$ such that

$$U(f, P^*) - L(f, P^*) < \frac{\epsilon}{2}. \tag{6.17}$$

Choose $M > 0$ such that

$$-M \leq f(x) \leq M \quad \text{for all } x \text{ in } [a, b]. \tag{6.18}$$

The crucial point in the proof is the following assertion: For any partition P of the interval $[a, b]$, we have the estimate

$$U(f, P) - L(f, P) \leq 2nM\|P\| + [U(f, P^*) - L(f, P^*)]. \tag{6.19}$$

Once this estimate is proven, we define $\delta = \epsilon/4nM$. Then, if P is a partition of $[a, b]$ such that $\|P\| < \delta$,

$$U(f, P) - L(f, P) < 2nM\delta + \frac{\epsilon}{2}$$

$$= \frac{\epsilon}{2} + \frac{\epsilon}{2} = \epsilon.$$

It remains to verify estimate (6.19). Let $P = \{x_0, \ldots, x_m\}$ be a partition of $[a, b]$. As usual, for each index i such that $1 \leq i \leq m$, we set

$$m_i = \inf\{f(x) \mid x \text{ in } [x_{i-1}, x_i]\} \quad \text{and} \quad M_i = \sup\{f(x) \mid x \text{ in } [x_{i-1}, x_i]\}.$$

We now separate the set of indices $\{1, \ldots, m\}$ into two subsets A and B. Define A to be the set of indices i in $\{1, \ldots, m\}$ such that the subinterval (x_{i-1}, x_i) contains a partition point of the partition P^*. Define B to be the set of indices i in $\{1, \ldots, m\}$ that do not have this property. Now $M_i - m_i \leq 2M$ and $x_i - x_{i-1} \leq \|P\|$ for every index i in $\{1, \ldots, m\}$, so since there are fewer than n indices in the set A,

$$\sum_{i \in A}(M_i - m_i)(x_i - x_{i-1}) \leq 2nM\|P\|.$$

On the other hand, if i is an index in the set B, then the subinterval $[x_{i-1}, x_i]$ is contained in one of the subintervals $[x_{j-1}^*, x_j^*]$ induced by the partition P^*, and so by the Refinement Lemma,

$$\sum_{i \in B}(M_i - m_i)(x_i - x_{i-1}) \leq U(f, P^*) - L(f, P^*).$$

Consequently,

$$U(f, P) - L(f, P) = \sum_{i \in A}(M_i - m_i)(x_i - x_{i-1}) + \sum_{i \in B}(M_i - m_i)(x_i - x_{i-1})$$
$$< 2nM\|P\| + [U(f, P^*) - L(f, P^*)],$$

so (6.19) is proven. ∎

COROLLARY 6.12 Suppose that the function $f: [a, b] \to \mathbb{R}$ is integrable. If $\{P_n\}$ is any sequence of partitions of $[a, b]$ such that $\lim_{n \to \infty} \|P_n\| = 0$, then

$$\lim_{n \to \infty} U(f, P_n) = \lim_{n \to \infty} L(f, P_n) = \int_a^b f. \qquad (6.20)$$

Proof Let $\epsilon > 0$. According to Theorem 6.11, we can choose $\delta > 0$ such that if P is any partition of $[a, b]$, then

$$U(f, P) - L(f, P) < \epsilon \quad \text{if} \quad \|P\| < \delta.$$

On the other hand, since $\lim_{n \to \infty} \|P_n\| = 0$, we can select a natural number N such that $\|P_n\| < \delta$ if $n \geq N$. Thus

$$0 \leq U(f, P_n) - L(f, P_n) < \epsilon \quad \text{for all integers } n \geq N.$$

Moreover, by the definition of the integral,

$$L(f, P_n) \leq \int_a^b f \leq U(f, P_n) \quad \text{for every natural number } n.$$

Consequently, for each integer $n \geq N$,

$$\left| \int_a^b f - L(f, P_n) \right| < \epsilon \quad \text{and} \quad \left| \int_a^b f - U(f, P_n) \right| < \epsilon.$$

This proves (6.20). ∎

For convenient future reference, we collect Proposition 6.8 and Corollary 6.12 in the single theorem that follows:

THEOREM 6.13 **The Darboux Sum Convergence Criterion** For a bounded function $f: [a, b] \to \mathbb{R}$ and a real number A, the following two assertions are equivalent:

(i) The function $f: [a, b] \to \mathbb{R}$ is integrable and $\int_a^b f = A$.

(ii) If $\{P_n\}$ is any sequence of partitions of $[a, b]$ such that $\lim_{n \to \infty} \|P_n\| = 0$, then

$$\lim_{n \to \infty} L(f, P_n) = \lim_{n \to \infty} U(f, P_n) = A.$$

Proof That (i) implies (ii) is the content of Corollary 6.12. To prove the converse, suppose that (ii) holds. For each natural number n, let P_n be the regular partition of $[a, b]$ into n subintervals. Then the sequence $\{\|P_n\|\}$ converges to 0, so (ii) implies that

$$\lim_{n \to \infty} L(f, P_n) = \lim_{n \to \infty} U(f, P_n) = A.$$

From this, using Proposition 6.8, we obtain (i). ∎

DEFINITION *Consider a function $f: [a, b] \to \mathbb{R}$, and let $P = \{x_0, \ldots, x_n\}$ be a partition of the interval $[a, b]$. For each index i such that $1 \le i \le n$, let c_i be a point in the interval $[x_{i-1}, x_i]$. Then the sum*

$$\sum_{i=1}^{n} f(c_i)(x_i - x_{i-1}) \tag{6.21}$$

is called a Riemann sum for the function $f: [a, b] \to \mathbb{R}$ based on the partition P.

It is convenient to denote the Riemann sum (6.21) by the symbol $R(f, P)$.* It is clear that if the function $f: [a, b] \to \mathbb{R}$ is bounded, then for each partition P of $[a, b]$,

$$L(f, P) \le R(f, P) \le U(f, P).$$

COROLLARY 6.14 Suppose that the function $f: [a, b] \to \mathbb{R}$ is integrable. For each natural number n, let P_n be a partition of $[a, b]$ and let $R(f, P_n)$ be a Riemann sum for $f: [a, b] \to \mathbb{R}$ based on P_n. Suppose that $\lim_{n \to \infty} \|P_n\| = 0$. Then

$$\lim_{n \to \infty} R(f, P_n) = \int_a^b f.$$

---

*The notation $R(f, P)$ does not explicitly exhibit the dependence of the Riemann sum (6.21) on the choice of the c_i's.

Proof   It is clear that for each natural number n,

$$L(f, P_n) \leq R(f, P_n) \leq U(f, P_n).$$

According to Corollary 6.12,

$$\lim_{n \to \infty} L(f, P_n) = \lim_{n \to \infty} U(f, P_n) = \int_a^b f.$$

The conclusion now follows from the Squeezing Principle for convergent sequences.

∎

EXAMPLE 6.14   For each natural number n, define P_n to be the regular partition of $[0, 1]$ into n subintervals. Consider the Riemann sum for the integral $\int_0^1 \sqrt{x}\, dx$ based on the partition P_n that we obtain by letting $c_i = i/n$ for $1 \leq i \leq n$. From Corollary 6.14 and the First Fundamental Theorem of Calculus, it follows that

$$\lim_{n \to \infty} \left[\frac{\sqrt{1} + \sqrt{2} + \cdots + \sqrt{n}}{n^{3/2}} \right] = \lim_{n \to \infty} \frac{1}{n} \left[\sqrt{\frac{1}{n}} + \cdots + \sqrt{\frac{n}{n}} \right] = \int_0^1 \sqrt{x}\, dx = \frac{2}{3}. \quad \square$$

We will conclude this section by proving an analogue of the Darboux Sum Convergence Criterion for Riemann sums. In order to do so, we will first prove the following:

LEMMA 6.15   Suppose that the function $f : [a, b] \to \mathbb{R}$ is bounded. For each partition P of $[a, b]$ and each positive number ϵ, there are Riemann sums $R(f, P)$ and $R'(f, P)$ for the function $f : [a, b] \to \mathbb{R}$ based on the partition P such that

$$0 \leq U(f, P) - R(f, P) < \epsilon \tag{6.22}$$

and

$$0 \leq R'(f, P) - L(f, P) < \epsilon. \tag{6.23}$$

Proof   Let $P = \{x_0, \ldots, x_n\}$. By definition,

$$U(f, P) = \sum_{k=1}^n M_i (x_i - x_{i-1})$$

where for each index i with $1 \leq i \leq n$,

$$M_i = \sup\{ f(x) \mid x \text{ in } [x_{i-1}, x_i] \}.$$

Fix an index i with $1 \leq i \leq n$. Since the number $M_i - \epsilon/(b - a)$ is not an upper bound for the set $\{ f(x) \mid x \text{ in } [x_{i-1}, x_i] \}$, there is a point c_i in the subinterval $[x_{i-1}, x_i]$ such that $f(c_i) > M_i - \epsilon/(b - a)$. Thus

$$M_i - \epsilon/(b - a) < f(c_i).$$

Multiply this inequality by $(x_i - x_{i-1})$ and sum the resulting n inequalities to obtain

$$U(f, P) - \epsilon = U(f, P) - \epsilon/(b - a) \sum_{k=1}^n (x_i - x_{i-1}) < \sum_{k=1}^n f(c_i)(x_i - x_{i-1}).$$

Define $R(f, P) = \sum_{k=1}^{n} f(c_i)(x_i - x_{i-1})$. This proves (6.22). The proof of (6.23) is entirely similar, except that one chooses a point c_i' in the subinterval $[x_{i-1}, x_i]$ such that $f(c_i') < m_i + \epsilon/(b - a)$. ∎

THEOREM 6.16 **The Riemann Sum Convergence Criterion**   Suppose that the function $f: [a, b] \to \mathbb{R}$ is bounded, and let A be a number. Then the following two assertions are equivalent:

(i) The function $f: [a, b] \to \mathbb{R}$ is integrable and $\int_a^b f = A$.

(ii) If $\{P_n\}$ is any sequence of partitions of $[a, b]$ such that $\lim_{n\to\infty} \|P_n\| = 0$, and for each natural number n, $R(f, P_n)$ is a Riemann sum for $f: [a, b] \to \mathbb{R}$ based on the partition P_n, then
$$\lim_{n\to\infty} R(f, P_n) = A.$$

Proof   That (i) implies (ii) is the assertion of Corollary 6.14.

We will use the Darboux Sum Convergence Criterion to verify that (ii) implies (i). Suppose that (ii) holds. Let $\{P_n\}$ be a sequence of partitions of $[a, b]$ such that $\lim_{n\to\infty} \|P_n\| = 0$. We must prove that
$$\lim_{n\to\infty} U(f, P_n) = \lim_{n\to\infty} L(f, P_n) = A. \tag{6.24}$$

Fix a natural number n. By the preceding lemma, taking $\epsilon = 1/n$, we may choose Riemann sums $R(f, P_n)$ and $R'(f, P_n)$ for the function $f: [a, b] \to \mathbb{R}$ based on the partition P_n such that
$$0 \le U(f, P_n) - R(f, P_n) < \frac{1}{n}$$

and
$$0 \le R'(f, P_n) - L(f, P_n) < \frac{1}{n}.$$

Consequently, for each natural number n,
$$R'(f, P_n) - \frac{1}{n} < L(f, P_n) \le U(f, P_n) < R(f, P_n) + \frac{1}{n}. \tag{6.25}$$

Now (ii) implies that
$$\lim_{n\to\infty} R(f, P_n) = \lim_{n\to\infty} R'(f, P_n) = A.$$

Inequality (6.25) and the Squeezing Principle for sequences imply (6.24). According to the Darboux Sum Convergence Criterion, the function $f: [a, b] \to \mathbb{R}$ is integrable and $\int_a^b f = A$. ∎

1. Let P_1 and P_2 be partitions of $[a, b]$. Show that if P_1 is a refinement of P_2, then $\|P_1\| \leq \|P_2\|$. Is the converse true?

2. For a fixed positive number β, find
$$\lim_{n \to \infty} \left[\frac{1^\beta + 2^\beta + \cdots + n^\beta}{n^{\beta+1}} \right].$$

3. Find
$$\lim_{n \to \infty} \left[\frac{1}{n+1} + \frac{1}{n+2} + \cdots + \frac{1}{2n} \right].$$

4. Find
$$\lim_{n \to \infty} \left[\sum_{k=1}^{n} \frac{k}{n^2 + k^2} \right].$$

5. Find
$$\lim_{n \to \infty} \left[\frac{1}{\sqrt{n \cdot n}} + \frac{1}{\sqrt{n(n+1)}} + \cdots + \frac{1}{\sqrt{n(n+n)}} \right].$$

6. Let $b > 1$. Find the value of the Riemann sum for $\int_1^b [1/\sqrt{x}]\, dx$ that one obtains for the partition $P = \{x_0, \ldots, x_n\}$ of $[1, b]$ by choosing $c_i = [(\sqrt{x_i} + \sqrt{x_{i-1}})/2]^2$ for $1 \leq k \leq n$.

7. Suppose that the function $f : [0, 1] \to \mathbb{R}$ is integrable. Prove that
$$\lim_{n \to \infty} \frac{1}{n} \left[f\left(\frac{1}{n}\right) + f\left(\frac{2}{n}\right) + \cdots + f\left(\frac{n-1}{n}\right) + f(1) \right] = \int_0^1 f.$$

8. Suppose that the function $f : [a, b] \to \mathbb{R}$ is Lipschitz; that is, there is a number c such that
$$|f(u) - f(v)| \leq c|u - v| \quad \text{for all } u \text{ and } v \text{ in } [a, b].$$
Let P be a partition of $[a, b]$ and $R(f, P)$ be a Riemann sum based on P. Prove that
$$\left| R(f, P) - \int_a^b f \right| \leq c\|P\|(b - a).$$

9. Let p and n be natural numbers with $n \geq 2$. Prove that
$$\sum_{k=1}^{n-1} k^p \leq \frac{n^{p+1}}{p+1} \leq \sum_{k=1}^{n} k^p.$$
(*Hint:* Use an induction argument on n.)

10. For a natural number p, use the preceding exercise and Corollary 6.12 to prove that
$$\int_0^1 x^p\, dx = \frac{1}{p+1}.$$

11. (Fermat's method for computing $\int_1^b x^\beta\, dx$.) Let $b > 1$ and $\beta \neq -1$. Define $f(x) = x^\beta$ for all x in $[1, b]$. For each natural number n, let $P_n = \{x_0, \ldots, x_n\}$ be the partition of $[1, b]$ defined by $x_i = b^{i/n}$ for $0 \leq i \leq n$.
    (a) Show that
$$\sum_{i=1}^{n} f(x_i)(x_i - x_{i-1}) = \frac{b^{1/n} - 1}{b^{1/n}} \left[\frac{1 - (b^{\beta+1})^{\frac{n+1}{n}}}{1 - b^{\frac{\beta+1}{n}}} - 1 \right].$$

(b)   Show that

$$\lim_{n\to\infty} \frac{1-(b^{1/n})^{\beta+1}}{1-b^{1/n}} = \beta+1.$$

(c)   Use (a) and (b) to show that

$$\int_1^b x^\beta\, dx = \lim_{n\to\infty} \sum_{i=1}^n f(x_i)(x_i - x_{i-1}) = \frac{b^{\beta+1}-1}{\beta+1}.$$

6.5   Linearity, Monotonicity, and Additivity over Intervals

THEOREM 6.17   **Linearity of the Integral**   Suppose that the functions $f:[a,b] \to \mathbb{R}$ and $g:[a,b] \to \mathbb{R}$ are integrable. Then for any two numbers α and β, the function $\alpha f + \beta g:[a,b] \to \mathbb{R}$ is integrable and

$$\int_a^b [\alpha f + \beta g] = \alpha \int_a^b f + \beta \int_a^b g. \qquad (6.26)$$

Proof   We will use the Riemann Sum Convergence Criterion to prove the theorem. Let $\{P_n\}$ be a sequence of partitions of the interval $[a,b]$ such that $\lim_{n\to\infty} \|P_n\| = 0$. For each natural number n, let $R(\alpha f + \beta g, P_n)$ be a Riemann sum for the function $\alpha f + \beta g:[a,b] \to \mathbb{R}$ based on the partition P_n. We must show that

$$\lim_{n\to\infty} R(\alpha f + \beta g, P_n) = \alpha \int_a^b f + \beta \int_a^b g. \qquad (6.27)$$

Fix a natural number n. The Riemann sum $R(\alpha f + \beta g, P_n)$ is defined by choosing points in the subintervals induced by the partition P_n; define $R(f, P_n)$ and $R(g, P_n)$ to be the Riemann sums for the functions $f:[a,b] \to \mathbb{R}$ and $g:[a,b] \to \mathbb{R}$ obtained by making the same choice of points in the subintervals induced by P_n. For such a choice of Riemann sums, we have

$$R(\alpha f + \beta g, P_n) = \alpha R(f, P_n) + \beta R(g, P_n). \qquad (6.28)$$

The Riemann Sum Convergence Criterion implies that

$$\lim_{n\to\infty} R(f, P_n) = \int_a^b f \quad \text{and} \quad \lim_{n\to\infty} R(g, P_n) = \int_a^b g. \qquad (6.29)$$

The linearity property of convergent sequences, together with (6.28) and (6.29), implies that (6.27) holds.   ∎

THEOREM 6.18   **Monotonicity of the Integral**   Suppose that the functions $f: [a, b] \to \mathbb{R}$ and $g: [a, b] \to \mathbb{R}$ are integrable and that

$$f(x) \le g(x) \quad \text{for all } x \text{ in } [a, b].$$

Then

$$\int_a^b f \le \int_a^b g.$$

Proof   Let $\{P_n\}$ be any sequence of partitions of $[a, b]$ such that

$$\lim_{n \to \infty} \|P_n\| = 0.$$

For each natural number n, let $R(f, P_n)$ and $R(g, P_n)$ be Riemann sums for the functions $f: [a, b] \to \mathbb{R}$ and $g: [a, b] \to \mathbb{R}$, obtained by making the same choice of points in the subintervals induced by P_n. Thus,

$$R(f, P_n) \le R(g, P_n).$$

The order preservation property of convergent sequences and the Riemann Sum Convergence Criterion imply that

$$\int_a^b f = \lim_{n \to \infty} R(f, P_n) \le \lim_{n \to \infty} R(g, P_n) = \int_a^b g. \qquad \blacksquare$$

THEOREM 6.19   **Additivity over Intervals**   Let $a < c < b$. Then the function $f: [a, b] \to \mathbb{R}$ is integrable if and only if both $f: [a, c] \to \mathbb{R}$ and $f: [c, b] \to \mathbb{R}$ are integrable, in which case

$$\int_a^b f = \int_a^c f + \int_c^b f. \tag{6.30}$$

Proof   First we suppose that the functions $f: [a, c] \to \mathbb{R}$ and $f: [c, b] \to \mathbb{R}$ are integrable. For each natural number n, let P_n' be the regular partition of the interval $[a, c]$ into n subintervals, let P_n'' be the regular partition of the interval $[c, b]$ into n subintervals, and let P_n be the partition of $[a, b]$ obtained from the union of the partition points of P_n' and P_n''; observe that

$$L(f, P_n) = L(f, P_n') + L(f, P_n'')$$

and

$$U(f, P_n) = U(f, P_n') + U(f, P_n'').$$

By the Darboux Sum Integrability Criterion,

$$\lim_{n \to \infty} L(f, P_n') = \lim_{n \to \infty} U(f, P_n') = \int_a^c f$$

and

$$\lim_{n \to \infty} L(f, P_n'') = \lim_{n \to \infty} U(f, P_n'') = \int_c^b f.$$

Thus, by the sum property of convergent sequences of numbers,

$$\lim_{n \to \infty} L(f, P_n) = \lim_{n \to \infty} U(f, P_n) = \int_a^c f + \int_c^b f.$$

It follows from Proposition 6.8 that the function $f:[a, b] \to \mathbb{R}$ is integrable and that

$$\int_a^b f = \int_a^c f + \int_c^b f.$$

Now suppose that the function $f:[a, b] \to \mathbb{R}$ is integrable. It is only necessary to show that the functions $f:[a, c] \to \mathbb{R}$ and $f:[c, b] \to \mathbb{R}$ are integrable, since then we have already verified formula (6.30). We will use the Integrability Criterion to show that $f:[a, c] \to \mathbb{R}$ is integrable. Let $\epsilon > 0$. Since $f:[a, b] \to \mathbb{R}$ is integrable, there is a partition P of the interval $[a, b]$ such that $U(f, P) - L(f, P) < \epsilon$. Define P^* to be the refinement of P obtained by adjoining the point c to P. The Refinement Lemma implies that

$$U(f, P^*) - L(f, P^*) \le U(f, P) - L(f, P) < \epsilon.$$

Let P' be the partition that P^* induces on $[a, c]$. Then

$$U(f, P') - L(f, P') \le U(f, P^*) - L(f, P^*) < \epsilon.$$

Thus $f:[a, c] \to \mathbb{R}$ is integrable. The proof that $f:[c, b] \to \mathbb{R}$ is integrable is the same. ∎

COROLLARY 6.20 Suppose that the functions $f:[a, b] \to \mathbb{R}$ and $|f|:[a, b] \to \mathbb{R}$ are integrable. Then

$$\left| \int_a^b f(x)\, dx \right| \le \int_a^b |f(x)|\, dx. \qquad (6.31)$$

Proof For all x in $[a, b]$,

$$-|f(x)| \le f(x) \le |f(x)|.$$

Thus, using the monotonicity and linearity of integration, it follows that

$$-\int_a^b |f(x)|\, dx \le \int_a^b f(x)\, dx \le \int_a^b |f(x)|\, dx,$$

which is equivalent to (6.31). ∎

EXERCISES

1. Suppose that the function $f:[a, b] \to \mathbb{R}$ has $f(x) = 0$ except at a finite number of points $z_1, \ldots, z_k$ in $[a, b]$. Define $M = \max_{1 \le i \le k} |f(z_i)|$. Prove that for any partition P of $[a, b]$, $|R(f, P)| \le (K + 1)M\|P\|$. Use this to prove that $\int_a^b f = 0$.
2. Suppose that the function $g:[a, b] \to \mathbb{R}$ is integrable and that the function $h:[a, b] \to \mathbb{R}$ has the property that $h(x) = g(x)$ except at a finite number of points in $[a, b]$. Prove that $h:[a, b] \to \mathbb{R}$ is integrable and that

$$\int_a^b g = \int_a^b h.$$

3. Suppose that the functions $g: [a, b] \to \mathbb{R}$ and $f: [a, b] \to \mathbb{R}$ are continuous. Prove that $\int_a^b [f + g]^2 \geq 0$. Use this to prove that

$$\int_a^b fg \leq \frac{1}{2} \left[\int_a^b f^2 + \int_a^b g^2 \right].$$

(This is the integral version of Cauchy's Inequality.)

4. Suppose that the functions $g: [a, b] \to \mathbb{R}$ and $f: [a, b] \to \mathbb{R}$ are continuous. Prove that

$$\int_a^b gf \leq \sqrt{\int_a^b g^2} \sqrt{\int_a^b f^2}.$$

(This is called the Cauchy-Schwarz Inequality for Integrals.) (*Hint:* For each number λ, define $p(\lambda) = \int_a^b [f - \lambda g]^2$. Show that $p(\lambda)$ is a quadratic polynomial for which $p(\lambda) \geq 0$ for all λ and analyze the discriminant of $p(\lambda)$.)

5. Use the Cauchy-Schwarz Inequality to verify that

$$\int_0^1 \sqrt{1 + x^4}\, dx \leq \sqrt{\frac{6}{5}}$$

and

$$\int_0^1 \sqrt{1 + x^3}\, dx \leq \sqrt{\frac{5}{2}}.$$

6. Suppose that the functions $f: [a, b] \to \mathbb{R}$ and $g: [a, b] \to \mathbb{R}$ are continuous. Prove the following integral version of the Triangle Inequality and the Reverse Triangle Inequality:

$$\int_a^b |f| - \int_a^b |g| \leq \int_a^b |f + g| \leq \int_a^b |f| + \int_a^b |g|.$$

7. Prove that

$$\frac{2}{\pi} x \leq \sin x \leq x \quad \text{if} \quad 0 \leq x \leq \frac{\pi}{2},$$

and use this to prove that

$$1 \leq \int_0^{\pi/2} \frac{\sin x}{x}\, dx \leq \frac{\pi}{2}.$$

8. Let $f: [a, b] \to \mathbb{R}$ and $g: [a, b] \to \mathbb{R}$ be continuous functions having the property that $f(x) \leq g(x)$ for all x in $[a, b]$. Prove that

$$\int_a^b f < \int_a^b g$$

if and only if there is a point x_0 in $[a, b]$ at which $f(x_0) < g(x_0)$.

9. The Monotonicity Property of the integral implies that if the functions $g: [0, \infty) \to \mathbb{R}$ and $h: [0, \infty) \to \mathbb{R}$ are continuous and $g(x) \leq h(x)$ for all $x \geq 0$, then

$$\int_0^x g \leq \int_0^x h \quad \text{for all } x \geq 0.$$

Use this to show that each of the following inequalities implies its successor:

$$\cos x \le 1 \quad \text{if} \quad x \ge 0$$
$$\sin x \le x \quad \text{if} \quad x \ge 0$$
$$1 - \cos x \le \frac{x^2}{2} \quad \text{if} \quad x \ge 0$$
$$x - \sin x \le \frac{x^3}{6} \quad \text{if} \quad x \ge 0.$$

Thus

$$x - \frac{x^3}{6} \le \sin x \le x \quad \text{if} \quad x \ge 0.$$

7

The Second Fundamental Theorem and Its Consequences

7.1 The Second Fundamental Theorem of Calculus

In Section 4.5, we first considered the question of whether, given a function $f: (a, b) \to \mathbb{R}$, there is a differentiable function $F: (a, b) \to \mathbb{R}$ such that

$$F'(x) = f(x) \quad \text{for all } x \text{ in } (a, b).$$

We call this equation the Fundamental Differential Equation (F.D.E.). As we have seen in Section 4.5,

(i) For certain functions $f: (a, b) \to \mathbb{R}$, such as polynomials, we can explicitly solve the F.D.E.

(ii) If the function $f: (a, b) \to \mathbb{R}$ does not have the Intermediate Value Property, then Darboux's Theorem asserts that there is no solution of the F.D.E.

(iii) For many functions $f: (a, b) \to \mathbb{R}$, we are unable to decide whether there is a solution of the F.D.E.

This is clearly not a satisfactory situation.

The importance of the Fundamental Differential Equation became evident in the statement of the First Fundamental Theorem of Calculus. However, quite independently of the problem of explicitly evaluating integrals, this equation is of great importance in mathematics. *In particular, it is the first step in the study of general differential equations.* In this section, we will prove that if the function $f: (a, b) \to \mathbb{R}$ is continuous, then the F.D.E. has a solution for which there is an explicit formula. Before proving this result, we derive two preliminary results that are of independent interest.

THEOREM 7.1   **The Mean Value Theorem for Integrals**   Suppose that the function $f: [a, b] \to \mathbb{R}$ is continuous. Then there is a point x_0 in the interval $[a, b]$ such that

$$\frac{1}{b-a} \int_a^b f = f(x_0).$$

FIGURE 7.1

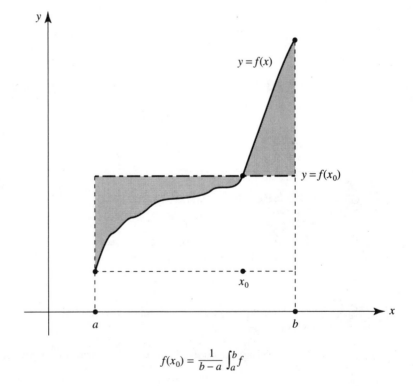

$$f(x_0) = \frac{1}{b-a} \int_a^b f$$

Proof   Since the function $f: [a, b] \to \mathbb{R}$ is continuous, we may use the Extreme Value Theorem to choose points x_m and x_M in the interval $[a, b]$ at which $f: [a, b] \to \mathbb{R}$ attains minimum and maximum values, respectively.

The monotonicity property of integration implies that

$$f(x_m)(b-a) \le \int_a^b f(x)\,dx \le f(x_M)(b-a),$$

and so

$$f(x_m) \le \frac{1}{b-a}\int_a^b f(x)\,dx \le f(x_M).$$

Thus, by the Intermediate Value Theorem, there is a point x_0 between x_m and x_M such that

$$f(x_0) = \frac{1}{b-a}\int_a^b f. \qquad \blacksquare$$

PROPOSITION 7.2 Suppose that the function $f:[a,b] \to \mathbb{R}$ is integrable. Define

$$F(x) = \int_a^x f \quad \text{for all } x \text{ in } [a,b].$$

Then the function $F:[a,b] \to \mathbb{R}$ is continuous.

Proof First of all, observe that, according to Theorem 6.19, for each point x in $[a,b]$, the function $f:[a,x] \to \mathbb{R}$ is integrable. Hence, the function $F:[a,b] \to \mathbb{R}$ is properly defined.

Now, since the function $f:[a,b] \to \mathbb{R}$ is integrable, it is bounded. Choose $M > 0$ such that

$$-M \le f(x) \le M \quad \text{for all } x \text{ in } [a,b]. \tag{7.1}$$

We claim that

$$|F(u) - F(v)| \le M|u - v| \quad \text{for all points } u \text{ and } v \text{ in } [a,b]. \tag{7.2}$$

Indeed, let u and v be points in $[a,b]$ with $u < v$. By the additivity over intervals property of the integral,

$$F(v) = \int_a^v f = \int_a^u f + \int_u^v f = F(u) + \int_u^v f,$$

so that

$$F(v) - F(u) = \int_u^v f. \tag{7.3}$$

But (7.1) implies, in particular, that

$$-M \le f(x) \le M \quad \text{if } u \le x \le v,$$

so that, by (7.3) and the monotonicity of the integral,

$$-M(v - u) \le F(v) - F(u) \le M(v - u).$$

Thus, (7.2) holds when $u < v$. Since (7.2) remains unchanged when u and v are interchanged, it also holds when $v < u$.

Finally, (7.2) immediately implies the continuity of the function $F:[a,b] \to \mathbb{R}$.

$\blacksquare$

EXAMPLE 7.1 Define

$$f(x) = \begin{cases} 2 & \text{if } 0 \le x \le 1 \\ x & \text{if } 1 < x \le 2. \end{cases}$$

Now define

$$F(x) = \int_0^x f \quad \text{if} \quad 0 \le x \le 2.$$

By the First Fundamental Theorem of Calculus,

$$F(x) = \begin{cases} 2x & \text{if } 0 \le x \le 1 \\ F(1) + \int_1^x f = 3/2 + x^2/2 & \text{if } 1 < x \le 2. \end{cases}$$

As the preceding theorem predicted, the function $F \colon [0, 2] \to \mathbb{R}$ is continuous. $\square$

When we strengthen the assumption in Proposition 7.2 by replacing the integrability of $f \colon [a, b] \to \mathbb{R}$ with the continuity of $f \colon [a, b] \to \mathbb{R}$, we obtain one of the most important theorems in mathematics.

THEOREM 7.3 **The Second Fundamental Theorem of Calculus** Suppose that the function $f \colon [a, b] \to \mathbb{R}$ is continuous. Define

$$F(x) = \int_a^x f \quad \text{for all } x \text{ in } [a, b].$$

Then

$$F'(x) = f(x) \quad \text{for all } x \text{ in } (a, b).$$

Proof We have already verified that the function $F \colon [a, b] \to \mathbb{R}$ is properly defined and is, in fact, continuous. Let x_0 be a point in (a, b). We must show that

$$\lim_{x \to x_0} \frac{F(x) - F(x_0)}{x - x_0} = f(x_0).$$

Let x be a point in (a, b) with $x \ne x_0$. By the additivity over intervals property of the integral,

$$F(x) - F(x_0) = \int_{x_0}^x f \quad \text{if} \quad x > x_0$$

and

$$F(x) - F(x_0) = -\int_x^{x_0} f \quad \text{if} \quad x < x_0.$$

Consequently, applying the Mean Value Theorem for Integrals, we see that we may select a point $c(x)$ between x_0 and x such that

$$\frac{F(x) - F(x_0)}{x - x_0} = f(c(x)). \tag{7.4}$$

But the function $f \colon [a, b] \to \mathbb{R}$ is continuous at x_0, so that

$$\lim_{x \to x_0} f(c(x)) = f(x_0).$$

Thus the conclusion follows from (7.4). ∎

As we have previously mentioned, *the principal importance of the Second Fundamental Theorem of Calculus is that it provides the crucial first step on the road to studying quite general differential equations.* We shall turn to this aspect in Section 7.2. Also, as we shall see in Section 7.3, this theorem can be used to verify various classical techniques for replacing complicated integrals by ones for which we can directly apply the First Fundamental Theorem of Calculus by inspection. Finally, in Section 7.4, we will see that the Second Fundamental Theorem is important in analyzing the errors that arise when we use approximation techniques for estimating integrals.

In the remainder of this section, we will consider some variations of the Second Fundamental Theorem.

COROLLARY 7.4 Suppose that the function $f: [a, b] \to \mathbb{R}$ is continuous. Define

$$H(x) = \int_x^b f \quad \text{for all } x \text{ in } [a, b].$$

Then

$$H'(x) = -f(x) \quad \text{for all } x \text{ in } (a, b).$$

Proof By the additivity over intervals property of the integral,

$$H(x) = \int_a^b f - \int_a^x f = k - F(x) \quad \text{for all } x \text{ in } [a, b],$$

where

$$k = \int_a^b f \quad \text{and} \quad F(x) = \int_a^x f \quad \text{for all } x \text{ in } (a, b).$$

The result now follows from the Second Fundamental Theorem of Calculus. ∎

Motivated by the previous result, we extend the meaning of the symbol $\int_a^b f$ as follows.

DEFINITION *Let c and d be numbers such that $c < d$. For an integrable function $f: [c, d] \to \mathbb{R}$, we define*

$$\int_d^c f \equiv -\int_c^d f.$$

With the above definition, the additivity over intervals property of the integral extends as follows: Let I be an interval and suppose that the function $f: I \to \mathbb{R}$ is continuous. Then for any three points x_1, x_2, and x_3 in I,

$$\int_{x_1}^{x_3} f = \int_{x_1}^{x_2} f + \int_{x_2}^{x_3} f.$$

We leave the proof of this as an exercise.

COROLLARY 7.5

Let I be an open interval, and suppose that the function $f: I \to \mathbb{R}$ is continuous. Fix a point x_0 in I and define

$$F(x) = \int_{x_0}^{x} f \quad \text{for all } x \text{ in } I.$$

Then the function $F: I \to \mathbb{R}$ is differentiable and

$$F'(x) = f(x) \quad \text{for all } x \text{ in } I.$$

Proof If $x > x_0$, then, according to the Second Fundamental Theorem, $F'(x) = f(x)$. If $x < x_0$, then

$$F(x) = -\int_{x}^{x_0} f,$$

so Corollary 7.4 implies that $F'(x) = f(x)$. Now choose a to be a point in I with $a < x_0$, and define $G(x) = \int_{a}^{x} f$ for x in I. Then by the Second Fundamental Theorem of Calculus, $G'(x_0) = f(x_0)$, and since the functions $F: I \to \mathbb{R}$ and $G: I \to \mathbb{R}$ differ by a constant function, $F'(x_0) = f(x_0)$. ∎

COROLLARY 7.6

Let I be an open interval, and suppose that the function $f: I \to \mathbb{R}$ is continuous. Let J be an open interval, and suppose that the function $\varphi: J \to \mathbb{R}$ is differentiable and that $\varphi(J) \subseteq I$. Fix a point x_0 in I and define

$$G(x) = \int_{x_0}^{\varphi(x)} f \quad \text{for all } x \text{ in } J.$$

Then the function $G: J \to \mathbb{R}$ is differentiable and

$$G'(x) = f(\varphi(x))\varphi'(x) \quad \text{for all } x \text{ in } J.$$

Proof Define $F(x) = \int_{x_0}^{x} f$ for x in I. Then $G = F \circ \varphi: J \to \mathbb{R}$ is the composition of differentiable functions, so the result follows from the Second Fundamental Theorem, as expressed in Corollary 7.5, and the Chain Rule. ∎

In the Leibnitz notation, the conclusion of Corollary 7.6 may be written as

$$\frac{d}{dx}\left[\int_{x_0}^{\varphi(x)} f(t)\, dt\right] = f(\varphi(x))\varphi'(x) \quad \text{for all } x \text{ in } J.$$

The Second Fundamental Theorem of Calculus was proven under the assumption that the function $f: [a, b] \to \mathbb{R}$ is continuous. In fact, if $f: [a, b] \to \mathbb{R}$ is merely integrable and we define $F(x) = \int_{a}^{x} f$ for all x in $[a, b]$, then $F'(x) = f(x)$ at each point x in (a, b) at which the function $f: [a, b] \to \mathbb{R}$ is continuous (see Exercise 11). Thus, if $f: [a, b] \to \mathbb{R}$ is bounded and $f: (a, b) \to \mathbb{R}$ is continuous, then the function $F: [a, b] \to \mathbb{R}$ defined by $F(x) = \int_{a}^{x} f$ for all x in $[a, b]$ has the property that $F: [a, b] \to \mathbb{R}$ is continuous and $F'(x) = f(x)$ at each point x in (a, b). This slight extension of the Second Fundamental Theorem will be useful in Section 7.3.

EXERCISES

1. Calculate the following derivatives:

   (a) $\dfrac{d}{dx}\left(\displaystyle\int_0^x x^2 t^2 \, dt\right)$

   (b) $\dfrac{d}{dx}\left(\displaystyle\int_1^{e^x} \ln t \, dt\right)$

   (c) $\dfrac{d}{dx}\left(\displaystyle\int_{-x}^x e^{t^2} \, dt\right)$

   (d) $\dfrac{d}{dx}\left(\displaystyle\int_1^x \cos(x+t) \, dt\right)$

2. For each of the following integrable functions $f:[a,b] \to \mathbb{R}$ define

   $$F(x) = \int_a^x f(t)\, dt \quad \text{for all } x \text{ in } [a,b]$$

   and find a formula for $F(x)$, $a \le x \le b$, that does not involve integrals.

   (a) $f:[1,4] \to \mathbb{R}$ defined by

   $$f(x) = \begin{cases} 2 & \text{if } 1 \le x \le 3 \\ 6 & \text{if } 3 < x \le 4. \end{cases}$$

   (b) $f:[0,2] \to \mathbb{R}$ defined by

   $$f(x) = \begin{cases} x^2 & \text{if } 0 \le x \le 1 \\ x & \text{if } 1 < x \le 2. \end{cases}$$

   (c) $f:[-1,1] \to \mathbb{R}$ defined by

   $$f(x) = \begin{cases} x & \text{if } -1 \le x < 0 \\ x+1 & \text{if } 0 \le x \le 1. \end{cases}$$

3. Suppose that the function $f:\mathbb{R} \to \mathbb{R}$ is differentiable. Define the function $H:\mathbb{R} \to \mathbb{R}$ by

   $$H(x) = \int_{-x}^x [f(t) + f(-t)]\, dt \quad \text{for all } x.$$

   Find $H''(x)$.

4. Suppose that the function $f:\mathbb{R} \to \mathbb{R}$ has a continuous second derivative. Prove that

   $$f(x) = f(0) + f'(0)x + \int_0^x (x-t)f''(t)\, dt \quad \text{for all } x.$$

   (*Hint:* Use the Identity Criterion.)

5. Suppose that the function $f:\mathbb{R} \to \mathbb{R}$ is continuous. Define

   $$G(x) = \int_0^x (x-t)f(t)\, dt \text{ for all } x.$$

   Prove that $G''(x) = f(x)$ for all x.

6. Define

   $$F(x) = \int_1^x \frac{1}{2\sqrt{t}-1}\, dt \quad \text{for all } x \ge 1.$$

   Prove that if $c > 0$, then there is a unique solution to the equation

   $$F(x) = c, \quad x > 1.$$

7. Suppose that the continuous function $f:[a, b] \to \mathbb{R}$ has the property that $\int_{x_1}^{x_2} f = 0$ whenever $a \le x_1 < x_2 \le b$. Prove that $f(x) = 0$ for all x in $[a, b]$.
8. Show that the Mean Value Theorem for Integrals does not hold if we replace the assumption that $f:[a, b] \to \mathbb{R}$ is continuous with the assumption that $f:[a, b] \to \mathbb{R}$ is integrable.
9. For numbers $a_1, \ldots, a_n$ define $p(x) = a_1 x + a_2 x^2 + \cdots + a_n x^n$ for all x. Suppose that

$$\frac{a_1}{2} + \frac{a_2}{3} + \cdots + \frac{a_n}{n+1} = 0.$$

Prove that there is some point x in the interval $(0, 1)$ such that $p(x) = 0$.
10. Show that the conclusion of the Mean Value Theorem for Integrals may be strengthened so that we can choose the point x_0 to be in (a, b), not just in $[a, b]$.
11. The Second Fundamental Theorem of Calculus has a somewhat more general form than we have stated: *For an integrable function $f:[a, b] \to \mathbb{R}$, we define $F(x) = \int_a^x f$ for all x in $[a, b]$. Then at each point x_0 in (a, b) at which the function $f:[a, b] \to \mathbb{R}$ is continuous, the function $F:[a, b] \to \mathbb{R}$ is differentiable and $F'(x_0) = f(x_0)$.* Use the monotonicity property of integration to prove this.
12. Let the function $f:[a, b] \to \mathbb{R}$ be continuous. Suppose that the function $F:[a, b] \to \mathbb{R}$ is continuous, that $F:(a, b) \to \mathbb{R}$ is differentiable, and that $F'(x) = f(x)$ for all x in (a, b). Use the Second Fundamental Theorem of Calculus to prove that

$$\frac{d}{dx}\left[F(x) - \int_a^x f\right] = 0 \quad \text{for all } x \text{ in } (a, b),$$

and from this derive a new proof of the First Fundamental Theorem of Calculus in the case when $f:[a, b] \to \mathbb{R}$ is assumed to be continuous, not just integrable.
13. Suppose that the functions $f:[a, b] \to \mathbb{R}$ and $g:[a, b] \to \mathbb{R}$ are continuous and α and β are any real numbers. Define

$$H(x) = \int_a^x [\alpha f + \beta g] - \alpha \int_a^x [f] - \beta \int_a^x [g] \quad \text{for all } x \text{ in } [a, b].$$

Prove that $H'(x) = 0$ for all x in (a, b) and use this to provide another proof of the linearity of the integral provided that the functions are assumed to be continuous, not just integrable.

7.2 The Existence of Solutions of Differential Equations

PROPOSITION 7.7 Let I be an open interval containing the point x_0, and suppose that the function $f: I \to \mathbb{R}$ is continuous. For any number y_0, the differential equation

$$\begin{cases} F'(x) = f(x) & \text{for all } x \text{ in } I \\ F(x_0) = y_0 \end{cases}$$

has a unique solution $F: I \to \mathbb{R}$ given by the formula

$$F(x) = y_0 + \int_{x_0}^x f \quad \text{for all } x \text{ in } I.$$

Proof   By definition, $F(x_0) = y_0$. The Second Fundamental Theorem of Calculus, as expressed in Corollary 7.5, implies that $F'(x) = f(x)$ for all x in I. Thus $F: I \to \mathbb{R}$ is a solution of the differential equation. The Identity Criterion (see Section 4.3) implies that there can be only one solution.   ∎

Recall that in Section 5.1 we *assumed* that there was a differentiable function $F: (0, \infty) \to \mathbb{R}$ that was a solution of the differential equation

$$\begin{cases} F'(x) = 1/x & \text{for all } x > 0 \\ F(1) = 0. \end{cases} \tag{7.5}$$

The Identity Criterion implies that there can be at most one solution. We can now *prove* that there is a solution.

PROPOSITION 7.8   Define

$$F(x) = \int_1^x \frac{1}{t}\, dt \quad \text{for all } x > 0.$$

Then the function $F: (0, \infty) \to \mathbb{R}$ is the solution of the differential equation (7.5).

Proof   By definition, $F(1) = 0$, and Corollary 7.5 implies that $F'(x) = 1/x$ for all $x > 0$.   ∎

We defined the natural logarithm $\ln: (0, \infty) \to \mathbb{R}$ to be the unique solution of the differential equation (7.5) provided that there is a solution. We now have the explicit integral formula

$$\ln x = \int_1^x \frac{1}{t}\, dt \quad \text{for all } x > 0.$$

We now consider the following prototypical example of a linear differential equation depending only on first derivatives.

Given a continuous function $h: \mathbb{R} \to \mathbb{R}$ and numbers a, x_0, and y_0, find a differentiable function $F: \mathbb{R} \to \mathbb{R}$ such that

$$\begin{cases} F'(x) + aF(x) = h(x) & \text{for all } x \\ F(x_0) = y_0. \end{cases} \tag{7.6}$$

PROPOSITION 7.9   There is at most one solution of the differential equation (7.6).

Proof   Suppose that the functions $F_1: \mathbb{R} \to \mathbb{R}$ and $F_2: \mathbb{R} \to \mathbb{R}$ are both solutions of (7.6). We will show that the difference function $g = F_1 - F_2: \mathbb{R} \to \mathbb{R}$ is identically 0, and this will prove that there is at most one solution of (7.6).

First, observe that

$$g'(x) + ag(x) = 0 \quad \text{for all } x. \tag{7.7}$$

Indeed,

$$
\begin{aligned}
g'(x) + ag(x) &= F_1'(x) - F_2'(x) + a[F_1(x) - F_2(x)] \\
&= [F_1'(x) + aF_1(x)] - [F_2'(x) + aF_2(x)] \\
&= h(x) - h(x) \\
&= 0 \quad \text{for all } x.
\end{aligned}
$$

According to Proposition 5.5,

$$
g(x) = g(0)e^{-ax} \quad \text{for all } x.
$$

But $g(x_0) = 0$, so $g(0) = 0$ and hence $g(x) = 0$ for all x. ∎

THEOREM 7.10 Suppose that the function $h: \mathbb{R} \to \mathbb{R}$ is continuous. Then the differential equation (7.6) has precisely one solution, given by the formula

$$
F(x) = y_0 e^{-a(x-x_0)} + e^{-ax} \int_{x_0}^{x} e^{at} h(t)\, dt \quad \text{for all } x. \tag{7.8}
$$

Proof Proposition 7.9 asserts that there is at most one solution of (7.6). It remains to prove that formula (7.8) defines a solution of (7.6), and to do this we need to compute $F': \mathbb{R} \to \mathbb{R}$.

Using the Chain Rule, the product rule for differentiation, and the Second Fundamental Theorem of Calculus, we have

$$
\begin{aligned}
F'(x) &= -ay_0 e^{-a(x-x_0)} - ae^{-ax} \int_{x_0}^{x} e^{at} h(t)\, dt + e^{-ax} e^{ax} h(x) \\
&= -aF(x) + h(x) \quad \text{for all } x,
\end{aligned}
$$

so that

$$
F'(x) + aF(x) = h(x) \quad \text{for all } x. \qquad \blacksquare
$$

EXAMPLE 7.2 Find the unique solution of the equation

$$
\begin{cases}
F'(x) - F(x) = x & \text{for all } x \\
F(0) = 2.
\end{cases}
$$

According to Theorem 7.10, the unique solution is given by the formula

$$
F(x) = 2e^x + e^x \int_0^x e^{-t} t\, dt \quad \text{for all } x.
$$

But the integral in this formula may be evaluated by using the First Fundamental Theorem of Calculus. After doing so, we obtain

$$
F(x) = 3e^x - x - 1 \quad \text{for all } x. \qquad \square
$$

EXERCISES

1. Find the unique solution of each of the following differential equations:

    (a) $\begin{cases} F'(x) + F(x) = x & \text{for all } x \\ F(0) = 1. \end{cases}$

    (b) $\begin{cases} F'(x) + 4F(x) = e^x & \text{for all } x \\ F(2) = 31. \end{cases}$

    (c) $\begin{cases} F'(x) + F(x) = x^2 & \text{for all } x \\ F(0) = -1. \end{cases}$

2. For numbers c and a, consider the differential equation

    $$\begin{cases} F'(x) = c(a - F(x)) & \text{for all } x. \\ F(0) = 0. \end{cases}$$

    Prove that the unique solution is given by the formula

    $$F(x) = a(1 - e^{-cx}) \quad \text{for all } x.$$

3. For an open interval I containing 0 and a function $f: I \to \mathbb{R}$ that has a continuous derivative, prove that

    $$f(x) = f(0) + \int_0^x f'(t)\, dt \quad \text{for all } x \text{ in } I.$$

    Use this formula to obtain explicit integral representations of the arcsine, the arccosine, and the arctangent.

4. Prove that

    $$\int_1^{12} \frac{1}{x}\, dx = 2\int_1^2 \frac{1}{x}\, dx + \int_1^3 \frac{1}{x}\, dx.$$

5. Suppose that the function $f: \mathbb{R} \to \mathbb{R}$ is continuous and that

    $$f(x) = \int_0^x f(t)\, dt \quad \text{for all } x.$$

    Prove that $f(x) = 0$ for all x.

6. Multiply both sides of the first line of (7.6) by e^{ax}, and observe that

    $$\frac{d}{dx}(e^{ax} F(x)) = e^{ax} h(x) \quad \text{for all } x.$$

    Use this to motivate formula (7.8), and also to give another proof of Theorem 7.10.

7. Suppose that the function $g: \mathbb{R} \to \mathbb{R}$ is continuous and that $g(x) > 0$ for all x. Define

    $$h(x) = \int_0^x \frac{1}{g(t)}\, dt \quad \text{for all } x,$$

    and let $J = h(\mathbb{R})$. Prove that if $f: J \to \mathbb{R}$ is the inverse of $h: \mathbb{R} \to \mathbb{R}$, then $f: J \to \mathbb{R}$ is a solution of the differential equation

    $$\begin{cases} f'(x) = g(f(x)) & \text{for all } x \text{ in } J \\ f(0) = 0. \end{cases}$$

<table>
<tr><td>**7.3**</td><td>## The Verification of Two Classical Integration Methods</td></tr>
</table>

For a continuous function $f: [a, b] \to \mathbb{R}$ such that its restriction $f: (a, b) \to \mathbb{R}$ has a continuous bounded derivative, using the First Fundamental Theorem of Calculus we obtain the formula

$$\int_a^b f'(x)\,dx = f(b) - f(a).$$

This formula may also be derived from the Second Fundamental Theorem of Calculus (see Exercise 12 of Section 7.1).

THEOREM 7.11   **Integration by Parts**   Suppose that the functions $h: [a, b] \to \mathbb{R}$ and $g: [a, b] \to \mathbb{R}$ are continuous and that both $h: (a, b) \to \mathbb{R}$ and $g: (a, b) \to \mathbb{R}$ have continuous bounded derivatives. Then

$$\int_a^b h(x)g'(x)\,dx = h(b)g(b) - h(a)g(a) - \int_a^b g(x)h'(x)\,dx. \qquad (7.9)$$

Proof   The product function $hg: [a, b] \to \mathbb{R}$ is continuous, $hg: (a, b) \to \mathbb{R}$ is differentiable, and according to the product rule for derivatives,

$$(hg)'(x) = h(x)g'(x) + g(x)h'(x) \quad \text{for all } x \text{ in } (a, b).$$

By the integration formula that preceded the statement of this theorem, we have

$$\int_a^b [hg' + gh'] = \int_a^b (hg)' = h(b)g(b) - h(a)g(a), \qquad (7.10)$$

and, on the other hand, the linearity property of the integral implies that

$$\int_a^b (hg' + gh') = \int_a^b hg' + \int_a^b gh'. \qquad (7.11)$$

Formula (7.9) follows from (7.10) and (7.11). ∎

EXAMPLE 7.3   By reformulating

$$\int_0^1 xe^x\,dx \quad \text{as} \quad \int_0^1 x\frac{d}{dx}(e^x)\,dx,$$

$$\int_0^\pi x\cos x\,dx \quad \text{as} \quad \int_0^\pi x\frac{d}{dx}(\sin x)\,dx,$$

and

$$\int_1^2 \ln x\,dx \quad \text{as} \quad \int_1^2 \ln x\frac{d}{dx}(x)\,dx,$$

each of the integrals on the left-hand side may be evaluated using integration by parts and the First Fundamental Theorem of Calculus.   □

THEOREM 7.12   **Integration by Substitution**   Let the function $f:[a, b] \to \mathbb{R}$ be continuous. Suppose that the function $g:[c, d] \to \mathbb{R}$ is also continuous, that $g:(c, d) \to \mathbb{R}$ has a bounded, continuous derivative, and, moreover, that the image of $g:(c, d) \to \mathbb{R}$ is in the interval (a, b). Then

$$\int_c^d f(g(x))g'(x)\,dx = \int_{g(c)}^{g(d)} f(x)\,dx. \tag{7.12}$$

Proof   Define the function $H:[c, d] \to \mathbb{R}$ by

$$H(x) = \int_c^x (f \circ g)g' - \int_{g(c)}^{g(x)} f \quad \text{for all } x \text{ in } [c, d].$$

Since the composition of continuous functions is continuous, it follows from Proposition 7.2 that the function $H:[c, d] \to \mathbb{R}$ is continuous. Moreover, from the Second Fundamental Theorem of Calculus and Corollary 7.6, we see that

$$H'(x) = f(g(x))g'(x) - f(g(x))g'(x) = 0 \quad \text{for all } x \text{ in } (c, d).$$

The Identity Criterion implies that the function $H:[c, d] \to \mathbb{R}$ is constant. In particular, since $H(c) = 0$, $H(d) = 0$ also; that is, formula (7.12) holds.   ∎

For an integrable function $f:[a, b] \to \mathbb{R}$ having the property that $f(x) \geq 0$ for all x in $[a, b]$, we *define* the area bounded by the graph of $f:[a, b] \to \mathbb{R}$ and the x-axis to be the integral $\int_a^b f(x)\,dx$. Of course, the integral itself was defined in order to make this definition reasonable.

Recall that in Section 5.2 we provided an analytic definition of the number π as follows: The function $\cos x = f(x)$ was defined to be the unique solution of a differential equation

$$\begin{cases} f''(x) + f(x) = 0 & \text{for all } x \\ f(0) = 1 \quad \text{and} \quad f'(0) = 0. \end{cases}$$

Then the number $\pi/2$ was defined to be the smallest positive number at which $\cos x = 0$. Of course, the number π has the geometric significance of being the area of a circle of unit radius. The next formula reconciles the analytic definition of π with its usual geometric significance.

**PROPOSITION
7.13**

$$\frac{\pi}{4} = \int_0^1 \sqrt{1 - x^2}\,dx.$$

FIGURE 7.2

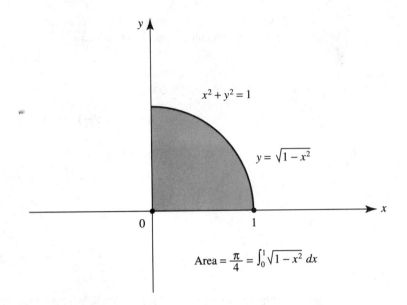

$$\text{Area} = \frac{\pi}{4} = \int_0^1 \sqrt{1-x^2}\, dx$$

Proof First, observe that $\sqrt{1-\sin^2 x} = \cos x$, for $0 \le x \le \pi/2$, since $\cos x \ge 0$ if $0 \le x \le \pi/2$, and $\sin^2 x + \cos^2 x = 1$. Moreover, $\cos^2 x = (1 + \cos 2x)/2$ for all x.

Define $g(x) = \sin x$ for $0 \le x \le \pi/2$. Then we may apply Theorem 7.12, together with the two preceding trigonometric identities, to see that since $\sin 0 = 0$ and $\sin \pi/2 = 1$,

$$\int_0^1 \sqrt{1-x^2}\, dx = \int_0^{\pi/2} \sqrt{1-\sin^2 x}\, \cos x\, dx$$

$$= \int_0^{\pi/2} \left[\frac{1 + \cos 2x}{2} \right] dx.$$

Since

$$\frac{d}{dx}\left(\frac{x}{2} + \frac{\sin 2x}{4} \right) = \frac{1 + \cos 2x}{2} \quad \text{for} \quad 0 \le x \le \frac{\pi}{2},$$

we may apply the First Fundamental Theorem to conclude that

$$\int_0^{\pi/2} \left[\frac{1 + \cos 2x}{2} \right] dx = \left(\frac{x}{2} + \frac{\sin 2x}{4} \right) \Big|_{x=0}^{x=\pi/2} = \frac{\pi}{4}. \qquad \blacksquare$$

EXAMPLE 7.4 Consider the integral

$$\int_0^1 e^{x^2}\, dx.$$

Define $f(x) = e^{x^2}$ for all x in $[0, 1]$. If we attempt to write $f : [0, 1] \to \mathbb{R}$ as $f = hg' : [0, 1] \to \mathbb{R}$ so that $\int_0^1 gh'$ can be calculated, we will find that we cannot do so.

Similarly, if we try substitution, we quickly encounter difficulties in choosing a function $g\colon [c, d] \to \mathbb{R}$ that will make $\int_c^d (f \circ g)g'$ easy to integrate. $\square$

The examples we have considered illustrate both the power and the limitations of the techniques of integration by parts and substitution. The object, of course, is to replace one integration problem with another in which we can directly, by inspection, apply the First Fundamental Theorem of Calculus. When we cannot make such a simplification, we need to develop methods for *estimating* integrals. We will turn to this in Section 7.4.*

EXERCISES

1. Evaluate the following integrals:

    (a) $\displaystyle \int_1^2 xe^{x^2}\, dx$

    (b) $\displaystyle \int_0^1 (1-x)^2\sqrt{2+x}\, dx$

    (c) $\displaystyle \int_2^3 x^3 e^{x^2}\, dx$

    (d) $\displaystyle \int_2^\pi x^2 \cos x\, dx$

2. Evaluate the following integrals:

    (a) $\displaystyle \int_1^e (\ln x)^2\, dx$

    (b) $\displaystyle \int_4^5 \frac{1+x}{1-x}\, dx$

    (c) $\displaystyle \int_4^9 \frac{1}{1-x^2}\, dx$

    (d) $\displaystyle \int_3^4 \left(\frac{1}{x^2 - 2x} + \frac{1}{1+\sqrt{x}} \right) dx$

3. Prove that for any two natural numbers n and m,

$$\int_0^1 x^m (1-x)^n\, dx = \int_0^1 (1-x)^m x^n\, dx.$$

4. Suppose that the function $f\colon \mathbb{R} \to \mathbb{R}$ has a continuous second derivative. Fix a number a. Prove that

$$\int_a^x f''(t)(x-t)\, dt = -(x-a)f'(a) + f(x) - f(a) \quad \text{for all } x.$$

5. Suppose that the function $f\colon \mathbb{R} \to \mathbb{R}$ has a continuous second derivative. Prove that for any two numbers a and b,

$$\int_a^b xf''(x)\, dx = bf'(b) + f(a) - af'(a) - f(b).$$

6. Prove that the area of a circle of radius r is πr^2.
7. Calculate the three integrals in Example 7.3.

---

*There is a precise way to assert and prove that for certain functions $f\colon \mathbb{R} \to \mathbb{R}$, it is not possible to find an "elementary" function $F\colon \mathbb{R} \to \mathbb{R}$ such that $F'(x) = f(x)$ for all x. Unfortunately, to do so requires a background in modern algebra that is outside the scope of this book; see the article "Integration in Finite Terms" by Maxwell Rosenlicht in the *American Mathematical Monthly*, Nov. 1972.

8. Suppose that the function $f: [0, \infty) \to \mathbb{R}$ is continuous and strictly increasing, and that $f: (0, \infty) \to \mathbb{R}$ is differentiable. Moreover, assume $f(0) = 0$. Consider the formula

$$\int_0^x f + \int_0^{f(x)} f^{-1} = xf(x) \quad \text{for all } x \geq 0.$$

Provide a geometric interpretation of this formula in terms of areas. Then prove this formula. (*Hint:* Differentiate the formula and apply the Identity Criterion.)

9. Suppose that the function $f: [0, \infty) \to \mathbb{R}$ is continuous and strictly increasing, with $f(0) = 0$ and $f([0, \infty)) = [0, \infty)$. Then define

$$F(x) = \int_0^x f \quad \text{and} \quad G(x) = \int_0^x f^{-1} \quad \text{for all } x \geq 0.$$

(a) Prove Young's Inequality:

$$ab \leq F(a) + G(b) \quad \text{for all } a \geq 0 \text{ and } b \geq 0.$$

(*Hint:* A sketch will help, as will the formula in Exercise 8.)

(b) Now use Young's Inequality with $f(x) = x^{p-1}$ for all $x \geq 0$, and $p > 1$ fixed, to prove that if the number q is chosen to have the property that $1/p + 1/q = 1$, then

$$ab \leq \frac{a^p}{p} + \frac{b^q}{q} \quad \text{for all } a \geq 0 \text{ and } b \geq 0.$$

7.4 The Approximation of Integrals

There are many functions $f: [a, b] \to \mathbb{R}$ that are integrable, but it is not possible by substitution, by integration by parts, or by any other device to reduce the calculation of $\int_a^b f(x)\, dx$ to an application by inspection of the First Fundamental Theorem of Calculus. In such cases, we approximate the value of the integral and we specify a bound for the error that has arisen in the approximation procedure.

The idea is to take a partition $P = \{x_0, \ldots, x_n\}$ of $[a, b]$. Then for each index i with $1 \leq i \leq n$, we approximate

$$\int_{x_{i-1}}^{x_i} f(x)\, dx \tag{7.13}$$

by some A_i and define E_i by

$$E_i \equiv \int_{x_{i-1}}^{x_i} f(x)\, dx - A_i. \tag{7.14}$$

Define $A \equiv \sum_{i=1}^n A_i$ and $E \equiv \sum_{i=1}^n E_i$, so that

$$\int_a^b f(x)\, dx - A = E.$$

The $E_i's$ are referred to as the *local errors*; E is called the *global error*. Once we have estimated the local errors, an estimate for the global error usually follows easily. We will look at two approximation methods, the Trapezoid Rule and Simpson's Rule.

For the Trapezoid Rule, consider a partition $P = \{x_0, \ldots, x_n\}$ of the interval $[a, b]$. For each index i with $1 \le i \le n$, we approximate the integral $\int_{x_{i-1}}^{x_i} f(x)\,dx$ by

$$A_i \equiv \frac{1}{2}(x_i - x_{i-1})(f(x_{i-1}) + f(x_i)).$$

If $f(x_i) \ge 0$ and $f(x_{i-1}) \ge 0$, the above A_i is simply the area of the trapezoid having vertices $(x_{i-1}, 0)$, $(x_{i-1}, f(x_{i-1}))$, $(x_i, f(x_i))$, and $(x_i, 0)$.

We first estimate the local error.

THEOREM 7.14   **The Local Error for the Trapezoid Rule**   Suppose that the function $f: [c, d] \to \mathbb{R}$ is continuous and that its restriction $f: (c, d) \to \mathbb{R}$ has two derivatives. Then there is a point ζ in the open interval (c, d) at which

$$\int_c^d f(x)\,dx - \frac{(d-c)(f(c) + f(d))}{2} = \frac{-(d-c)^3}{12} f''(\zeta). \qquad (7.15)$$

FIGURE 7.3

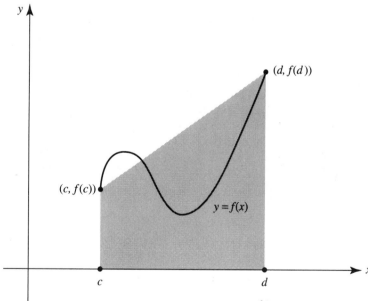

The Trapezoid Approximation of $\int_c^d f$

Proof   Let $m = (d+c)/2$ and $t_0 = (d-c)/2$, and define an auxiliary function $E: [0, t_0] \to \mathbb{R}$ by

$$E(t) = \left[\int_{m-t}^{m+t} f(x)\,dx \right] - t[f(m+t) + f(m-t)] \quad \text{for} \quad 0 \le t \le t_0.$$

Since $m + t_0 = d$ and $m - t_0 = c$, the left-hand side of (7.15) is precisely $E(t_0)$. Now define another function $H: [0, t_0] \to \mathbb{R}$ by

$$H(t) = E(t) - \left(\frac{t}{t_0}\right)^3 E(t_0) \quad \text{for} \quad 0 \le t \le t_0.$$

It follows from Proposition 7.2 that the function $E: [0, t_0] \to \mathbb{R}$ is continuous, so the function $H: [0, t_0] \to \mathbb{R}$ is also continuous. Moreover, from the Second Fundamental Theorem of Calculus and the Chain Rule, it follows that

$$E'(t) = f(m + t) + f(m - t) - [f(m + t) + f(m - t)] - t[f'(m + t) - f'(m - t)]$$
$$= -t[f'(m + t) - f'(m - t)] \quad \text{for} \quad 0 < t < t_0.$$

Hence

$$H'(t) = -t[f'(m + t) - f'(m - t)] - \frac{3t^2}{t_0^3} E(t_0) \quad \text{for} \quad 0 < t < t_0.$$

It is clear that $H(0) = H(t_0) = 0$. We may apply Rolle's Theorem to the function $H: [0, t_0] \to \mathbb{R}$ to choose a point t_* in $(0, t_0)$ at which $H'(t_*) = 0$; that is,

$$-t_*[f'(m + t_*) - f'(m - t_*)] - \frac{3t_*^2}{t_0^3} E(t_0) = 0.$$

Now apply the Mean Value Theorem to the function $f': [m - t_*, m + t_*] \to \mathbb{R}$ and choose a point ζ in $(m - t_*, m + t_*)$ at which

$$f'(m + t_*) - f'(m - t_*) = 2t_* f''(\zeta).$$

Substituting the last equality in the preceding equation, we arrive at

$$2t_*^2 \left[f''(\zeta) + \frac{3}{2t_0^3} E(t_0) \right] = 0.$$

But $t_* \ne 0$, so

$$E(t_0) = -\frac{2t_0^3}{3} f''(\zeta) = \frac{-(d - c)^3}{12} f''(\zeta) \qquad \blacksquare$$

THEOREM 7.15   **The Global Error for the Trapezoid Rule**   Suppose that the function $f: [a, b] \to \mathbb{R}$ is continuous and that its restriction $f: (a, b) \to \mathbb{R}$ has a bounded second derivative. For a partition $P = \{x_0, \ldots, x_n\}$ of the interval $[a, b]$,

$$\int_a^b f = \sum_{i=1}^n \frac{(x_i - x_{i-1})(f(x_{i-1}) + f(x_i))}{2} + E$$

with

$$|E| \le \frac{M \|P\|^2 (b - a)}{12}, \qquad (7.16)$$

where

$$M \equiv \sup\{|f''(x)| \mid x \text{ in } (a, b)\}.$$

Proof   For each index i such that $1 \leq i \leq n$, we may apply the local error estimate for the Trapezoid Rule to choose a point ζ_i in (x_{i-1}, x_i) at which

$$\int_{x_{i-1}}^{x_i} f = \frac{(x_i - x_{i-1})(f(x_i) + f(x_{i-1}))}{2} - \frac{(x_i - x_{i-1})^3 f''(\zeta_i)}{12}.$$

Sum these n equalities to see that the first formula in (7.16) holds, where

$$E = -\sum_{i=1}^n \frac{(x_i - x_{i-1})^3 f''(\zeta_i)}{12}.$$

However, by the Triangle Inequality and the definitions of $\|P\|$ and M,

$$|E| \leq \frac{\|P\|^2}{12} \sum_{i=1}^n (x_i - x_{i-1})|f''(\zeta_i)|$$

$$\leq \frac{\|P\|^2 M}{12} \sum_{i=1}^n (x_i - x_{i-1}) = \frac{M\|P\|^2(b-a)}{12}. \qquad \blacksquare$$

EXAMPLE 7.5   We apply the Trapezoid Rule to estimate $\ln 2 = \int_1^2 1/t\, dt$. Define $f(t) = 1/t$ for $1 \leq t \leq 2$, and note that

$$0 \leq f''(t) \leq 2 \quad \text{for} \quad 1 \leq t \leq 2.$$

For a natural number n, let P_n be the partition obtained by dividing the interval $[1,2]$ into n subintervals of equal length. Then (see Exercise 3),

$$\ln 2 = \frac{1}{n}\left[\frac{1}{2} + \frac{n}{n+1} + \frac{n}{n+2} + \cdots + \frac{n}{2n-1} + \frac{1}{4}\right] + E_n,$$

where

$$0 \leq E_n \leq \frac{1}{6n^2}.$$

Taking $n = 10$, a brief calculation yields .69 as a lower approximation of $\ln 2$, and the error is at most $1/600$; thus, $.69 < \ln 2 < .692$. $\qquad\square$

From the Local Error Estimate for the Trapezoid Rule, we note that the Trapezoid Rule gives the *exact value* of the integral when $f: \mathbb{R} \to \mathbb{R}$ has a line as its graph. Moreover, when

$$f''(x) \geq 0 \quad \text{for all } x \text{ in } (a,b),$$

which means that the function $f:[a,b] \to \mathbb{R}$ is convex, the Trapezoid Rule gives an *upper* approximation to the integral. Each of these observations is clear geometrically.

The second approximation method that we will consider is called Simpson's Rule. Though it is not as easy to motivate geometrically, this rule is, in general, more accurate than the Trapezoid Rule. Given an integrable function $f:[a,b] \to \mathbb{R}$ and a partition $P = \{x_0, \ldots, x_n\}$ of the interval $[a,b]$, for each index i with $1 \leq i \leq n$, Simpson's Rule approximates the integral $\int_{x_{i-1}}^{x_i} f$ by

$$A_i \equiv \frac{(x_i - x_{i-1})}{6}\left[f(x_{i-1}) + 4f\left(\frac{x_{i-1}+x_i}{2}\right) + f(x_i)\right]. \qquad (7.17)$$

One way to compare approximation methods is to see for what functions the approximation of the integral agrees precisely with the value of the integral. For the Trapezoid Rule, there is exact agreement provided that the function $f:[a, b] \to \mathbb{R}$ is a polynomial of degree less than 2; that is, the graph of $f:[a, b] \to \mathbb{R}$ is a line. We will show that for Simpson's Rule there is exact agreement provided that the function $f:[a, b] \to \mathbb{R}$ is a polynomial of degree less than 4.*

In order to derive the local error estimate for Simpson's Rule it is first convenient to note the following slight extension of Rolle's Theorem.

THEOREM 7.16   **A Generalized Rolle's Theorem**   Suppose that the function $g:[c, d] \to \mathbb{R}$ is continuous. For a natural number n, suppose that its restriction $g:(c, d) \to \mathbb{R}$ has $n + 1$ derivatives. Let x_0 be a point in (c, d) at which

$$g(x_0) = g'(x_0) = \cdots = g^{(n)}(x_0) = 0.$$

Then for each point $x \neq x_0$ in $[c, d]$ at which $g(x) = 0$, there is a point ζ strictly between x_0 and x at which

$$g^{(n+1)}(\zeta) = 0.$$

Proof   We will assume that $x > x_0$. If we apply Rolle's Theorem to the function $g:[x_0, x] \to \mathbb{R}$, we can choose a point z_1 in (x_0, x) at which $g'(z_1) = 0$. Now apply Rolle's Theorem to the function $g':[x_0, z_1] \to \mathbb{R}$ to choose a point z_2 in (x_0, z_1) at which $g''(z_2) = 0$. By continuing this procedure n times, we find a point $z_{n+1} = \zeta$ in (x_0, x) at which $g^{n+1}(\zeta) = 0$.   ∎

THEOREM 7.17   **The Local Error for Simpson's Rule**   Suppose that the function $f:[c, d] \to \mathbb{R}$ is continuous and that its restriction $f:(c, d) \to \mathbb{R}$ has four derivatives. Then there is a point ζ in the open interval (c, d) at which

$$\int_c^d f(x)\, dx - \frac{(d-c)}{6}\left[f(c) + 4f\left(\frac{c+d}{2}\right) + f(d)\right] = -\frac{1}{2880}(d-c)^5 f^{(4)}(\zeta).$$

$$(7.18)$$

Proof   Let $m = (c+d)/2$ and $t_0 = (d-c)/2$, and define the auxiliary function $E:[-t_0, t_0] \to \mathbb{R}$ by

$$E(t) = \int_{m-t}^{m+t} f - \frac{t}{3}[f(m+t) + 4f(m) + f(m-t)] \quad \text{for} \quad -t_0 \leq t \leq t_0.$$

---

*The formula in Simpson's Rule is motivated as follows: For a function $f:[c, d] \to \mathbb{R}$, there is a unique quadratic polynomial $p:\mathbb{R} \to \mathbb{R}$ that agrees with the function $f:[c, d] \to \mathbb{R}$, at $x = c$, $x = (c+d)/2$, and $x = d$, and it can be shown that for this polynomial,

$$\int_c^d p = \frac{(d-c)}{6}\left[f(c) + 4f\left(\frac{c+d}{2}\right) + f(d)\right].$$

Observe that the left-hand side of (7.18) is $E(t_0)$. Now define the function $H : [-t_0, t_0] \to \mathbb{R}$ by

$$H(t) = E(t) - \left(\frac{t}{t_0}\right)^5 E(t_0) \quad \text{for} \quad -t_0 \le t \le t_0. \tag{7.19}$$

Proposition 7.2 implies that the function $E : [-t_0, t_0] \to \mathbb{R}$ is continuous, so the function $H : [-t_0, t_0] \to \mathbb{R}$ is also continuous. It is clear that $H(0) = H(t_0) = 0$, and we will now show that $H'(0) = H''(0) = 0$ so that we can apply the Generalized Rolle's Theorem. We have the following straightforward calculation of derivatives at each point t in $(-t_0, t_0)$:

$$
\begin{aligned}
E'(t) &= f(m+t) + f(m-t) - \frac{1}{3}[f(m+t) + 4f(m) + f(m-t)] \\
&\quad - \frac{t}{3}[f'(m+t) - f'(m-t)] \\
&= \frac{2}{3}[f(m+t) - 2f(m) + f(m-t)] - \frac{t}{3}[f'(m+t) - f'(m-t)],
\end{aligned}
$$

$$
\begin{aligned}
E''(t) &= \frac{2}{3}[f'(m+t) - f'(m-t)] - \frac{1}{3}[f'(m+t) - f'(m-t)] \\
&\quad - \frac{t}{3}[f''(m+t) + f''(m-t)] \\
&= \frac{1}{3}[f'(m+t) - f'(m-t)] - \frac{t}{3}[f''(m+t) + f''(m-t)],
\end{aligned}
$$

and

$$E'''(t) = -\frac{t}{3}[f'''(m+t) - f'''(m-t)].$$

These calculations, together with (7.19), show that $H(0) = H'(0) = H''(0) = 0$ and that

$$H'''(t) = -\frac{t}{3}[f'''(m+t) - f'''(m-t)] - \frac{60t^2}{t_0^5}E(t_0) \quad \text{for} \quad -t_0 < t < t_0.$$

Consequently, since $H(t_0) = 0$, we can apply the Generalized Rolle's Theorem with $n = 2$ to choose a point t_* in $(0, t_0)$ at which $H'''(t_*) = 0$; that is,

$$-\frac{t_*}{3}[f'''(m+t_*) - f'''(m-t_*)] - \frac{60t_*^2}{t_0^5}E(t_0) = 0. \tag{7.20}$$

Finally, we can apply the Mean Value Theorem to the function $f''' : [m - t_*, m + t_*] \to \mathbb{R}$ to choose a point ζ in $(m - t_*, m + t_*)$ at which

$$f'''(m+t_*) - f'''(m-t_*) = 2t_* f^{(4)}(\zeta).$$

Substituting the last equality in (7.20) leads to

$$t_*^2 \left[-\frac{2}{3}f^{(4)}(\zeta) - \frac{60}{t_0^5}E(t_0) \right] = 0,$$

so since $t_* \ne 0$, we have

$$E(t_0) = \frac{-t_0^5}{90}f^{(4)}(\zeta). \tag{7.21}$$

However, $t_0 = (d - c)/2$, and since $E(t_0)$ is the left-hand side of (7.18), we see that (7.21) is the same as (7.18). ∎

COROLLARY 7.18

For a polynomial $p: \mathbb{R} \to \mathbb{R}$ of degree at most 3 and numbers $c < d$,

$$\int_c^d p(x)\, dx = \frac{1}{6}(d - c)\left[p(c) + 4p\left(\frac{c+d}{2}\right) + p(d) \right].$$

Proof Since $p^{(4)}(\zeta) = 0$ for every number ζ, the result immediately follows from the preceding theorem. ∎

THEOREM 7.19

The Global Error for Simpson's Rule Suppose that the function $f: [a, b] \to \mathbb{R}$ is continuous and that its restriction $f: (a, b) \to \mathbb{R}$ has a bounded fourth derivative. Let $P = \{x_0, \ldots, x_n\}$ be a partition of the interval $[a, b]$. Then

$$\int_a^b f = \frac{1}{6}\sum_{i=1}^n (x_i - x_{i-1})\left[f(x_i) + 4f\left(\frac{x_i + x_{i-1}}{2}\right) + f(x_{i-1}) \right] + E, \qquad (7.22)$$

with

$$|E| \le \frac{M\|P\|^4(b - a)}{2880},$$

where

$$M \equiv \sup\{|f^{(4)}(x)| \mid a < x < b\}.$$

Proof Let i be an index such that $1 \le i \le n$. We can apply the local error estimate for Simpson's Rule to choose a point ζ_i in (x_{i-1}, x_i) at which

$$\int_{x_{i-1}}^{x_i} f - \frac{(x_i - x_{i-1})}{6}\left[f(x_i) + 4f\left(\frac{x_i + x_{i-1}}{2}\right) + f(x_{i-1}) \right]$$

$$= -\frac{1}{2880}(x_i - x_{i-1})^5 f^{(4)}(\zeta_i).$$

Summing these n equalities, we see that (7.22) holds where

$$E = -\frac{1}{2880}\sum_{i=1}^n (x_i - x_{i-1})^5 f^{(4)}(\zeta_i).$$

However, the Triangle Inequality and the definitions of $\|P\|$ and M yield

$$|E| \le \frac{\|P\|^4}{2880}\sum_{i=1}^n (x_i - x_{i-1})|f^{(4)}(\zeta_i)|$$

$$\le \frac{M\|P\|^4}{2880}\sum_{i=1}^n (x_i - x_{i-1})$$

$$= \frac{M\|P\|^4(b - a)}{2880}.$$

∎

1. Use the First Fundamental Theorem of Calculus to compute each of the following integrals, then compute the approximations using the Trapezoid Rule and Simpson's Rule with the partition $P = \{c, d\}$. Then compare the actual errors generated against the error estimates provided by Theorems 7.14 and 7.17.

   (a) $\displaystyle\int_1^2 (2x + 3)\, dx$ $\qquad$ (b) $\displaystyle\int_0^1 x^2\, dx$

   (c) $\displaystyle\int_0^1 x^4\, dx$

2. For each of the following integrals, verify Corollary 7.18 by direct computation.

   (a) $\displaystyle\int_0^1 (x^2 + x^3)\, dx$ $\qquad$ (b) $\displaystyle\int_2^3 (x + 1)^2\, dx$

3. Suppose that the function $f : [a, b] \to \mathbb{R}$ is continuous and that its restriction $f : (a, b) \to \mathbb{R}$ has a bounded second derivative. Let n be a natural number and let P_n be the regular partition of $[a, b]$ into n subintervals of equal length. Show that

$$\int_a^b f(x)\, dx = \left(\frac{b-a}{n}\right)\left[\frac{f(a)}{2} + \sum_{k=1}^{n-1} f\left(a + \frac{k}{n}(b-a)\right) + \frac{f(b)}{2}\right] + E,$$

   where $\qquad$ $\displaystyle |E| \le \frac{(b-a)^3}{12n^2}\sup\{|f''(x)| \mid x \text{ in } (a, b)\}.$

4. Use Exercise 3 with $n = 3$ to estimate $\ln 4$ and give an upper bound for the error.
5. Use Exercise 3 with $n = 4$ to estimate $\int_0^1 \sqrt{1 + x^2}\, dx$ and give an upper bound for the error.
6. Use Simpson's Rule with $P = \{1, 3/2, 2\}$ to estimate $\ln 2$ and give an upper bound for the error.
7. An approximation rule similar to the Trapezoid Rule is the Midpoint Rule. This rule approximates the integral $\int_c^d f(x)\, dx$ by $(d - c)f([d + c]/2)$. Prove that if the function $f : [c, d] \to \mathbb{R}$ is continuous and its restriction $f : (c, d) \to \mathbb{R}$ has a second derivative, then for some point ζ in (c, d),

$$\int_c^d f(x)\, dx = (d - c)f\left(\frac{c + d}{2}\right) + \frac{1}{24}(d - c)^3 f''(\zeta).$$

   (*Hint:* Let $m = (c + d)/2$, let $t_0 = (d - c)/2$, and define

$$H(t) = \left[\int_{m-t}^{m+t} f\right] - 2t f(m) - \left(\frac{t}{t_0}\right)^3 \int_{m-t_0}^{m+t_0} f \quad \text{for} \quad -t_0 \le t \le t_0.$$

   Apply the Generalized Rolle's Theorem with $n = 1$ to the function $H : [-t_0, t_0] \to \mathbb{R}$.)
8. Find a global error estimate for the Midpoint Rule.
9. Use the local error estimates for the Midpoint Rule (see Exercise 7) and the Trapezoid Rule for the evaluation of

$$\int_{\ln a}^{\ln b} e^x\, dx$$

   to prove that if $0 < a < b$, then

$$\sqrt{ab} < \frac{b-a}{\ln b - \ln a} < \frac{a+b}{2}.$$

(The geometric mean is less than the logarithmic mean, which is less than the arithmetic mean.)

8

Approximation by Taylor Polynomials

8.1   Taylor Polynomials and Order of Contact

Polynomials are the simplest kind of functions. Accordingly, for a general function $f: D \to \mathbb{R}$, it is natural to seek a polynomial that is a good approximation of $f: D \to \mathbb{R}$.

DEFINITION   *Let I be an open interval containing the point x_0. Two functions $f: I \to \mathbb{R}$ and $g: I \to \mathbb{R}$ are said to have contact of order 0 at x_0 provided that $f(x_0) = g(x_0)$. For a natural number n, the functions $f: I \to \mathbb{R}$ and $g: I \to \mathbb{R}$ are said to have contact of order n at x_0 provided that $f: I \to \mathbb{R}$ and $g: I \to \mathbb{R}$ have n derivatives and*

$$f^{(k)}(x_0) = g^{(k)}(x_0) \quad for \quad 0 \le k \le n.$$

EXAMPLE 8.1 Define $f(x) = \sqrt{2 - x^2}$ and $g(x) = e^{1-x}$ for $0 < x < \sqrt{2}$. Then

$$f(1) = g(1) \quad \text{and} \quad f'(1) = g'(1), \quad \text{but} \quad f''(1) \neq g''(1).$$

Hence the functions $f: (0, \sqrt{2}) \to \mathbb{R}$ and $g: (0, \sqrt{2}) \to \mathbb{R}$ have contact of order 1 at $x_0 = 1$, but do not have contact of order 2 there. At the point $(1, 1)$, which lies on both graphs, the tangent lines to the functions are the same. $\square$

The following formula is clear: For each pair of nonnegative integers k and ℓ,

$$\frac{d^k}{dx^k}[(x - x_0)^\ell]\bigg|_{x=x_0} = \begin{cases} k! & \text{if } k = \ell \\ 0 & \text{if } k \neq \ell. \end{cases} \tag{8.1}$$

PROPOSITION 8.1 Let I be an open interval containing the point x_0 and n be a nonnegative integer. Suppose that the function $f: I \to \mathbb{R}$ has n derivatives. Then there is a unique polynomial of degree at most n that has contact of order n with the function $f: I \to \mathbb{R}$ at x_0. This polynomial is defined by the formula

$$p_n(x) = f(x_0) + f'(x_0)(x - x_0) + \cdots + \frac{f^{(k)}(x_0)}{k!}(x - x_0)^k + \cdots + \frac{f^{(n)}(x_0)}{n!}(x - x_0)^n. \tag{8.2}$$

Proof If $n = 0$, the result is clear; there is only one constant function whose value at x_0 is $f(x_0)$. So suppose that $n \geq 1$. From formula (8.1) it follows that

$$\frac{d^k}{dx^k}[p_n(x)]\bigg|_{x=x_0} = f^{(k)}(x_0) \quad \text{for} \quad 0 \leq k \leq n,$$

so the function $f: I \to \mathbb{R}$ and the polynomial $p_n: I \to \mathbb{R}$ have contact of order n at x_0.

It remains to prove uniqueness. However, if we take a general polynomial of degree at most n, written in powers of $(x - x_0)$ as

$$p(x) = c_0 + c_1(x - x_0) + \cdots + c_n(x - x_0)^n,$$

then, again from formula (8.1), it is clear that

$$\frac{d^k}{dx^k}[p(x)]\bigg|_{x=x_0} = k!c_k \quad \text{for} \quad 0 \leq k \leq n,$$

so that if the polynomial $p: I \to \mathbb{R}$ has contact of order n with $f: I \to \mathbb{R}$ at x_0, we must have $k!c_k = f^{(k)}(x_0)$ for $0 \leq k \leq n$; that is, $p = p_n$. ∎

The polynomial $p_n: \mathbb{R} \to \mathbb{R}$ defined by (8.2) is called the nth *Taylor polynomial* for the function $f: I \to \mathbb{R}$ at the point x_0.

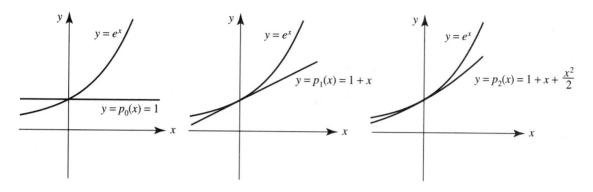

FIGURE 8.1

EXAMPLE 8.2   Define $f(x) = e^x$ for all x. For each natural number k, $f^{(k)}(x) = e^x$ for all x. Thus the nth Taylor polynomial for $f: \mathbb{R} \to \mathbb{R}$ at the point $x = 0$ is defined by

$$p_n(x) = 1 + x + \cdots + \frac{x^n}{n!}. \qquad \square$$

EXAMPLE 8.3   Define $f(x) = \ln(1 + x)$ for $x > -1$. For each natural number k,

$$f^{(k)}(x) = \frac{(-1)^{k+1}(k-1)!}{(1+x)^k} \qquad \text{for all } x > -1.$$

Thus the nth Taylor polynomial for $f: (-1, \infty) \to \mathbb{R}$ at $x = 0$ is defined by

$$p_n(x) = x - \frac{x^2}{2} + \cdots + \frac{(-1)^{n+1}}{n} x^n. \qquad \square$$

EXAMPLE 8.4   Define $f(x) = \cos x$ for all x. For each natural number k, $f^{(2k)}(x) = (-1)^k \cos x$, and $f^{(2k+1)}(x) = (-1)^{k+1} \sin x$ for all x. Thus, for each nonnegative integer n, the Taylor polynomials for the cosine function at $x = 0$ are given by

$$p_{2n}(x) = p_{2n+1}(x) = 1 - \frac{x^2}{2!} + \cdots + \frac{(-1)^n}{(2n)!} x^{2n}. \qquad \square$$

EXAMPLE 8.5   Define $f(x) = \sqrt{x}$ for $x > 0$. For each natural number k,

$$f^{(k)}(x) = \frac{1}{2}\left(\frac{1}{2} - 1\right) \cdots \left(\frac{1}{2} - k + 1\right) x^{1/2-k} \qquad \text{for all } x > 0.$$

Thus the third Taylor polynomial for the function $f: (0, \infty) \to \mathbb{R}$ at $x = 1$ is

$$p_3(x) = 1 + \frac{1}{2}(x - 1) - \frac{1}{8}(x - 1)^2 + \frac{1}{16}(x - 1)^3. \qquad \square$$

For two functions that have a high order of contact at a point, it is reasonable to expect that near this point the difference between them will be small. In particular, if I is an open interval containing the point x_0 and $p_n: \mathbb{R} \to \mathbb{R}$ is the nth Taylor polynomial for the function $f: I \to \mathbb{R}$ at x_0, one expects that for another point x in I, the difference

$f(x) - p_n(x)$ can be estimated and shown to be small if x is close to x_0 and n is large. What is really surprising is that frequently it happens that

$$\lim_{n \to \infty} [f(x) - p_n(x)] = 0$$

even when the point x is far away from x_0. As we will show in Section 8.6, it can also happen that the Taylor polynomials for certain functions do not provide good approximations at any point x other than x_0, no matter how large the index n is.

We define $R_n(x) \equiv f(x) - p_n(x)$ for all x in I, so that

$$f(x) = p_n(x) + R_n(x) \quad \text{for all } x \text{ in } I,$$

and call $R_n : I \to \mathbb{R}$ the nth *remainder.* In Section 8.2, we will begin a rigorous analysis of this remainder.

EXERCISES

1. For each of the following pairs of functions, determine its highest order of contact at the indicated point:
   (a) $f(x) = x^2$ and $g(x) = \sin x$ for all x; $x_0 = 0$.
   (b) $f(x) = e^{x^2}$ and $g(x) = 1 + 2x^2$ for all x; $x_0 = 0$.
   (c) $f(x) = \ln x$ and $g(x) = (x - 1)^3 + \ln x$ for all $x > 0$; $x_0 = 1$.
2. Compute the third Taylor polynomial for each of the following functions at the indicated point:
   (a) $f(x) = \int_0^x (1/1 + t^2)\, dt$ for all x; $x_0 = 0$.
   (b) $f(x) = \sin x$ for all x; $x_0 = 0$.
   (c) $f(x) = \sqrt{2 - x}$ for all $x < 2$; $x_0 = 1$.
3. Define $f(x) = x^6 e^x$ for all x. Find the sixth Taylor polynomial for the function $f : \mathbb{R} \to \mathbb{R}$ at $x = 0$.
4. Suppose that the function $f : \mathbb{R} \to \mathbb{R}$ has three derivatives and that the third Taylor polynomial at $x = 0$ is $p_3(x) = 1 + 4x - x^2 + x^3/6$. Show that there is an open interval containing the point 0 such that $f : I \to \mathbb{R}$ is positive, strictly increasing, and strictly concave.
5. Suppose that the function $f : \mathbb{R} \to \mathbb{R}$ has a second derivative and that

$$\begin{cases} f''(x) + f(x) = e^{-x} & \text{for all } x \\ f(0) = 0 \quad \text{and} \quad f'(0) = 2. \end{cases}$$

   Find the fourth Taylor polynomial for $f : \mathbb{R} \to \mathbb{R}$ at $x = 0$.

8.2 The Lagrange Remainder Theorem

For easy reference, we record again here Theorem 4.21 as the following lemma:

LEMMA 8.2   Let I be an open interval and n be a nonnegative integer, and suppose that the function $f: I \to \mathbb{R}$ has n derivatives. Suppose also that at the point x_0 in I,

$$f^{(k)}(x_0) = 0 \quad \text{for} \quad 0 \le k \le n - 1.$$

Then for each point $x \ne x_0$ in I, there is a point c strictly between x and x_0 at which

$$f(x) = \frac{f^{(n)}(c)}{n!}(x - x_0)^n.$$

The general remainder theorem is a simple extension of the above lemma.

THEOREM 8.3   **The Lagrange Remainder Theorem**   Let I be an open interval containing the point x_0 and let n be a nonnegative integer. Suppose that the function $f: I \to \mathbb{R}$ has $n + 1$ derivatives. Then for each point x in I, there is a point c strictly between x and x_0 such that

$$f(x) = \sum_{k=0}^{n} \frac{f^{(k)}(x_0)}{k!}(x - x_0)^k + \frac{f^{(n+1)}(c)}{(n+1)!}(x - x_0)^{n+1}. \qquad (8.3)$$

Proof   Consider the nth Taylor polynomial for the function $f: I \to \mathbb{R}$ at x_0,

$$p_n(x) = \sum_{k=0}^{n} \frac{f^{(k)}(x_0)}{k!}(x - x_0)^k.$$

Since the functions $f: I \to \mathbb{R}$ and $p_n: I \to \mathbb{R}$ have contact of order n at x_0, it follows that if we define the function $E: I \to \mathbb{R}$ by

$$E(x) = f(x) - p_n(x) \quad \text{for all } x \text{ in } I,$$

then

$$E(x_0) = E'(x_0) = \cdots = E^{(n)}(x_0) = 0.$$

According to the above lemma, if x is in I, then there is a point c strictly between x and x_0 such that

$$E(x) = \frac{E^{(n+1)}(c)}{(n+1)!}(x - x_0)^{n+1}.$$

But since $p_n: \mathbb{R} \to \mathbb{R}$ is a polynomial of degree at most n,

$$E^{(n+1)}(c) = f^{(n+1)}(c),$$

so from the previous equation it follows that

$$f(x) - p_n(x) = E(x) = \frac{f^{(n+1)}(c)}{(n+1)!}(x - x_0)^{n+1}. \qquad \blacksquare$$

COROLLARY 8.4   Suppose that $p: \mathbb{R} \to \mathbb{R}$ is a polynomial of degree at most n, and let x_0 be any point. Then the nth Taylor polynomial for $p: \mathbb{R} \to \mathbb{R}$ at x_0 equals $p: \mathbb{R} \to \mathbb{R}$ itself.

Proof Fix $x \neq x_0$. According to the Lagrange Remainder Theorem, we may choose a point c strictly between x and x_0 such that

$$p(x) - p_n(x) = \frac{p^{(n+1)}(c)}{(n+1)!}(x - x_0)^{n+1}.$$

But $p: \mathbb{R} \to \mathbb{R}$ is a polynomial of degree at most n, so $p^{n+1}(c) = 0$. Thus, $p_n(x) = p(x)$. ∎

We will use the Lagrange Remainder Theorem to get a precise estimate of the number e. First, we will derive the following crude estimate of e.

LEMMA 8.5
$$e < 3. \tag{8.4}$$

Proof Since the function ln: $(0, \infty) \to \mathbb{R}$ is strictly increasing,

$$e < 3 \quad \text{if and only if} \quad 1 = \ln e < \ln 3.$$

However, using the integral representation of the natural logarithm, we have

$$\ln 3 = \int_1^3 \frac{1}{t}\, dt$$

$$= \int_1^2 \frac{1}{t}\, dt + \int_2^3 \frac{1}{t}\, dt$$

$$= \int_1^0 \frac{(-1)}{2 - s}\, ds + \int_0^1 \frac{1}{2 + s}\, ds$$

$$= \int_0^1 \frac{4}{4 - s^2}\, ds.$$

But $4/(4 - s^2) > 1$ if $0 < s \leq 1$, so

$$\ln 3 = \int_0^1 \frac{4}{4 - s^2}\, ds > 1. \qquad \blacksquare$$

THEOREM 8.6 For each natural number n and each nonzero number x, there is a point c strictly between 0 and x such that

$$e^x = 1 + x + \frac{x^2}{2!} + \cdots + \frac{x^n}{n!} + \frac{e^c}{(n+1)!}x^{n+1}. \tag{8.5}$$

In particular,

$$0 < e^x - \left[1 + x + \cdots + \frac{x^n}{n!}\right] < \frac{3}{(n+1)!} \quad \text{if} \quad 0 \leq x \leq 1. \tag{8.6}$$

Proof Formula (8.5) follows directly from the Lagrange Remainder Theorem and Example 8.2. According to the preceding lemma, $e < 3$, and since the function $\exp\colon \mathbb{R} \to \mathbb{R}$ is strictly increasing, it follows that

$$1 = e^0 \le e^c < e^1 < 3 \quad \text{if} \quad 0 < c < x \le 1.$$

Thus estimate (8.6) follows from (8.5). ∎

PROPOSITION 8.7 The number e is irrational.

Proof We will argue by contradiction. Suppose that e is rational. Then there are natural numbers n_0 and m_0 such that $e = n_0/m_0$. Then (8.6), with $x = 1$, becomes

$$0 < \frac{n_0}{m_0} - \left[2 + \frac{1}{2!} + \cdots + \frac{1}{n!}\right] \le \frac{3}{(n+1)!} \quad \text{for every natural number } n.$$

Now multiply this inequality by $n!$ to get

$$0 < \frac{n!n_0}{m_0} - n!\left[2 + \frac{1}{2!} + \cdots + \frac{1}{n!}\right] \le \frac{3}{n+1} \quad \text{for every natural number } n.$$

However, if $n > 3$ and $n \ge m_0$ the above inequality implies the existence of an integer in the interval $(0, 3/4)$. This contradiction proves that e is irrational. ∎

THEOREM 8.8 For each natural number n and each number $x > -1$, there is a number c strictly between 0 and x such that

$$\ln(1 + x) = x - \frac{x^2}{2} + \cdots + \frac{(-1)^{n+1}}{n}x^n + \frac{(-1)^n}{(n+1)(1+c)^{n+1}}x^{n+1}. \tag{8.7}$$

Proof Formula (8.7) follows from the Lagrange Remainder Theorem and Example 8.3. ∎

Recall that in Section 2.2, we showed that the sequence

$$\left\{1 + \frac{1}{2} + \cdots + \frac{1}{n}\right\}$$

is strictly increasing but unbounded above; that is, the harmonic series diverges. In Section 5.1, we showed that the sequence $\{\ln(n + 1)\}$ is strictly increasing but unbounded above. In fact, these two results are equivalent.

PROPOSITION 8.9

$$\lim_{n \to \infty}\left[1 + \frac{1}{2} + \cdots + \frac{1}{n} - \ln(n + 1)\right] = \gamma \quad \text{where} \quad 0 < \gamma \le 1.$$

Proof For each natural number n, define

$$c_n = 1 + \frac{1}{2} + \cdots + \frac{1}{n} - \ln(n + 1).$$

We will show that the sequence $\{c_n\}$ is strictly increasing and bounded above by 1. The conclusion of the proposition will then be a consequence of the Monotone Convergence Theorem.

For each natural number k, $\ln(1 + 1/k) = \ln(1 + k) - \ln(k)$. Thus for $n \geq 2$, we may write each c_n as the sum

$$c_n = (1 - \ln 2) + \sum_{k=2}^{n} \left(\frac{1}{k} - \ln\left(1 + \frac{1}{k}\right) \right).$$

Now from formula (8.7), with $n = 1$ and $x = 1/k$, it follows (see Exercise 4) that

$$0 < \frac{1}{k} - \ln\left(1 + \frac{1}{k}\right) < \frac{1}{2k^2} \quad \text{for every natural number } k. \tag{8.8}$$

Thus the sequence $\{c_n\}$ is strictly increasing; it remains to be shown that it is bounded above. In order to do so, we first observe that (8.8) implies that for each integer $n \geq 2$,

$$\sum_{k=2}^{n} \left[\frac{1}{k} - \ln\left(1 + \frac{1}{k}\right) \right] \leq \sum_{k=2}^{n} \left[\frac{1}{2k^2} \right]$$

$$\leq \sum_{k=2}^{n} \left[\frac{1}{2k(k-1)} \right]$$

$$= \frac{1}{2} \sum_{k=2}^{n} \left[\frac{1}{k-1} - \frac{1}{k} \right]$$

$$= \frac{1}{2} \left[1 - \frac{1}{n} \right]$$

$$\leq \frac{1}{2}.$$

On the other hand, (8.8), with $k = 1$, asserts that $1 - \ln 2 < 1/2$, so for every natural number $n \geq 2$,

$$c_n = [1 - \ln 2] + \sum_{k=2}^{n} \left[\frac{1}{k} - \ln\left(1 + \frac{1}{k}\right) \right] \leq \frac{1}{2} + \frac{1}{2} = 1. \qquad \blacksquare$$

The above number γ is called *Euler's constant*. It is unknown whether γ is rational or irrational.

EXERCISES

1. Prove that

$$1 + \frac{x}{2} - \frac{x^2}{8} < \sqrt{1+x} < 1 + \frac{x}{2} \quad \text{if} \quad x > 0.$$

In particular, show that $1.375 < \sqrt{2} < 1.5$.

2. Prove that

$$1 + \frac{x}{3} - \frac{x^2}{9} < (1+x)^{1/3} < 1 + \frac{x}{3} \quad \text{if} \quad x > 0.$$

3. Expand the polynomial $p(x) = x^5 - x^3 + x$ in powers of $(x-1)$.

4. Use formula (8.7) to prove that

$$0 < \frac{1}{k} - \ln\left(1 + \frac{1}{k}\right) < \frac{1}{2k^2} \quad \text{for every natural number } k.$$

5. Prove that for every pair of numbers a and b,

$$|\sin(a+b) - (\sin a + b\cos a)| \le \frac{b^2}{2}.$$

6. Let I be an open interval containing the point x_0 and let n be a natural number. Suppose that the function $f: I \to \mathbb{R}$ has $n+1$ derivatives. Show that the Lagrange Remainder Theorem is equivalent to the following: For each number h such that $x_0 + h$ is in I, there is a number θ, strictly between 0 and 1, such that

$$f(x_0 + h) = \sum_{k=0}^{n} \frac{f^{(k)}(x_0)}{k!} h^k + \frac{1}{(n+1)!} f^{(n+1)}(x_0 + \theta h) h^{n+1}.$$

7. Using Corollary 8.4, show that if $p: \mathbb{R} \to \mathbb{R}$ is a polynomial of degree n and the number x_0 is a root of $p(x)$—that is, $p(x_0) = 0$—then there is a polynomial $q: \mathbb{R} \to \mathbb{R}$ such that $p(x) = (x - x_0)q(x)$.

8. A number x_0 is said to be a *root of order k of the polynomial* $p: \mathbb{R} \to \mathbb{R}$ provided that k is a natural number such that $p(x) = (x - x_0)^k r(x)$, where $r: \mathbb{R} \to \mathbb{R}$ is a polynomial and $r(x_0) \ne 0$. Prove that x_0 is a root of order k of the polynomial $p: \mathbb{R} \to \mathbb{R}$ if and only if

$$p(x_0) = p'(x_0) = \cdots = p^{(k-1)}(x_0) = 0 \quad \text{and} \quad p^{(k)}(x_0) \ne 0.$$

9. (a) For nonnegative integers n and k such that $k \le n$, show that

$$(1+x)^n = 1 + \binom{n}{1}x + \binom{n}{2}x^2 + \cdots + \binom{n}{n-1}x^{n-1} + x^n.$$

   (b) Use (a) to prove the Binomial Formula: For each natural number n and any pair of numbers a and b,

$$(a+b)^n = \sum_{k=0}^{n} \binom{n}{k} a^k b^{n-k}.$$

10. Suppose that each of the functions $f: \mathbb{R} \to \mathbb{R}$ and $g: \mathbb{R} \to \mathbb{R}$ has $n+1$ continuous derivatives. Prove that $f: \mathbb{R} \to \mathbb{R}$ and $g: \mathbb{R} \to \mathbb{R}$ have contact of order n at 0 if and only if

$$\lim_{x \to 0} \frac{f(x) - g(x)}{x^n} = 0.$$

11. Use the Lagrange Remainder Theorem to verify the following criterion for identifying local extreme points: Let I be an open interval containing the point x_0 and let n be a natural number. Suppose that the function $f: I \to \mathbb{R}$ has $n+1$ derivatives and that $f^{(n+1)}: I \to \mathbb{R}$ is continuous. Assume that $f^{(k)}(x_0) = 0$ if $1 \le k \le n$, and that $f^{(n+1)}(x_0) \ne 0$.
   (a) If $n+1$ is even and $f^{(n+1)}(x_0) > 0$, then x_0 is a local minimizer.
   (b) If $n+1$ is even and $f^{(n+1)}(x_0) < 0$, then x_0 is a local maximizer.

(c)   If $n + 1$ is odd, then x_0 is neither a local maximizer nor a local minimizer.
12.   Use Theorem 8.8 to show that if $0 < x \leq 1$, then

$$\ln(1 + x) = \sum_{k=1}^{\infty} \frac{(-1)^{k+1}}{k} x^k.$$

13.   Let I be an open interval containing the point x_0, and suppose that the function $f : I \to \mathbb{R}$ has a continuous third derivative with $f'''(x) > 0$ for all x in I.
   (a)   Prove that if $x_0 + h$ is in I, there is a unique number $\theta = \theta(h)$ in the interval $(0, 1)$ such that

$$f(x_0 + h) = f(x_0) + f'(x_0)h + f''(x_0 + \theta h)\frac{h^2}{2}.$$

   (b)   Prove that

$$\lim_{h \to 0} \theta(h) = \frac{1}{3}.$$

8.3   The Convergence of Taylor Polynomials

For a sequence of numbers $\{a_k\}$ that is indexed by the nonnegative integers, we define

$$s_n = \sum_{k=0}^{n} a_k \quad \text{for every nonnegative integer } n,$$

and obtain a new sequence $\{s_n\}$. The sequence $\{s_n\}$ is called the *sequence of partial sums* for the series $\sum_{k=0}^{\infty} a_k$, and a_k is called the kth *term* of the series $\sum_{k=0}^{\infty} a_k$. We write

$$\sum_{k=0}^{\infty} a_k = \lim_{n \to \infty} \left[\sum_{k=1}^{n} a_k \right]$$

if the sequence $\{s_n\}$ converges. If the sequence $\{s_n\}$ does not converge, then we say that the series $\sum_{k=0}^{\infty} a_k$ *diverges*.

Let I be an open interval containing the point x_0 and suppose that the function $f : I \to \mathbb{R}$ has derivatives of all orders. The nth Taylor polynomial for $f : I \to \mathbb{R}$ at x_0 is defined by

$$p_n(x) = \sum_{k=0}^{n} \frac{f^{(k)}(x_0)}{k!}(x - x_0)^k.$$

In conformity with the above series notation, if x is a point in I at which

$$\lim_{n \to \infty} p_n(x) = f(x), \tag{8.9}$$

we write
$$f(x) = \sum_{k=0}^{\infty} \frac{f^{(k)}(x_0)}{k!}(x - x_0)^k. \tag{8.10}$$

This formula is called a *Taylor series expansion* of the function $f: I \to \mathbb{R}$ about the point x_0. By its very definition, (8.10) holds at x if and only if

$$\lim_{n \to \infty} [f(x) - p_n(x)] = 0. \tag{8.11}$$

In this section, we will use the Lagrange Remainder Theorem to determine when $\lim_{n\to\infty}[f(x) - p_n(x)] = 0$. First, we will prove a useful preliminary result.

LEMMA 8.10   For any number c,

$$\lim_{n \to \infty} \frac{c^n}{n!} = 0.$$

Proof   Choose k to be a natural number such that $k \geq 2|c|$. Then if $n \geq k$,

$$0 \leq \left| \frac{c^n}{n!} \right|$$

$$= \left[\frac{|c|}{1} \cdots \frac{|c|}{k} \right] \left[\frac{|c|}{k+1} \cdots \frac{|c|}{n} \right]$$

$$\leq |c|^k \left(\frac{1}{2} \right)^{n-k}$$

$$= (2|c|)^k \left(\frac{1}{2} \right)^n$$

But $\lim_{n\to\infty}(1/2)^n = 0$, and so $\lim_{n\to\infty} c^n/n! = 0$ also. ∎

THEOREM 8.11   Let I be an open interval containing the point x_0 and suppose that the function $f: I \to \mathbb{R}$ has derivatives of all orders. Suppose also that there are positive numbers r and M such that the interval $[x_0 - r, x_0 + r]$ is contained in I and for every natural number n and every point x in $[x_0 - r, x_0 + r]$,

$$|f^{(n)}(x)| \leq M^n. \tag{8.12}$$

Then

$$f(x) = \sum_{k=0}^{\infty} \frac{f^{(k)}(x_0)}{k!}(x - x_0)^k \quad \text{if} \quad |x - x_0| \leq r. \tag{8.13}$$

Proof   The nth Taylor polynomial $p_n: \mathbb{R} \to \mathbb{R}$ for $f: I \to \mathbb{R}$ at x_0 is defined by

$$p_n(x) = \sum_{k=0}^{n} \frac{f^{(k)}(x_0)}{k!}(x - x_0)^k,$$

and, according to the Lagrange Remainder Theorem, for each point x in I, there is a point c strictly between x and x_0 such that

$$|f(x) - p_n(x)| = \frac{|f^{(n+1)}(c)|}{(n+1)!}|x - x_0|^{n+1}.$$

In view of inequality (8.12), it follows that for every natural number n and every point x in $[x_0 - r, x_0 + r]$,

$$|f(x) - p_n(x)| \le \frac{M^{n+1}}{(n+1)!}|x - x_0|^{n+1} \le \frac{c^{n+1}}{(n+1)!}, \tag{8.14}$$

where $c = Mr$. According to Lemma 8.10, $\lim_{n\to\infty} c^n/n! = 0$. Thus, from (8.14), we see that

$$\lim_{n\to\infty}[f(x) - p_n(x)] = 0 \quad \text{if} \quad |x - x_0| \le r.$$

This is precisely assertion (8.13). ∎

COROLLARY 8.12

$$e^x = \sum_{k=0}^{\infty}\frac{x^k}{k!} \quad \text{for all } x. \tag{8.15}$$

$$\cos x = \sum_{k=0}^{\infty}\frac{(-1)^k}{(2k)!}x^{2k} \quad \text{for all } x. \tag{8.16}$$

Proof First, we will prove (8.15). Define $f(x) = e^x$ for all x, and let $x_0 = 0$. Fix $r > 0$. If we define $M = e^r$, it follows that for every natural number n and every point x in the interval $[-r, r]$,

$$|f^{(n)}(x)| \le M \le M^n.$$

According to Theorem 8.11, if $|x| < r$, then

$$f(x) = \sum_{k=0}^{\infty}\frac{x^k}{k!}.$$

But the choice of $r > 0$ was arbitrary, and so the Taylor expansion (8.15) is verified.

The proof of (8.16) is similar. We define $f(x) = \cos x$ for all x and observe that $|f^{(n)}(x)| \le 1$ for every natural number n and every number x. Then the proof proceeds as above. ∎

EXERCISES

1. Show that the Taylor expansion of the following functions at the given points converges for all points x:
   (a) $f(x) = \sin x$ at the point $x_0 = 0$.
   (b) $f(x) = \cos x$ at the point $x_0 = \pi$.
2. Define $f(x) = 1/x$ if $0 < x < 2$.
   (a) Find $p_n : \mathbb{R} \to \mathbb{R}$, the nth Taylor polynomial at $x_0 = 1$.
   (b) Use the Geometric Sum Formula to show that for every natural number n,

   $$f(x) - p_n(x) = \frac{(1-x)^{n+1}}{x} \quad \text{if} \quad 0 < x < 2.$$

   (c) Use part (b) to prove that

   $$f(x) = \sum_{k=0}^{\infty}\frac{f^{(k)}(1)}{k!}(x-1)^k \quad \text{if} \quad |x-1| < 1.$$

3. Suppose that the function $F: \mathbb{R} \to \mathbb{R}$ has derivatives of all orders and that

$$\begin{cases} F'(x) - F(x) = 0 & \text{for all } x \\ F(0) = 2. \end{cases}$$

Find a formula for the coefficients of the nth Taylor polynomial for $F: \mathbb{R} \to \mathbb{R}$ at $x = 0$. Show that the Taylor expansion converges at every point.

4. Suppose that the function $F: \mathbb{R} \to \mathbb{R}$ has derivatives of all orders and that

$$\begin{cases} F''(x) - F'(x) - F(x) = 0 & \text{for all } x \\ F(0) = 1 \quad \text{and} \quad F'(0) = 1. \end{cases}$$

Find a recursive formula for the coefficients of the nth Taylor polynomial for $F: \mathbb{R} \to \mathbb{R}$ at $x = 0$. Show that the Taylor expansion converges at every point.

5. For a pair of numbers α and β, suppose that the function $f: \mathbb{R} \to \mathbb{R}$ has derivatives of all orders and that

$$f''(x) + \alpha f'(x) + \beta f(x) = 0 \quad \text{for all } x.$$

(a) Show that for every natural number n,

$$f^{(n+2)}(x) + \alpha f^{(n+1)}(x) + \beta f^{(n)}(x) = 0 \quad \text{for all } x.$$

(b) Use (a) to show that

$$f(x) = \sum_{k=0}^{\infty} \frac{f^{(k)}(x_0)}{k!}(x - x_0)^k \quad \text{for all } x.$$

8.4 A Power Series for the Logarithm

In this section, we will analyze the validity of the Taylor expansion of the natural logarithm. It turns out that in order to do so, it is convenient first to translate the natural logarithm and consider the function $f: (-1, \infty) \to \mathbb{R}$ defined by

$$f(x) = \ln(1 + x) \quad \text{if} \quad x > -1.$$

A direct calculation of derivatives shows that for each natural number k,

$$f^{(k)}(x) = \frac{(-1)^{k+1}(k-1)!}{(1+x)^k} \quad \text{for all } x > -1.$$

In particular, the nth Taylor polynomial for $f: (-1, \infty) \to \mathbb{R}$ at $x = 0$ is defined by

$$p_n(x) = x - \frac{x^2}{2} + \cdots + \frac{(-1)^{n+1}}{n}x^n. \tag{8.17}$$

Rather than trying to use the Lagrange Remainder Theorem to study the difference $f(x) - p_n(x)$, it is better to jointly exploit the integral formula for the natural logarithm and the Geometric Sum Formula in order to derive a more explicit formula for the difference. Indeed, observe that for each natural number n, the Geometric Sum Formula

$$\frac{1}{1-r} = 1 + r + \cdots + r^{n-1} + \frac{r^n}{1-r} \quad \text{if} \quad r \neq 1$$

becomes, if one substitutes $1 - t$ for r,

$$\frac{1}{t} = 1 + (1 - t) + \cdots + (1 - t)^{n-1} + \frac{(1 - t)^n}{t} \quad \text{if} \quad t \neq 0.$$

Thus, using the linearity of integration and the integral representation of the logarithm, we have

$$\ln(1 + x) = \int_1^{1+x} \frac{1}{t}\, dt$$

$$= \int_1^{1+x} [1 + (1 - t) + \cdots + (1 - t)^{n-1}]\, dt + \int_1^{1+x} \frac{(1 - t)^n}{t}\, dt$$

$$= x - \frac{x^2}{2} + \cdots + \frac{(-1)^{n+1}}{n} x^n + \int_1^{1+x} \frac{(1 - t)^n}{t}\, dt$$

$$= P_n(x) + \int_1^{1+x} \frac{(1 - t)^n}{t}\, dt \quad \text{if} \quad x > -1. \tag{8.18}$$

THEOREM 8.13

$$\ln(1 + x) = \sum_{k=1}^{\infty} \frac{(-1)^{k+1} x^k}{k} \quad \text{if} \quad -1 < x \leq 1. \tag{8.19}$$

Proof   Formula (8.18) implies that for each natural number n,

$$\ln(1 + x) - \sum_{k=1}^{n} (-1)^{k+1} \frac{x^k}{k} = \int_1^{1+x} \frac{(1 - t)^n}{t}\, dt \quad \text{if} \quad x > -1.$$

Thus, to verify (8.19), we must show that

$$\lim_{n \to \infty} \left[\int_1^{1+x} \frac{(1 - t)^n}{t}\, dt \right] = 0 \quad \text{if} \quad -1 < x \leq 1. \tag{8.20}$$

First, suppose $0 \leq x \leq 1$. Then for each natural number n,

$$\left| \int_1^{1+x} \frac{(1 - t)^n}{t}\, dt \right| = \int_1^{1+x} \frac{(t - 1)^n}{t}\, dt$$

$$\leq \int_1^{1+x} (t - 1)^n\, dt$$

$$= \frac{x^{n+1}}{n + 1}$$

$$\leq \frac{1}{n + 1}.$$

Since $\lim_{n\to\infty} 1/n = 0$, we see that (8.20) holds if $0 \le x \le 1$.

Now suppose that $-1 < x < 0$. Then for each natural number n,

$$\left| \int_1^{1+x} \frac{(1-t)^n}{t} \, dt \right| = \int_{1+x}^1 \frac{(1-t)^n}{t} \, dt$$

$$\le \frac{1}{1+x} \int_{1+x}^1 (1-t)^n \, dt$$

$$= \left(\frac{1}{1+x} \right) \frac{|x|^{n+1}}{n+1}$$

$$\le \left(\frac{1}{1+x} \right) \frac{1}{n+1}.$$

Since $\lim_{n\to\infty} 1/n = 0$, we also see that (8.20) holds if $-1 < x < 0$. ∎

In spite of the fact that the function $f(x) = \ln(1+x)$ has derivatives of all orders for all $x > -1$, the Taylor expansion (8.19) is not valid if $x > 1$. Indeed, in view of (8.18) and Bernoulli's Inequality, it follows that if $x > 1$ and n is any natural number, then

$$| \ln(1+x) - p_n(x) | = \int_1^{1+x} \frac{(1-t)^n}{t} \, dt$$

$$\ge \frac{1}{1+x} \int_1^{1+x} (1-t)^n \, dt$$

$$= \frac{1}{1+x} \cdot \frac{x^{n+1}}{n+1}$$

$$= \frac{1}{1+x} \cdot \frac{[1+x-1]^{n+1}}{n+1}$$

$$\ge \frac{1}{1+x} \cdot \frac{1+(n+1)(x-1)}{n+1}$$

$$\ge \frac{x-1}{1+x}.$$

Thus, $\lim_{n\to\infty} [f(x) - p_n(x)] \ne 0$ if $x > 1$.

EXERCISES

1. Prove that for each natural number n,

$$| \ln(1+x) - p_n(x) | \le \frac{1}{1+x} \cdot \frac{|x|^{n+1}}{n+1} \quad \text{if} \quad -1 < x \le 0,$$

and

$$| \ln(1+x) - p_n(x) | \le \frac{x^{n+1}}{n+1} \quad \text{if} \quad 0 \le x \le 1.$$

Estimate $\ln(1.1)$ with an error of at most 10^{-4}.

2. Show that with the error estimates in the previous exercise, we need $n = 10{,}000$ to estimate $\ln 2$ with an error bound of 10^{-4}. How does the identity $\ln 2 = \ln 4/3 - \ln 2/3$ allow us to estimate $\ln 2$ more efficiently?

3. Explain how the identity

$$s = \left(1 + \frac{s-1}{s+1}\right) \Big/ \left(1 - \frac{s-1}{s+1}\right) \quad \text{if} \quad s \neq 0$$

allows us to efficiently compute $\ln(1+x)$ if $-1 < x < 1$ and x is close to -1 or 1.

4. Verify the integral inequalities in the proof of Theorem 8.13.

5. At what points x in the interval $(-1, 1]$ can one use the Lagrange Remainder Theorem to verify the expansion

$$\ln(1+x) = \sum_{k=1}^{\infty} (-1)^{k+1} \frac{x^k}{k!}?$$

8.5 The Cauchy Integral Remainder Formula and the Binomial Expansion

If I is an open interval containing the point x_0 and the function $f: I \to \mathbb{R}$ is differentiable, then for each point x in I, there is a point c strictly between x and x_0 such that

$$f(x) = f(x_0) + f'(c)(x - x_0). \tag{8.21}$$

If we further assume that the derivative $f': I \to \mathbb{R}$ is continuous, then, by the First Fundamental Theorem of Calculus,

$$f(x) = f(x_0) + \int_{x_0}^{x} f'(t)\, dt. \tag{8.22}$$

The proof of the Lagrange Remainder Theorem was rooted in the Lagrange Mean Value Theorem as expressed in (8.21). The proof of the following Remainder Theorem will exploit the First Fundamental Theorem of Calculus as expressed in (8.22).

THEOREM 8.14 **The Cauchy Integral Remainder Formula** Let I be an open interval containing the point x_0 and n be a natural number. Suppose that the function $f: I \to \mathbb{R}$ has $n+1$ derivatives and that $f^{(n+1)}: I \to \mathbb{R}$ is continuous. Then for each point x in I,

$$f(x) = \sum_{k=0}^{n} \frac{f^{(k)}(x_0)}{k!}(x - x_0)^k + \frac{1}{n!} \int_{x_0}^{x} f^{(n+1)}(t)(x-t)^n\, dt. \tag{8.23}$$

Proof   By the First Fundamental Theorem of Calculus,

$$f(x) = f(x_0) + \int_{x_0}^{x} f'(t)\,dt. \tag{8.24}$$

Integrating by parts, we see that

$$\int_{x_0}^{x} f'(t)\,dt = -\int_{x_0}^{x} f'(t)\frac{d}{dt}(x-t)\,dt$$

$$= -f'(t)(x-t)\bigg|_{t=x_0}^{t=x} + \int_{x_0}^{x} f''(t)(x-t)\,dt \tag{8.25}$$

$$= f'(x_0)(x-x_0) + \int_{x_0}^{x} f''(t)(x-t)\,dt.$$

From (8.24) and (8.25) we obtain (8.23) when $n = 1$. The general formula follows by induction. The inductive step depends on observing that if $1 \le k \le n-1$, then

$$\frac{1}{k!}\int_{x_0}^{x} f^{(k+1)}(t)(x-t)^k\,dt = \frac{-1}{(k+1)!}\int_{x_0}^{x} f^{(k+1)}(t)\frac{d}{dt}[(x-t)^{k+1}]\,dt$$

$$= \frac{1}{(k+1)!}f^{(k+1)}(x_0)(x-x_0)^{k+1}$$

$$+ \frac{1}{(k+1)!}\int_{x_0}^{x} f^{(k+2)}(t)(x-t)^{k+1}\,dt. \qquad \blacksquare$$

Recall from Section 1.3 that for each natural number n and pair of numbers a and b, we have the

Binomial Formula

$$(a+b)^n = \sum_{k=0}^{n}\binom{n}{k}a^{n-k}b^k. \tag{8.26}$$

This formula can be proved directly, using elementary algebra. Another proof can be given by first applying Corollary 8.4 to show that

$$(1+x)^n = \sum_{k=0}^{n}\binom{n}{k}x^k \quad \text{for all } x. \tag{8.27}$$

Then, if $a \ne 0$, substitute $x = b/a$ in (8.27) and multiply by a^n to obtain (8.26).

We will now extend formula (8.27) to the case of exponents that are not necessarily natural numbers. Of course, if β is not a nonnegative integer, then the function $(1+x)^\beta$ is not a polynomial, so the right-hand side of (8.27), rather than being a polynomial, will be an infinite series. In order to find an infinite series expansion of $(1+x)^\beta$, it is useful to extend the definition of the binomial coefficients. For each natural number n, and each number β, we define

$$\binom{\beta}{k} \equiv \frac{\beta(\beta-1)\cdots(\beta-k+1)}{k!},$$

and define

$$\binom{\beta}{0} \equiv 1.$$

THEOREM 8.15 **Newton's Binomial Expansion** Let β be any real number. Then

$$(1+x)^\beta = \sum_{k=0}^\infty \binom{\beta}{k} x^k \quad \text{if} \quad -1 < x < 1. \tag{8.28}$$

To verify the Binomial Expansion is to prove that

$$\lim_{n\to\infty}\left[(1+x)^\beta - \sum_{k=0}^n \binom{\beta}{k} x^k\right] = 0 \quad \text{if} \quad -1 < x < 1.$$

The crucial step in the proof is to show that the Binomial Expansion is a Taylor expansion about $x = 0$ so that the Cauchy Integral Remainder Formula provides an integral representation for the remainders. We summarize this step in the following lemma.

LEMMA 8.16 For any number β and any natural number n, if $x > -1$, then

$$(1+x)^\beta - \sum_{k=0}^n \binom{\beta}{k} x^k = (n+1)\binom{\beta}{n+1}\int_0^x (1+t)^{\beta-n-1}(x-t)^n\,dt. \tag{8.29}$$

Proof Define the function $f:(-1,\infty) \to \mathbb{R}$ by

$$f(x) = (1+x)^\beta \quad \text{if} \quad x > -1.$$

Observe that for each natural number k,

$$f^{(k)}(x) = \beta(\beta-1)\cdots(\beta-k+1)(1+x)^{\beta-k} \quad \text{if} \quad x > -1,$$

so that

$$\frac{f^{(k)}(x)}{k!} = \binom{\beta}{k}(1+x)^{\beta-k}$$

and, in particular,

$$\frac{f^{(k)}(0)}{k!} = \binom{\beta}{k}.$$

Thus, the nth Taylor polynomial for $f:(-1,\infty) \to \mathbb{R}$ at $x = 0$ is

$$p_n(x) = \sum_{k=0}^n \binom{\beta}{k} x^k.$$

According to the Cauchy Integral Remainder Theorem, for each natural number n and each number $x > -1$,

$$f(x) - p_n(x) = \frac{1}{n!} \int_0^x f^{(n+1)}(t)(x - t)^n \, dt$$

$$= \frac{1}{n!} \int_0^x \binom{\beta}{n+1}(n + 1)!(1 + t)^{\beta-n-1}(x - t)^n \, dt$$

$$= (n + 1)\binom{\beta}{n+1} \int_0^x (1 + t)^{\beta-n-1}(x - t)^n \, dt. \qquad \blacksquare$$

In order to analyze the behavior of the difference (8.29) when n is large, it is convenient first to prove the following lemma, which will also be useful in Chapter 9.

LEMMA 8.17   **The Ratio Lemma for Sequences**   Suppose that $\{c_n\}$ is a sequence of nonzero numbers that has the property that

$$\lim_{n\to\infty} \frac{|c_{n+1}|}{|c_n|} = \ell.$$

(i) If $\ell < 1$, then

$$\lim_{n\to\infty} c_n = 0.$$

(ii) If $\ell > 1$, then the sequence $\{c_n\}$ is unbounded.

Proof   First, suppose that $0 \le \ell < 1$. Define $\alpha = (\ell + 1)/2$. Since $\ell < \alpha$, we may choose a natural number N such that

$$\frac{|c_{n+1}|}{|c_n|} \le \alpha \quad \text{for all integers } n \ge N.$$

For each natural number k, if we successively apply the preceding inequality k times, we see that

$$|c_{N+k}| \le |c_N|\alpha^k.$$

Hence, if we define $M = |c_N|\alpha^{-N}$, it follows that

$$|c_n| \le M\alpha^n \quad \text{for all integers } n \ge N.$$

However, $0 \le \alpha < 1$, so $\lim_{n\to\infty} \alpha^n = 0$. The preceding inequality implies that $\lim_{n\to\infty} c_n = 0$.

Now suppose that $\ell > 1$. Define $\beta = (\ell + 1)/2$. Since $\beta < \ell$, we may choose a natural number N such that

$$\frac{|c_{n+1}|}{|c_n|} \ge \beta \quad \text{for all integers } n \ge N.$$

Hence, for each natural number k,

$$|c_{N+k}| \ge |c_N|\beta^k, \qquad (8.30)$$

and since, by Bernoulli's Inequality,

$$\beta^k \ge 1 + k(\beta - 1),$$

(8.30) implies that the sequence $\{c_n\}$ is unbounded. $\blacksquare$

LEMMA 8.18 Let β be any number. Then

$$\lim_{n\to\infty} n\binom{\beta}{n}x^n = 0 \quad \text{if} \quad |x| < 1.$$

Proof Observe that for each natural number n,

$$(n+1)\binom{\beta}{n+1}\Big/ n\binom{\beta}{n} = \frac{n+1}{n}\cdot\frac{\beta-n}{n+1}.$$

Thus,

$$\lim_{n\to\infty}\left|(n+1)\binom{\beta}{n+1}|x|^{n+1}\Big/ n\binom{\beta}{n}|x|^n\right| = |x|.$$

The conclusions follow immediately from the Ratio Lemma. ∎

Proof of Newton's Binomial Expansion First, we consider the case when $-1 < x < 0$. When we write $(x-t) = -(t-x)$ and interchange the limits of integration, formula (8.29) becomes

$$f(x) - p_n(x) = (-1)^{n+1}(n+1)\binom{\beta}{n+1}\int_x^0\left(\frac{t-x}{1+t}\right)^n(1+t)^{\beta-1}\,dt. \quad (8.31)$$

But observe that

$$0 \le \left(\frac{t-x}{1+t}\right) \le -x = |x| \quad \text{if} \quad -1 < x \le t \le 0,$$

so for each natural number n,

$$0 \le \left(\frac{t-x}{1+t}\right)^n(1+t)^{\beta-1} \le |x|^n \quad \text{if} \quad -1 < x \le t \le 0. \quad (8.32)$$

From (8.31) and (8.32), it follows that for each natural number n,

$$|f(x)-p_n(x)| = (n+1)\binom{\beta}{n+1}\int_x^0\left(\frac{t-x}{1+t}\right)^n(1+t)^{\beta-1}\,dt$$

$$\le (n+1)\binom{\beta}{n+1}\int_x^0 |x|^n\,dt$$

$$\le (n+1)\binom{\beta}{n+1}|x|^n\int_x^0 dt$$

$$= (n+1)\binom{\beta}{n+1}|x|^{n+1} \quad \text{if} \quad -1 < x < 0. \quad (8.33)$$

According to Lemma 8.18, if $|x| < 1$,

$$\lim_{n\to\infty}(n+1)\binom{\beta}{n+1}|x|^{n+1} = 0,$$

so from (8.33) we conclude that the Binomial Expansion is valid if $-1 < x < 0$.

It remains to consider the case when $0 < x < 1$. In this case, from (8.29), we obtain

$$|f(x) - p_n(x)| = (n+1)\binom{\beta}{n+1}\int_0^x (1+t)^{\beta-n-1}(x-t)^n \, dt$$

$$= (n+1)\binom{\beta}{n+1}\int_0^x \left[\frac{x-t}{1+t}\right]^n (1+t)^{\beta-1} \, dt$$

$$\leq (n+1)\binom{\beta}{n+1}x^n \int_0^x (1+t)^{\beta-1} \, dt$$

$$= (n+1)\binom{\beta}{n+1}x^{n+1}\left[\frac{(1+x)^\beta - 1}{\beta x}\right]. \qquad (8.34)$$

Again using Lemma 8.18, from (8.34) we conclude that the Binomial Expansion is valid if $0 < x < 1$. ∎

EXERCISES

1. Verify all of the details in the derivations of the inequalities (8.32), (8.33), and (8.34).
2. Show that for $\beta = -1$, the Binomial Expansion reduces to the Geometric Series.
3. Show that for β a natural number, the Binomial Expansion reduces to the Binomial Formula.
4. Prove that if the functions $g : [a, b] \to \mathbb{R}$ and $h : [a, b] \to \mathbb{R}$ are continuous with $h(x) \geq 0$ for all x in $[a, b]$, then there is a point c in (a, b) such that

$$\int_a^b h(x)g(x) \, dx = g(c)\int_a^b h(x) \, dx.$$

5. Use Exercise 4 to show that the Cauchy Integral Remainder Theorem implies the Lagrange Remainder Theorem if $f^{n+1} : I \to \mathbb{R}$ is assumed to be continuous.
6. Apply the Cauchy Integral Remainder Theorem in the analysis of the expansion

$$\ln(1+x) = \sum_{k=1}^{\infty}(-1)^{k+1}\frac{x^k}{k} \quad \text{if} \quad -1 < x \leq 1.$$

7. Show that for $0 \leq x < 1$, the Lagrange Remainder Theorem can be used to verify the Binomial Expansion.
8. Prove that the Binomial Expansion does not converge if $|x| > 1$.
9. For what values of r does the sequence $\{n^3 r^n\}$ converge?

8.6   An Infinitely Differentiable Function That Is Not Analytic

We will now present an explicit example of a function $f : \mathbb{R} \to \mathbb{R}$ that has derivatives of all orders and yet the only point at which its Taylor expansion about $x = 0$ agrees with its functional value is at $x = 0$.

THEOREM 8.19   Define

$$f(x) = \begin{cases} e^{-(1/x^2)} & \text{if } x \neq 0 \\ 0 & \text{if } x = 0. \end{cases}$$

Then the function $f: \mathbb{R} \to \mathbb{R}$ has derivatives of all orders. However, the only point at which

$$f(x) = \sum_{k=0}^{\infty} \frac{f^{(k)}(0)}{k!} x^k \qquad (8.35)$$

is at $x = 0$.

Proof   To prove the theorem it will suffice to prove that $f: \mathbb{R} \to \mathbb{R}$ has derivatives of all orders and that for each natural number n, $f^{(n)}(0) = 0$. Once this is proven, simply observe that the right-hand side of (8.35) is identically zero, and $f(x) = 0$ if and only if $x = 0$.

Step 1: We claim that for any polynomial $q: \mathbb{R} \to \mathbb{R}$,

$$\lim_{x \to 0} q\left(\frac{1}{x}\right) e^{-(1/x^2)} = 0. \qquad (8.36)$$

In order to verify this, it suffices to show that for each natural number n,

$$\lim_{x \to 0} \frac{e^{-(1/x^2)}}{x^n} = 0. \qquad (8.37)$$

Indeed, let n be a natural number. According to (8.5),

$$e^b > \frac{b^n}{n!} \quad \text{if} \quad b > 0,$$

so that

$$e^{(1/x^2)} \geq \frac{1}{n! x^{2n}} \quad \text{if} \quad x \neq 0,$$

and hence

$$0 \leq \left| \frac{e^{-(1/x^2)}}{x^n} \right| \leq n! |x|^n \quad \text{if} \quad x \neq 0.$$

This inequality implies (8.37), which in turn implies (8.36).

Step 2: We will argue by induction to show that for each natural number n, there is a polynomial $q_n: \mathbb{R} \to \mathbb{R}$ such that

$$f^{(n)}(x) = q_n\left(\frac{1}{x}\right) e^{-(1/x^2)} \quad \text{if} \quad x \neq 0. \qquad (8.38)$$

Indeed, $f'(x) = (2/x^3)e^{-(1/x^2)}$ if $x \neq 0$, so (8.38) holds when $n = 1$, where $q_1(t) = 2t^3$. Suppose (8.38) holds with $n = k$. Then

$$f^{(k+1)}(x) = \left[q_k'\left(\frac{1}{x}\right)\left(\frac{-1}{x^2}\right) + q_k\left(\frac{1}{x}\right)\left(\frac{2}{x^3}\right) \right] e^{-(1/x^2)} \quad \text{if} \quad x \neq 0,$$

so (8.38) holds if $n = k + 1$ where $q_{k+1}(t) = q_k'(t)(-t^2) + q_k(t)(2t^3)$. The Principle of Mathematical Induction implies that (8.38) holds for all natural numbers.

From step 2 it follows that the function $f: \mathbb{R} \to \mathbb{R}$ has derivatives of all orders at every point $x \neq 0$. To complete the proof, we will show, again by induction, that for each natural number n,

$$f^{(n)}(0) = 0. \tag{8.39}$$

Indeed, if $n = 1$, then, using (8.36) with $q(t) = t$ for all t, it follows that

$$\lim_{x \to 0} \frac{f(x) - f(0)}{x} = \lim_{x \to 0} \frac{1}{x} e^{-(1/x^2)} = 0.$$

Now suppose that k is a natural number such that $f^{(k)}(0) = 0$. Then, using (8.38), together with (8.36) with $q(t) = t q_k(t)$ for all t, it follows that

$$\lim_{x \to 0} \frac{f^{(k)}(x) - f^{(k)}(0)}{x} = \lim_{x \to 0} \frac{1}{x} q_k \left(\frac{1}{x} \right) e^{-(1/x^2)} = 0,$$

so $f^{(k+1)}(0) = 0$. The Principle of Mathematical Induction implies that for each natural number n, $f^{(n)}(0) = 0$. ∎

A function $g: \mathbb{R} \to \mathbb{R}$ that has derivatives of all orders is said to be *infinitely differentiable*. A function $g: \mathbb{R} \to \mathbb{R}$ that has derivatives of all orders such that

$$g(x) = \sum_{k=0}^{\infty} \frac{g^{(k)}(0) x^k}{k!} \quad \text{for all } x$$

is said to be *analytic*. We have exhibited a function $f: \mathbb{R} \to \mathbb{R}$ that is infinitely differentiable and not analytic.

EXERCISES

1. Let the function $f: \mathbb{R} \to \mathbb{R}$ be as in Theorem 8.19. Explicitly compute $f''(x)$.

2. Let the function $f: \mathbb{R} \to \mathbb{R}$ be as in Theorem 8.19. Show that there is no positive number M such that for each natural number n,

$$|f^{(n)}(x)| \leq M^n \quad \text{for all } x.$$

3. For n a natural number, a function $f: \mathbb{R} \to \mathbb{R}$ is said to be n *times continuously differentiable* provided that $f: \mathbb{R} \to \mathbb{R}$ has an nth derivative and $f^{(n)}: \mathbb{R} \to \mathbb{R}$ is continuous. Define

$$h(x) = \int_0^x |t| \, dt \quad \text{for all } x.$$

Show that the function $h: \mathbb{R} \to \mathbb{R}$ is once continuously differentiable but is not twice continuously differentiable. For each natural number n, find a function that is n times continuously differentiable but is not $n + 1$ times continuously differentiable.

4. Suppose that the function $g: \mathbb{R} \to \mathbb{R}$ has derivatives of all orders, and that for each natural number n, there are positive numbers number c_n and δ_n such that

$$|g(x)| \leq c_n |x|^n \quad \text{if} \quad |x| < \delta_n.$$

Prove that for each natural number n, $g^{(n)}(0) = 0$.

8.7   The Weierstrass Approximation Theorem

As we have seen in Section 8.6, even if a function has derivatives of all orders, the Taylor polynomial for the function computed at a point x_0 in its domain may not provide a good approximation for the function at any point other than x_0. Nevertheless, there is the following remarkable theorem.

THEOREM 8.20   **The Weierstrass Approximation Theorem**   Let I be a closed and bounded interval and suppose that the function $f: I \to \mathbb{R}$ is continuous. Then for each positive number ϵ, there is a polynomial $p: \mathbb{R} \to \mathbb{R}$ such that

$$|f(x) - p(x)| < \epsilon \quad \text{for all points } x \text{ in } I. \tag{8.40}$$

What is remarkable about this theorem is that there is no assumption about differentiability. For instance, we allow the possibility that there is no point at which the function $f: I \to \mathbb{R}$ is differentiable. Of course, the polynomial that satisfies (8.40) will not, in general, be a Taylor polynomial.

The proof of the Approximation Theorem, which we will present, is due to Bernstein and is quite ingenious. At its roots lie the following three identities:

For each natural number n and any number x,

$$\sum_{k=0}^{n} \binom{n}{k} x^k (1 - x)^{n-k} = 1, \tag{8.41}$$

$$\sum_{k=0}^{n} \frac{k}{n} \binom{n}{k} x^k (1 - x)^{n-k} = x, \tag{8.42}$$

and if $n \geq 2$,

$$\sum_{k=0}^{n} \frac{k(k - 1)}{n(n - 1)} \binom{n}{k} x^k (1 - x)^{n-k} = x^2. \tag{8.43}$$

The first identity (8.41) follows from the Binomial Formula, formula (8.26), by setting $a = x$ and $b = 1 - x$. Identities (8.42) and (8.43) are consequences of (8.41). Indeed, if in the identity (8.41) we replace n by $n - 1$ and multiply both sides by x, then since

$$\binom{n - 1}{k - 1} = \frac{k}{n} \binom{n}{k} \quad \text{if} \quad 1 \leq k \leq n,$$

we obtain (8.42). Similarly, if in the identity (8.41) we replace n by $n - 2$ and multiply both sides by x^2, then since

$$\binom{n - 2}{k - 2} = \frac{k(k - 1)}{n(n - 1)} \binom{n}{k} \quad \text{if} \quad 2 \leq k \leq n,$$

we obtain (8.43).

For a natural number n, and an integer k such that $0 \leq k \leq n$, it is notationally convenient to define

$$g_k(x) = x^k (1 - x)^{n-k} \quad \text{for all } x \text{ in } \mathbb{R}.$$

LEMMA 8.21   For each number x and each natural number $n \geq 2$,

$$\sum_{k=0}^{n} \left(x - \frac{k}{n} \right)^2 \binom{n}{k} x^k (1-x)^{n-k} = \frac{x(1-x)}{n}. \tag{8.44}$$

Proof   For each integer $n \geq 2$, it follows from (8.41) and (8.42) that

$$\sum_{k=0}^{n} \left(x - \frac{k}{n} \right)^2 \binom{n}{k} g_k(x) = \sum_{k=0}^{n} \left[x^2 - \frac{2xk}{n} + \frac{k^2}{n^2} \right] \binom{n}{k} g_k(x)$$

$$= x^2 \sum_{k=0}^{n} \binom{n}{k} g_k(x) - 2x \sum_{k=0}^{n} \frac{k}{n} \binom{n}{k} g_k(x) + \sum_{k=0}^{n} \frac{k^2}{n^2} \binom{n}{k} g_k(x)$$

$$= x^2 - 2x^2 + \sum_{k=0}^{n} \frac{k^2}{n^2} \binom{n}{k} g_k(x).$$

On the other hand, from (8.42) and (8.43) we have

$$\sum_{k=0}^{n} \frac{k^2}{n^2} \binom{n}{k} g_k(x) = \frac{n-1}{n} \sum_{k=0}^{n} \frac{k^2}{n(n-1)} \binom{n}{k} g_k(x)$$

$$= \frac{n-1}{n} \sum_{k=0}^{n} \left[\frac{k(k-1)}{n(n-1)} + \frac{k}{n(n-1)} \right] \binom{n}{k} g_k(x)$$

$$= \left[\frac{n-1}{n} \right] \left[x^2 + \frac{x}{n-1} \right].$$

Hence,

$$\sum_{k=0}^{n} \left(x - \frac{k}{n} \right)^2 \binom{n}{k} g_k(x) = x^2 - 2x^2 + \left[\frac{n-1}{n} \right] \left[x^2 + \frac{x}{n-1} \right] = \frac{x(1-x)}{n}. \quad \blacksquare$$

Proof of Weierstrass Approximation Theorem   We will first consider the case when $I = [0, 1]$; the general case follows easily from this case. Let $\epsilon > 0$. According to Theorem 3.14, the function $f: I \to \mathbb{R}$ is uniformly continuous. Hence we can choose $\delta > 0$ such that

$$|f(u) - f(v)| < \frac{\epsilon}{2} \quad \text{for all points } u \text{ and } v \text{ in } I \text{ such that } |u - v| \leq \delta. \tag{8.45}$$

Also, it follows from the Extreme Value Theorem that the function $f: I \to \mathbb{R}$ is bounded. Thus we can choose a number $M > 0$ such that

$$|f(x)| \leq M \quad \text{for all } x \text{ in } I. \tag{8.46}$$

Using the Archimedean Property of $\mathbb{R}$, we can select a natural number n such that

$$n > \frac{4M}{\epsilon \delta^2}. \tag{8.47}$$

Define the polynomial $p: \mathbb{R} \to \mathbb{R}$ by

$$p(x) = \sum_{k=0}^{n} f\left(\frac{k}{n}\right)\binom{n}{k}x^k(1-x)^{n-k} \quad \text{for all } x.$$

We will show that for this choice of polynomial, the required approximation property (8.40) holds. Indeed, let x be a point in I. Then if $0 \le k \le n$, either $|x - k/n| < \delta$ or $|x - k/n| \ge \delta$. If $|x - k/n| < \delta$, it follows from (8.45) that $|f(x) - f(k/n)| < \epsilon/2$. If $|x - k/n| \ge \delta$, then, in view of (8.46),

$$\left| f(x) - f\left(\frac{k}{n}\right)\right| \le 2M \le \frac{2M}{\delta^2}\left(x - \frac{k}{n}\right)^2.$$

Thus, $\quad \left| f(x) - f\left(\frac{k}{n}\right)\right| \le \frac{\epsilon}{2} + \frac{2M}{\delta^2}\left(x - \frac{k}{n}\right)^2 \quad \text{for} \quad 0 \le k \le n. \quad (8.48)$

From (8.41) it follows that

$$f(x) = \sum_{k=0}^{n} f(x)\binom{n}{k}x^k(1-x)^{n-k},$$

so $\quad f(x) - p(x) = \sum_{k=0}^{n}\left[f(x) - f\left(\frac{k}{n}\right)\right]\binom{n}{k}x^k(1-x)^{n-k}.$

Using the Triangle Inequality, (8.48), (8.41), and (8.44), it follows that

$$|f(x) - p(x)| \le \sum_{k=0}^{n}\left| f(x) - f\left(\frac{k}{n}\right)\right| \binom{n}{k}x^k(1-x)^{n-k}$$

$$\le \sum_{k=0}^{n}\left[\frac{\epsilon}{2} + \frac{2M}{\delta^2}\left(x - \frac{k}{n}\right)^2\right]\binom{n}{k}x^k(1-x)^{n-k}$$

$$= \frac{\epsilon}{2} + \frac{2M}{\delta^2}\sum_{k=0}^{n}\left(x - \frac{k}{n}\right)^2\binom{n}{k}x^k(1-x)^{n-k}$$

$$= \frac{\epsilon}{2} + \frac{2M}{n\delta^2}x(1-x)$$

$$< \frac{\epsilon}{2} + \frac{2M}{n\delta^2}.$$

Consequently, since n satisfies (8.47), $|f(x) - p(x)| < \epsilon$.

This proves the theorem if $I = [0, 1]$. Now let $I = [a, b]$. Define $g(t) = a + t(b - a)$ if $0 \le t \le 1$. Then the composite function $f \circ g: [0, 1] \to \mathbb{R}$ is continuous. By what we have just proven, there is a polynomial $q: \mathbb{R} \to \mathbb{R}$ such that $|f(g(t)) - q(t)| < \epsilon$ for all points t in $[0, 1]$. Now define $p(x) = q((x - a)/(b - a))$ for all x. Then $p: \mathbb{R} \to \mathbb{R}$ is a polynomial for which the approximation property (8.40) holds. ∎

EXERCISES

1. Show that if $n \geq k \geq 1$, then

$$\frac{k}{n}\binom{n}{k} = \binom{n-1}{k-1}.$$

   Use this, together with (8.41) with n replaced by $n-1$, to verify (8.42).

2. Show that if $n \geq k \geq 2$, then

$$\frac{k(k-1)}{n(n-1)}\binom{n}{k} = \binom{n-2}{k-2}.$$

   Use this, together with (8.41) with n replaced by $n-2$, to verify (8.43).

3. In the proof of the Approximation Theorem, where did we use the fact that $g_k(x) \geq 0$ for all x in $[0, 1]$ and $0 \leq k \leq n$?

4. Show that the Approximation Theorem does not hold if we replace I by $\mathbb{R}$, by showing that if $f(x) = e^x$ for all x, then $f: \mathbb{R} \to \mathbb{R}$ cannot be uniformly approximated by polynomials.

5. Define $f(x) = |x - 1/2|$ for $0 \leq x \leq 1$. Use the proof of the Approximation Theorem to find an explicit polynomial $p: \mathbb{R} \to \mathbb{R}$ such that $|f(x) - p(x)| < 1/4$ for all x in $[0, 1]$.

6. Verify the assertion about the composition that was made on the last line of the proof of the Approximation Theorem.

7. Suppose that the function $h: [-1, 1] \to \mathbb{R}$ is continuous. Prove that there is a sequence $\{p_k: \mathbb{R} \to \mathbb{R}\}$ of polynomials having the property that

$$h(x) = \sum_{k=1}^{\infty} p_k(x) \quad \text{for all points } x \text{ in } [-1, 1].$$

The Convergence of Sequences and Series of Functions

9.1   Sequences and Series of Numbers

In Chapter 2, we studied the convergence of sequences of numbers. In particular, in Section 2.2 we proved the following important result.

THEOREM 9.1   **The Monotone Convergence Theorem**   A monotone sequence of numbers converges if and only if it is bounded.

This is a criterion for convergence that is intrinsic to the sequence itself; it does not require any information about the proposed limit. But the Monotone Convergence Theorem does require that the sequence be monotone. As the sequence $\{(-1)^n\}$ shows, in general it is not true that any bounded sequence converges. We will now establish a criterion for convergence that applies to *all* sequences of numbers.

DEFINITION *A sequence of numbers $\{a_n\}$ is said to be a Cauchy sequence provided that for each positive number ϵ there is a natural number N such that*

$$|a_n - a_m| < \epsilon \quad if \quad n \geq N \quad and \quad m \geq N.$$

We will prove that a sequence of numbers converges if and only if it is a Cauchy sequence. This too is a criterion for convergence that is intrinsic to the sequence itself; it does not require any information about the proposed limit. Moreover, monotonicity is not required. We will prove this result in stages.

PROPOSITION 9.2   Every convergent sequence is Cauchy.

Proof   Suppose that $\{a_n\}$ is a sequence that converges to the number a. Let $\epsilon > 0$. We need to find a natural number N such that

$$|a_n - a_m| < \epsilon \quad if \quad n \geq N \quad and \quad m \geq N.$$

But since $\{a_n\}$ converges to a, we may choose a natural number N such that

$$|a_k - a| < \frac{\epsilon}{2} \quad for\ every\ integer\ k \geq N.$$

Thus, if $n \geq N$ and $m \geq N$, the Triangle Inequality implies that

$$|a_n - a_m| = |(a_n - a) + (a - a_m)|$$

$$\leq |a_n - a| + |a_m - a|$$

$$< \frac{\epsilon}{2} + \frac{\epsilon}{2} = \epsilon. \qquad \blacksquare$$

LEMMA 9.3   Every Cauchy sequence is bounded.

Proof   Suppose that $\{a_n\}$ is a Cauchy sequence. For $\epsilon = 1$, we can choose a natural number N such that

$$|a_n - a_m| < 1 \quad if \quad n \geq N \quad and \quad m \geq N.$$

In particular, we have

$$|a_n - a_N| < 1 \quad for\ all\ integers\ n \geq N.$$

But, by the Reverse Triangle Inequality,

$$|a_n| - |a_N| \leq |a_n - a_N| \quad for\ every\ natural\ number\ n.$$

Consequently, we see that

$$|a_n| \leq |a_N| + 1 \quad for\ all\ integers\ n \geq N.$$

Define $M = \max\{|a_N| + 1, |a_1|, |a_2|, \ldots, |a_{N-1}|\}$. Then

$$|a_n| \leq M \quad for\ every\ natural\ number\ n. \qquad \blacksquare$$

THEOREM 9.4   **The Cauchy Convergence Criterion for Sequences**   A sequence of numbers converges if and only if it is a Cauchy sequence.

Proof   According to Proposition 9.2, every convergent sequence is a Cauchy sequence. The converse remains to be proven. Suppose that $\{a_n\}$ is a Cauchy sequence. The preceding lemma asserts that $\{a_n\}$ is bounded. Thus, by the Bolzano-Weierstrass Theorem, $\{a_n\}$ has a subsequence $\{a_{n_k}\}$ that converges to a number a.

We claim that the whole sequence $\{a_n\}$ converges to a. Indeed, let $\epsilon > 0$. We need to find a natural number N such that

$$|a_n - a| < \epsilon \quad \text{for all integers } n \geq N.$$

Since $\{a_n\}$ is a Cauchy sequence, we can choose a natural number N such that

$$|a_n - a_m| < \frac{\epsilon}{2} \quad \text{if} \quad n \geq N \quad \text{and} \quad m \geq N. \tag{9.1}$$

On the other hand, since the subsequence $\{a_{n_k}\}$ converges to a, there is a natural number K such that

$$|a_{n_k} - a| < \frac{\epsilon}{2} \quad \text{if} \quad k \geq K. \tag{9.2}$$

Now choose any natural number k such that $k \geq K$ and $n_k \geq N$. Using the inequalities (9.1) and (9.2), together with the Triangle Inequality, it follows that if $n \geq N$, then

$$|a_n - a| = |(a_n - a_{n_k}) + (a_{n_k} - a)|$$
$$\leq |a_n - a_{n_k}| + |a_{n_k} - a|$$
$$< \frac{\epsilon}{2} + \frac{\epsilon}{2} = \epsilon.$$ ∎

Recall that for a sequence of numbers $\{a_k\}$ that is indexed by the natural numbers, we define

$$s_n = \sum_{k=1}^{n} a_k \quad \text{for every natural number } n$$

and obtain a new sequence $\{s_n\}$. The sequence $\{s_n\}$ is called the *sequence of partial sums* for the series $\sum_{k=1}^{\infty} a_k$, and a_k is called the kth *term* of the series $\sum_{k=1}^{\infty} a_k$. We write

$$\sum_{k=1}^{\infty} a_k = \lim_{n \to \infty} \left[\sum_{k=1}^{n} a_k \right]$$

if the sequence $\{s_n\}$ converges. If the sequence $\{s_n\}$ does not converge, we say that the series $\sum_{k=1}^{\infty} a_k$ *diverges*.*

---

*For a sequence of numbers $\{a_k\}$ indexed by the nonnegative integers, we define $s_n = \sum_{k=0}^{n} a_k$ for every nonnegative integer n, and then define

$$\sum_{k=0}^{\infty} a_k = \lim_{n \to \infty} \left[\sum_{k=0}^{n} a_k \right]$$

if the sequence $\{s_n\}$ converges. This change in the initial index for the terms of a series has no material effect on the theory.

PROPOSITION 9.5

Suppose that the series $\sum_{k=1}^{\infty} a_n$ converges. Then $\lim_{n \to \infty} a_n = 0$.

Proof Define $\{s_n\}$ to be the sequence of partial sums for the series $\sum_{k=1}^{\infty} a_n$ and define s to be the limit of the sequence $\{s_n\}$. Since $\lim_{n \to \infty} s_n = s$, we also have $\lim_{n \to \infty} s_{n-1} = s$. Thus, by the difference property of convergent sequences,

$$\lim_{n \to \infty} [s_n - s_{n-1}] = 0.$$

However, for each natural number $n \geq 2$, $a_n = s_n - s_{n-1}$ and hence $\lim_{n \to \infty} a_n = 0$. ∎

As we have already seen in Chapter 2, the Harmonic Series

$$\sum_{n=1}^{\infty} \frac{1}{n}$$

does not converge, despite the fact that $\lim_{n \to \infty} 1/n = 0$. Thus the convergence of the sequence of terms $\{a_n\}$ to 0 is a necessary, but not sufficient, condition for the series $\sum_{n=1}^{\infty} a_n$ to converge. The remainder of this section will be devoted to presenting conditions on the terms of a series that are sufficient to ensure that the series converges.

Recall that one of the first results we proved about convergent sequences was that

$$\lim_{n \to \infty} r^n = 0 \quad \text{if} \quad |r| < 1. \tag{9.3}$$

This limit, together with the Geometric Sum Formula, is exactly what is needed to establish the convergence of the Geometric Series $\sum_{k=0}^{\infty} r^k$ provided that $|r| < 1$.

PROPOSITION 9.6

For a number r such that $|r| < 1$,

$$\sum_{k=0}^{\infty} r^k = \frac{1}{1-r}.$$

Proof The Geometric Sum Formula asserts that for each nonnegative integer n,

$$\sum_{k=0}^{n} r^k = \frac{1 - r^{n+1}}{1 - r}.$$

But $|r| < 1$, so $\lim_{n \to \infty} r^{n+1} = 0$ and hence, by the linearity property of convergent sequences of numbers,

$$\lim_{n \to \infty} \left[\sum_{k=0}^{n} r^k \right] = \lim_{n \to \infty} \left[\frac{1 - r^{n+1}}{1 - r} \right] = \frac{1}{1 - r}. \qquad \blacksquare$$

Given two sequences $\{a_k\}$ and $\{b_k\}$ and two numbers α and β, observe that for each natural number n,

$$\sum_{k=1}^{n} (\alpha a_k + \beta b_k) = \alpha \sum_{k=1}^{n} a_k + \beta \sum_{k=1}^{n} b_k.$$

Thus, from the linearity property of convergent sequences, it follows that if the two series $\sum_{k=1}^{\infty} a_k$ and $\sum_{k=1}^{\infty} b_k$ are convergent, then so is the series $\sum_{k=1}^{\infty} (\alpha a_k + \beta b_k)$, and moreover,

$$\sum_{k=1}^{\infty} (\alpha a_k + \beta b_k) = \alpha \sum_{k=1}^{\infty} a_k + \beta \sum_{k=1}^{\infty} b_k.$$

We have two principal general criteria for a sequence of numbers to converge, namely the Monotone Convergence Theorem and the Cauchy Convergence Criterion. Applying these criteria to series—that is, to sequences of partial sums—we obtain criteria for the convergence of series. First we examine consequences of the Monotone Convergence Theorem.

THEOREM 9.7 Suppose that $\{a_k\}$ is a sequence of nonnegative numbers. Then the series $\sum_{k=1}^{\infty} a_k$ converges if and only if there is a positive number M such that

$$a_1 + \cdots + a_n \le M \quad \text{for every natural number } n.$$

Proof Since the terms of the series $\sum_{k=1}^{\infty} a_k$ are nonnegative, the sequence of partial sums is monotonically increasing. The Monotone Convergence Theorem asserts that the sequence of partial sums converges if and only if the sequence of partial sums is bounded. ∎

COROLLARY 9.8 **The Comparison Test** Suppose that $\{a_k\}$ and $\{b_k\}$ are sequences of numbers such that for each natural number k,

$$0 \le a_k \le b_k.$$

(i) The series $\sum_{k=1}^{\infty} a_k$ converges if the series $\sum_{k=1}^{\infty} b_k$ converges.

(ii) The series $\sum_{k=1}^{\infty} b_k$ diverges if the series $\sum_{k=1}^{\infty} a_k$ diverges.

Proof Observe that for each natural number n,

$$\sum_{k=1}^{n} a_k \le \sum_{k=1}^{n} b_k.$$

The result follows from this inequality and Theorem 9.7. ∎

EXAMPLE 9.1 Consider the series

$$\sum_{k=1}^{\infty} \frac{1}{\sqrt{k}\, 2^k}.$$

Since for every natural number k, $1/\sqrt{k}\, 2^k \le 1/2^k$, and the Geometric Series converges, it follows from the Comparison Test that the series $\sum_{k=1}^{\infty} 1/\sqrt{k}\, 2^k$ also converges. □

EXAMPLE 9.2 Consider the series

$$\sum_{k=1}^{\infty} \frac{1}{2 + \sqrt{k}}.$$

Since for each integer $k \geq 2$, $1/(2 + \sqrt{k}) \geq 1/2k$, and the harmonic series $\sum_{k=1}^{\infty} 1/k$ diverges, it follows from the Comparison Test that the series $\sum_{k=1}^{\infty} 1/(2 + \sqrt{k})$ also diverges. $\qquad \square$

COROLLARY 9.9 **The Integral Test** Let $\{a_k\}$ be a sequence of nonnegative numbers and suppose that the function $f:[1, \infty) \to \mathbb{R}$ is monotonically decreasing and has the property that

$$f(k) = a_k \quad \text{for every natural number } k.$$

Then the series $\sum_{k=1}^{\infty} a_k$ is convergent if and only if the sequence $\{\int_1^n f(x)dx\}$ is bounded.

Proof Since the function $f:[1, \infty) \to \mathbb{R}$ is monotonically decreasing, its restriction to each bounded interval is integrable. Moreover, for each natural number k and each point x in the interval $[k, k+1]$,

$$a_k = f(k) \geq f(x) \geq f(k+1) = a_{k+1},$$

so the monotonicity property of integration implies that for each natural number n,

$$\sum_{k=1}^{n} a_k \geq \int_1^{n+1} f(x)\,dx \geq \sum_{k=2}^{n+1} a_k.$$

FIGURE 9.1

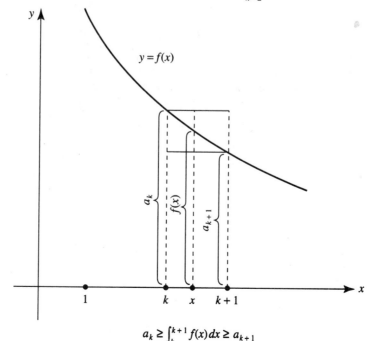

$$a_k \geq \int_k^{k+1} f(x)\,dx \geq a_{k+1}$$

This inequality implies that the sequence of partial sums for the series $\sum_{k=1}^{\infty} a_k$ is bounded if and only if the sequence $\{\int_1^n f(x)\,dx\}$ is bounded. In view of Theorem 9.7, it follows that the series $\sum_{k=1}^{\infty} a_k$ is convergent if and only if the sequence $\{\int_1^n f(x)\,dx\}$ is bounded. ∎

EXAMPLE 9.3 Consider the series

$$\sum_{k=1}^{\infty} \frac{1}{(k+1)\ln(k+1)}.$$

Using the First Fundamental Theorem of Calculus, we see that for every natural number n,

$$\int_1^n \frac{1}{(x+1)\ln(x+1)}\,dx = \ln(\ln(n+1)) - \ln(\ln 2).$$

Since the sequence $\{\ln(\ln(n+1)) - \ln(\ln 2)\}$ is not bounded, it follows from the Integral Test that the series $\sum_{k=1}^{\infty} 1/[(k+1)\ln(k+1)]$ diverges. □

COROLLARY 9.10

The p-Test For a positive number p, the series

$$\sum_{k=1}^{\infty} \frac{1}{k^p}$$

converges if and only if $p > 1$.

Proof Define $f(x) = x^{-p}$ for $x \geq 1$. The function $f: [1, \infty) \to \mathbb{R}$ is monotone decreasing. For each natural number n, the First Fundamental Theorem of Calculus implies that

$$\int_1^n f(x)\,dx = \begin{cases} (n^{1-p} - 1)/(1-p) & \text{if } p \neq 1 \\ \ln n & \text{if } p = 1. \end{cases}$$

Hence the sequence $\{\int_1^n f(x)\,dx\}$ is bounded if and only if $p > 1$. Using the Integral Test, we conclude that the series $\sum_{k=1}^{\infty} 1/k^p$ converges if and only if $p > 1$. ∎

EXAMPLE 9.4 Consider the series

$$\sum_{k=1}^{\infty} \frac{k}{e^k}.$$

In Section 8.2, we used the Lagrange Remainder Theorem to prove that

$$e^b > 1 + b + \frac{b^2}{2} + \frac{b^3}{6} > \frac{b^3}{6} \quad \text{if} \quad b > 0.$$

Thus for each natural number k, $k/e^k < 6/k^2$. The p-Test implies that the series $\sum_{k=1}^{\infty} 1/k^2$ converges, and hence so does the series $\sum_{k=1}^{\infty} 6/k^2$. The Comparison Test now implies that the series $\sum_{k=1}^{\infty} k/e^k$ also converges. □

When the terms of a series fail to be of one sign, it is not possible to directly invoke the Monotone Convergence Theorem in order to check convergence. However, for series whose terms alternate in sign we can indirectly use the Monotone Convergence Criterion to obtain the following convergence test.

THEOREM 9.11 **The Alternating Series Test** Suppose that $\{a_k\}$ is a monotonically decreasing sequence of nonnegative numbers that converges to 0. Then the series

$$\sum_{k=1}^{\infty} (-1)^{k+1} a_k$$

converges.

Proof Define

$$s_n = \sum_{k=1}^{n} (-1)^{k+1} a_k \quad \text{for every natural number } n.$$

In order to prove that the sequence of partial sums $\{s_n\}$ converges, we will first show that the subsequence $\{s_{2n}\}$ converges. Indeed, for each natural number n, observe that, since the sequence $\{a_k\}$ is monotonically decreasing,

$$s_{2n+2} - s_{2n} = a_{2n+1} - a_{2n+2} \geq 0,$$

and since the sequence $\{a_k\}$ also consists of nonnegative numbers,

$$s_{2n} = \sum_{k=1}^{n} (a_{2k-1} - a_{2k}) = a_1 - \sum_{k=1}^{n-1} (a_{2k} - a_{2k+1}) - a_{2n} \leq a_1.$$

We conclude that $\{s_{2n}\}$ is monotonically increasing and bounded above by a_1. By the Monotone Convergence Theorem, the sequence $\{s_{2n}\}$ converges. Define $s = \lim_{n \to \infty} s_{2n}$. But

$$s_{2n+1} = s_{2n} + a_{2n+1} \quad \text{for every natural number } n.$$

Since $\lim_{n \to \infty} a_n = 0$, it follows that the sequence $\{s_{2n+1}\}$ converges to the same limit s.

We claim that the whole sequence $\{s_n\}$ converges to s. Indeed, let $\epsilon > 0$. We can choose natural numbers N_1 and N_2 such that

$$|s_{2n} - s| < \epsilon \quad \text{for all integers } n \geq N_1$$

and

$$|s_{2n+1} - s| < \epsilon \quad \text{for all integers } n \geq N_2.$$

Define $N = \max\{2N_1, \, 2N_2 + 1\}$. Then

$$|s_n - s| < \epsilon \quad \text{for all integers } n \geq N.$$

EXAMPLE 9.5 From the Alternating Series Test, it follows that the series

$$\sum_{k=1}^{\infty} \frac{(-1)^{k+1}}{k}$$

converges. In fact, in Section 8.4 we proved that it converged to $\ln 2$. □

For series whose terms are neither of one sign nor alternating in sign, it is natural to apply the Cauchy Convergence Criterion for Sequences to the sequence of partial sums in order to determine if the series converges.

It is sometimes useful, particularly when considering series, to restate the definition of a Cauchy sequence as follows: The sequence $\{s_n\}$ is a Cauchy sequence provided that for each positive number ϵ there is a natural number N such that for each integer $n \geq N$ and any natural number k,

$$|s_{n+k} - s_n| < \epsilon.$$

THEOREM 9.12 **The Cauchy Convergence Criterion for Series** The series $\sum_{k=1}^{\infty} a_k$ converges if and only if for each positive number ϵ there is a natural number N such that

$$|a_{n+1} + \cdots + a_{n+k}| < \epsilon \quad \text{for all integers } n \geq N \text{ and all natural numbers } k.$$

Proof Apply the Cauchy Convergence Criterion for Sequences to the sequence of partial sums. ■

DEFINITION *The series $\sum_{k=1}^{\infty} a_k$ is said to converge absolutely provided that the series $\sum_{k=1}^{\infty} |a_k|$ converges.*

COROLLARY 9.13 **The Absolute Convergence Test** The series $\sum_{k=1}^{\infty} a_k$ converges if the series $\sum_{k=1}^{\infty} |a_k|$ converges.

Proof From the Triangle Inequality, we conclude that for each pair of natural numbers n and k,

$$\left| \sum_{j=n+1}^{n+k} a_j \right| \leq \sum_{j=n+1}^{n+k} |a_j|.$$

Since the series $\sum_{k=1}^{\infty} |a_k|$ converges, it follows from the Cauchy Convergence Criterion for Series that the sequence of partial sums for $\sum_{k=1}^{\infty} |a_k|$ is a Cauchy sequence. The preceding inequality implies that the sequence of partial sums for $\sum_{k=1}^{\infty} a_k$ is also a Cauchy sequence. Once more using the Cauchy Convergence Criterion for Series, it follows that the series $\sum_{k=1}^{\infty} a_k$ converges. ■

EXAMPLE 9.6   The series

$$\sum_{k=1}^{\infty} \frac{\sin k}{k^2}$$

converges. To verify this, first observe that by the *p*-test, with $p = 2$, the series $\sum_{k=1}^{\infty} 1/k^2$ converges. Since for every natural number k, $|\sin k| \leq 1$, it follows from the Comparison Test that the series $\sum_{k=1}^{\infty} |\sin k|/k^2$ also converges. The Absolute Convergence Test now implies that the series $\sum_{k=1}^{\infty} \sin k/k^2$ converges.   □

A series that converges but does not converge absolutely is said to *converge conditionally*. The series $\sum_{k=1}^{\infty}(-1)^{k+1}/k$ converges conditionally, since the Harmonic Series diverges, but, by the Alternating Series Test, the series $\sum_{k=1}^{\infty}(-1)^{k+1}/k$ converges.

THEOREM 9.14   For the series $\sum_{k=1}^{\infty} a_k$, suppose that there is a number r with $0 \leq r < 1$ and a natural number N such that

$$|a_{n+1}| \leq r|a_n| \quad \text{for all integers } n \geq N. \tag{9.4}$$

Then the series $\sum_{k=1}^{\infty} a_k$ is absolutely convergent.

Proof   First, observe that for each natural number k, if we apply the inequality (9.4) successively k times, we obtain

$$|a_{N+k}| \leq r^k |a_N|. \tag{9.5}$$

From this inequality and the Geometric Sum Formula, we conclude that for each natural number k,

$$|a_1| + \cdots + |a_{N+k}| = |a_1| + \cdots + |a_{N-1}| + |a_N| + \cdots + |a_{N+k}|$$

$$\leq |a_1| + \cdots + |a_{N-1}| + |a_N|[1 + r + \cdots + r^k]$$

$$= |a_1| + \cdots + |a_{N-1}| + |a_N|\left[\frac{1 - r^{k+1}}{1 - r}\right]$$

$$\leq |a_1| + \cdots + |a_{N-1}| + |a_N|\left[\frac{1}{1 - r}\right]. \tag{9.6}$$

Define
$$M = |a_1| + \cdots + |a_{N-1}| + |a_N|\left[\frac{1}{1 - r}\right].$$

Then, from (9.6), it follows that

$$|a_1| + \cdots + |a_n| \leq M \quad \text{for every natural number } n.$$

This means that the sequence of partial sums of the series $\sum_{k=1}^{\infty} |a_k|$ is bounded. According to Theorem 9.7, the series $\sum_{k=1}^{\infty} |a_k|$ converges.   ■

**COROLLARY
9.15**

The Ratio Test for Series For the series $\sum_{k=1}^{\infty} a_k$, suppose that

$$\lim_{n \to \infty} \frac{|a_{n+1}|}{|a_n|} = \ell.$$

(i) If $\ell < 1$, the series $\sum_{n=1}^{\infty} a_n$ converges absolutely.

(ii) If $\ell > 1$, the series $\sum_{n=1}^{\infty} a_n$ diverges.

Proof First, suppose that $\ell < 1$. Define $r = (1 + \ell)/2$. Then $\ell < r$, since $\ell < 1$, and so we can choose a natural number N such that

$$\frac{|a_{n+1}|}{|a_n|} < r \quad \text{for all integers } n \geq N.$$

Also, $r < 1$, since $\ell < 1$. The conclusion now follows from Theorem 9.14.

Now suppose that $\ell > 1$. Then it follows from the Ratio Lemma for Sequences (Lemma 8.17) that the sequence $\{a_n\}$ does not converge to 0. Thus the series $\sum_{n=1}^{\infty} a_n$ diverges. ∎

The theory of convergent and divergent series is a broad and deep subject. The present section gives but a brief glimpse of some ways in which the Monotone Convergence Theorem and the Cauchy Convergence Criterion for sequences of numbers can be applied to obtain criteria that are sufficient for a series to converge.

EXERCISES

1. Examine the following series for convergence:

   (a) $\displaystyle\sum_{k=1}^{\infty} \frac{a^k}{k^p}$ where $a > 0$ and $p > 0$

   (b) $\displaystyle\sum_{k=1}^{\infty} \frac{1}{2k + 3}$

   (c) $\displaystyle\sum_{k=1}^{\infty} \frac{(-1)^k}{k}$

   (d) $\displaystyle\sum_{k=1}^{\infty} \frac{1}{k(k + 1)}$

   (e) $\displaystyle\sum_{k=1}^{\infty} ke^{-k^2}$

(f) $\displaystyle\sum_{k=1}^{\infty}\left(\frac{k+1}{k^2+1}\right)^3$

(g) $\displaystyle\sum_{k=1}^{\infty}k\sin\left(\frac{1}{k}\right)$

2. For any positive number α, prove that the series

$$\sum_{k=1}^{\infty}\frac{k^{\alpha}}{e^k}$$

converges.

3. Fix a positive number α and consider the series

$$\sum_{k=1}^{\infty}\frac{1}{(k+1)[\ln(k+1)]^{\alpha}}.$$

For what values of α does this series converge?

4. Under the assumptions of the Alternating Series Test, define

$$s=\sum_{k=1}^{\infty}(-1)^{k+1}a_k.$$

Prove that for every natural number n,

$$\left|s-\sum_{k=1}^{n}(-1)^{k+1}a_k\right|\le a_{n+1}.$$

5. Use the Cauchy Convergence Criterion for Series to provide another proof of the Alternating Series Test.

6. If a sequence converges, then each of its subsequences converges to the same limit, but the convergence of a subsequence does not imply the convergence of the whole sequence. Based on this, prove that

$$\text{if}\qquad\sum_{k=1}^{\infty}a_k=\ell,\qquad\text{then}\qquad\sum_{k=1}^{\infty}(a_{2k}+a_{2k-1})=\ell,$$

but that the converse does not necessarily hold. (*Hint:* Consider the series $\sum_{k=1}^{\infty}(-1)^k$.)

7. For the series $\sum_{k=1}^{\infty}a_k$, suppose that there is a number r with $0\le r<1$ and a natural number N such that

$$|a_k|^{1/k}<r\qquad\text{for all integers }k\ge N.$$

Prove that $\sum_{k=1}^{\infty}a_k$ converges absolutely. This is known as the Cauchy Root Test.

8. Suppose that $\sum_{k=1}^{\infty}a_k$ and $\sum_{k=1}^{\infty}b_k$ are series of positive numbers such that

$$\lim_{n\to\infty}\left(\frac{a_k}{b_k}\right)=\ell\quad\text{and}\quad\ell>0.$$

Prove that the series $\sum_{k=1}^{\infty}a_k$ converges if and only if the series $\sum_{k=1}^{\infty}b_k$ converges.

9.2 Pointwise Convergence and Uniform Convergence of Sequences of Functions

In Section 9.1, we studied sequences and series of *numbers*. We now turn to the study of sequences of *functions*.

DEFINITION *Given a function $f: D \to \mathbb{R}$ and a sequence of functions $\{f_n: D \to \mathbb{R}\}$, the sequence $\{f_n: D \to \mathbb{R}\}$ is said to converge pointwise to $f: D \to \mathbb{R}$ provided that for each point x in D,*

$$\lim_{n \to \infty} f_n(x) = f(x).$$

EXAMPLE 9.7 For each natural number n, define

$$f_n(x) = x^n \quad \text{for} \quad 0 \le x \le 1.$$

Since $\{f_n(1)\}$ is a constant sequence, whose constant value is 1, $\lim_{n \to \infty} f_n(1) = 1$. On the other hand,

$$\lim_{n \to \infty} x^n = 0 \quad \text{if} \quad 0 \le x < 1.$$

FIGURE 9.2

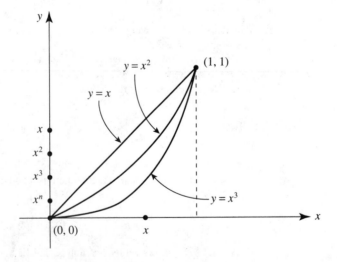

Thus the sequence of functions $\{f_n: [0, 1] \to \mathbb{R}\}$ converges pointwise to the function $f: [0, 1] \to \mathbb{R}$ defined by

$$f(x) = \begin{cases} 1 & \text{if } x = 1 \\ 0 & \text{if } 0 \le x < 1. \end{cases}$$

□

EXAMPLE 9.8   For each natural number n, define

$$f_n(x) = \sum_{k=0}^{n} \frac{x^k}{k!} \quad \text{for} \quad 0 \le x \le 1.$$

According to formula (8.15), the sequence of functions $\{f_n : [0, 1] \to \mathbb{R}\}$ converges pointwise to the function $f : [0, 1] \to \mathbb{R}$, defined by $f(x) = e^x$ for $0 \le x \le 1$. In infinite series notation, this simply means that

$$e^x = \sum_{k=0}^{\infty} \frac{x^k}{k!} \quad \text{for} \quad 0 \le x \le 1. \qquad \Box$$

EXAMPLE 9.9   For each natural number n, define

$$f_n(x) = e^{-nx^2} \quad \text{for all } x.$$

FIGURE 9.3

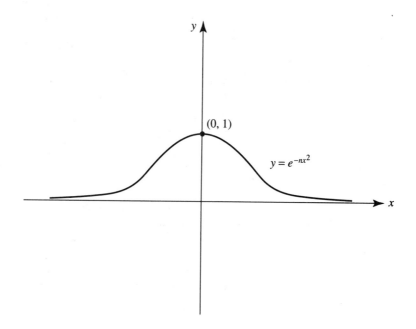

Then $\{f_n(0)\}$ is a constant sequence, whose constant value is 1, so $\lim_{n \to \infty} f_n(0) = 1$. On the other hand, since $e^b > 1 + b$ if $b > 0$, it follows that

$$\frac{1}{e^b} < \frac{1}{1+b} \quad \text{for all } b > 0.$$

Thus, for each natural number n and each $x \ne 0$,

$$0 < f_n(x) < \frac{1}{1+nx^2},$$

so $\lim_{n\to\infty} f_n(x) = 0$ if $x \neq 0$. It follows that the sequence of functions $\{f_n : \mathbb{R} \to \mathbb{R}\}$ converges pointwise to the function $f : \mathbb{R} \to \mathbb{R}$ defined by

$$f(x) = \begin{cases} 0 & \text{if } x \neq 0 \\ 1 & \text{if } x = 0. \end{cases}$$ □

EXAMPLE 9.10 For each natural number n, and each number x with $|x| < 1$, define

$$f_n(x) = \sum_{k=0}^{n} x^k,$$

so that according to the Geometric Sum Formula,

$$f_n(x) = \frac{1 - x^{n+1}}{1 - x}.$$

Since $\lim_{n\to\infty} x^{n+1} = 0$, if $|x| < 1$, the sequence of functions $\{f_n : (-1, 1) \to \mathbb{R}\}$ converges pointwise to the function $f : (-1, 1) \to \mathbb{R}$ defined by $f(x) = 1/(1 - x)$ for $|x| < 1$. We are already familiar with this example; it is the Geometric Series. □

EXAMPLE 9.11 For each natural number n, and each number x in the interval $[0, 1]$, define

$$f_n(x) = \begin{cases} 1 & \text{if } x = k2^{-n} \text{ for some natural number } k \\ 0 & \text{otherwise.} \end{cases}$$

Then we see that the sequence $\{f_n : [0, 1] \to \mathbb{R}\}$ converges pointwise to the function $f : [0, 1] \to \mathbb{R}$ defined by

$$f(x) = \begin{cases} 1 & \text{if } x = k2^{-n}, \text{ for some natural numbers } k \text{ and } n \\ 0 & \text{otherwise.} \end{cases}$$ □

For a sequence of functions $\{f_n : D \to \mathbb{R}\}$ that converges pointwise to the function $f : D \to \mathbb{R}$, we wish to determine the properties of the individual f_n's that are inherited by the limit function $f : D \to \mathbb{R}$. Three natural questions come to mind.

Question A

Suppose that each function $f_n : D \to \mathbb{R}$ is continuous. Is the limit function $f : D \to \mathbb{R}$ also continuous?

Question B

If $D = I$ is an open interval and each function $f_n : I \to \mathbb{R}$ is differentiable, is the limit function $f : I \to \mathbb{R}$ also differentiable? If so, does the sequence of derivatives

$\{f'_n: I \to \mathbb{R}\}$ converge pointwise to $f': I \to \mathbb{R}$—that is, is the derivative of the limit equal to the limit of the derivatives?

Question C

If $D = [a, b]$ and each function $f_n: [a, b] \to \mathbb{R}$ is integrable, is the limit function $f: [a, b] \to \mathbb{R}$ also integrable? If so, is

$$\lim_{n \to \infty} \left[\int_a^b f_n \right] = \int_a^b f?$$

That is, is the integral of the limit equal to the limit of the integrals?

It turns out that the answer to each of the above questions is negative. Example 9.7 shows that the pointwise limit of continuous functions need not be continuous. Example 9.9 shows that the pointwise limit of differentiable functions need not be differentiable. Finally, Example 9.11 exhibits a sequence of integrable functions that converge pointwise to a nonintegrable function.

All is not lost, however. If we strengthen the assumption of pointwise convergence to what we will call *uniform convergence*, then the first and third questions have affirmative answers, and Question B has a satisfactory answer. What is of equal importance is that in many interesting situations we can verify uniform convergence.

DEFINITION   *Given a function $f: D \to \mathbb{R}$ and a sequence of functions $\{f_n: D \to \mathbb{R}\}$, the sequence $\{f_n: D \to \mathbb{R}\}$ is said to converge uniformly to $f: D \to \mathbb{R}$ provided that for each positive number ϵ there is a natural number N such that*

$$|f(x) - f_n(x)| < \epsilon \quad \text{for all integers } n \geq N \text{ and all points } x \text{ in } D. \qquad (9.7)$$

It is clear from the above definition that uniform convergence implies pointwise convergence; however, the converse is not true. To understand the distinction between uniform and pointwise convergence, observe that the sequence $\{f_n: D \to \mathbb{R}\}$ converges pointwise to $f: D \to \mathbb{R}$ provided that for each fixed point x in D, the sequence of numbers $\{f_n(x)\}$ converges to the number $f(x)$; thus, for a given point x in D and a positive number ϵ, there is a natural number N such that $|f_n(x) - f(x)| < \epsilon$ for all integers $n \geq N$. The index N that responds to the ϵ challenge may depend on the point x. For uniform convergence, the requirement is that given an $\epsilon > 0$ challenge, we can respond with an index N such that $|f_n(x) - f(x)| < \epsilon$ for all integers $n \geq N$ and for all points x in D.

In terms of graphs, the sequence $\{f_n: D \to \mathbb{R}\}$ converges uniformly to $f: D \to \mathbb{R}$ if for each positive number ϵ there is a natural number N such that if $n \geq N$, the graph of the function $f_n: D \to \mathbb{R}$ lies between the graphs of the functions $f + \epsilon: D \to \mathbb{R}$ and $f - \epsilon: D \to \mathbb{R}$.

FIGURE 9.4

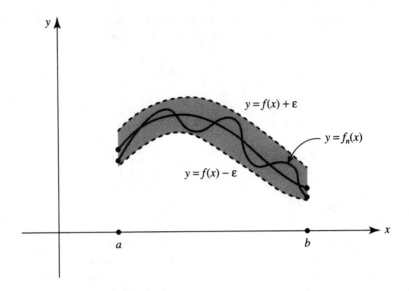

Let us revisit our first two examples of pointwise convergence and analyze them for uniform convergence.

EXAMPLE 9.12 Let the sequence $\{f_n : [0, 1] \to \mathbb{R}\}$ and the function $f : [0, 1] \to \mathbb{R}$ be as in Example 9.7. The convergence is not uniform. Indeed, for $\epsilon = 1/2$, there is no natural number N having the property that

$$|f_n(x) - f(x)| < \frac{1}{2} \quad \text{for all integers } n \geq N \text{ and all points } x \text{ in } [0, 1],$$

because no matter what natural number N is chosen, by taking $x = (3/4)^{\frac{1}{N+1}}$ we have

$$f_{N+1}(x) - f(x) = \frac{3}{4} > \frac{1}{2}. \qquad \square$$

EXAMPLE 9.13 Let the sequence $\{f_n : [0, 1] \to \mathbb{R}\}$ and the function $f : [0, 1] \to \mathbb{R}$ be as in Example 9.8. We claim that $\{f_n : [0, 1] \to \mathbb{R}\}$ converges uniformly to $f : [0, 1] \to \mathbb{R}$. To verify this claim, we need the estimate obtained from the Lagrange Remainder Theorem. According to estimate (8.6), for any point x in the interval $[0, 1]$,

$$|f(x) - f_n(x)| \leq \frac{3}{(n + 1)!} \quad \text{for every natural number } n. \qquad (9.8)$$

Now let $\epsilon > 0$. By the Archimedean property of $\mathbb{R}$, we can choose a natural number N such that $N > 3/\epsilon$. Thus,

$$|f(x) - f_n(x)| < \epsilon \quad \text{for all integers } n \geq N \text{ and all points } x \text{ in } [0, 1]. \qquad \square$$

In Section 9.1, we proved the Cauchy Convergence Criterion for the convergence of a sequence of numbers. There is a similar criterion for the uniform convergence of a sequence of functions.

DEFINITION   *The sequence of functions $\{f_n: D \to \mathbb{R}\}$ is said to be uniformly Cauchy provided that for each positive number ϵ there is a natural number N such that*

$$|f_{n+k}(x) - f_n(x)| < \epsilon \qquad (9.9)$$

for every integer $n \geq N$, every natural number k, and every point x in D.

THEOREM 9.16   **The Weierstrass Uniform Convergence Criterion**   The sequence of functions $\{f: D \to \mathbb{R}\}$ converges uniformly to a function $f: D \to \mathbb{R}$ if and only if the sequence $\{f_n: D \to \mathbb{R}\}$ is uniformly Cauchy.

Proof   Suppose that $\{f_n: D \to \mathbb{R}\}$ converges uniformly to $f: D \to \mathbb{R}$. We will show that $\{f_n: D \to \mathbb{R}\}$ is uniformly Cauchy. Indeed, let $\epsilon > 0$. We can select a natural number N such that

$$|f_n(x) - f(x)| < \frac{\epsilon}{2} \qquad \text{for all integers } n \geq N \text{ and every point } x \text{ in } D.$$

Using the Triangle Inequality, it follows that

$$|f_{n+k}(x) - f_n(x)| = |f_{n+k}(x) - f(x) + f(x) - f_n(x)|$$

$$\leq |f_{n+k}(x) - f(x)| + |f_n(x) - f(x)|$$

$$< \frac{\epsilon}{2} + \frac{\epsilon}{2} = \epsilon$$

for every integer $n \geq N$, every natural number k, and every point x in D. Thus, the sequence $\{f_n: D \to \mathbb{R}\}$ is a uniformly Cauchy sequence.

To prove the converse, we suppose that the sequence of functions $\{f_n: D \to \mathbb{R}\}$ is uniformly Cauchy. Let x be a point in D. Then clearly the sequence of real numbers $\{f_n(x)\}$ is a Cauchy sequence and so, by the Cauchy Convergence Criterion for sequences of numbers, $\{f_n(x)\}$ converges. Denote the limit by $f(x)$. This defines a function $f: D \to \mathbb{R}$ that is the only candidate for a function to which $\{f_n: D \to \mathbb{R}\}$ may converge uniformly.

Now let us prove that $\{f_n: D \to \mathbb{R}\}$ does converge uniformly to $f: D \to \mathbb{R}$. Let $\epsilon > 0$. Since $\{f_n: D \to \mathbb{R}\}$ is uniformly Cauchy, we can select a natural number N such that

$$|f_{n+k}(x) - f_n(x)| < \frac{\epsilon}{2} \qquad (9.10)$$

for every integer $n \geq N$, every natural number k, and every point x in D. Let x be a point in D. Choose $n \geq N$. Observe that from inequality (9.10) we have

$$f_n(x) - \frac{\epsilon}{2} < f_{n+k}(x) < f_n(x) + \frac{\epsilon}{2} \qquad \text{for every natural number } k. \qquad (9.11)$$

But $$\lim_{k \to \infty} f_{n+k}(x) = f(x)$$

so that from (9.11) we obtain

$$f_n(x) - \frac{\epsilon}{2} \le f(x) \le f_n(x) + \frac{\epsilon}{2}.$$

Hence,

$$|f_n(x) - f(x)| < \epsilon \quad \text{for all integers } n \ge N \text{ and all points } x \text{ in } D.$$

It follows that $\{f_n : D \to \mathbb{R}\}$ converges uniformly to $f : D \to \mathbb{R}$.   ■

EXAMPLE 9.14   For each natural number n and each number x with $|x| \le 1$, define

$$f_n(x) = \sum_{k=1}^{n} \frac{x^k}{k 2^k}.$$

Observe, using the Triangle Inequality and the Geometric Sum Formula, that for each pair of natural numbers n and k and each number x with $|x| \le 1$,

$$|f_{n+k}(x) - f_n(x)| \le \frac{|x|^{n+1}}{(n+1)2^{n+1}} + \cdots + \frac{|x|^{n+k}}{(n+k)2^{n+k}}$$

$$\le \frac{1}{2^{n+1}} + \cdots + \frac{1}{2^{n+k}}$$

$$\le \frac{1}{2^n}. \tag{9.12}$$

But $\lim_{n \to \infty} (1/2)^n = 0$, and this, together with the inequality (9.12), implies that the sequence $\{f_n : [-1, 1] \to \mathbb{R}\}$ is uniformly Cauchy. According to the Weierstrass Uniform Convergence Criterion, there is a function $f : [-1, 1] \to \mathbb{R}$ to which the sequence $\{f_n : [-1, 1] \to \mathbb{R}\}$ converges uniformly.   □

EXERCISES

1. For each natural number n and each number x, define
$$f_n(x) = \frac{1 - |x|^n}{1 + |x|^n}.$$
Find the function $f : \mathbb{R} \to \mathbb{R}$ to which the sequence $\{f_n : \mathbb{R} \to \mathbb{R}\}$ converges pointwise. Prove that the convergence is not uniform.

2. For each natural number n and each number $x \ge 2$, define
$$f_n(x) = \frac{1}{1 + x^n}.$$
Find the function $f : [2, \infty) \to \mathbb{R}$ to which the sequence $\{f_n : [2, \infty) \to \mathbb{R}\}$ converges pointwise. Prove that the convergence is uniform.

3. For each natural number n and each number x in $(0, 1)$, define
$$f_n(x) = \frac{1}{nx + 1}.$$
Find the function $f : (0, 1) \to \mathbb{R}$ to which the sequence $\{f_n : (0, 1) \to \mathbb{R}\}$ converges pointwise. Prove that the convergence is not uniform.

4. For each natural number n and each number x in $[0, 1]$, define

$$f_n(x) = \frac{x}{nx + 1}.$$

Find the function $f: [0, 1] \to \mathbb{R}$ to which the sequence $\{f_n: [0, 1] \to \mathbb{R}\}$ converges pointwise. Prove that the convergence is uniform.

5. Determine whether the sequences in Examples 9.9, 9.10, and 9.11 converge uniformly.

6. Suppose that the sequences $\{f_n: D \to \mathbb{R}\}$ and $\{g_n: D \to \mathbb{R}\}$ converge uniformly to the functions $f: D \to \mathbb{R}$ and $g: D \to \mathbb{R}$, respectively. For any two numbers α and β, prove that the sequence $\{\alpha f_n + \beta g_n: D \to \mathbb{R}\}$ converges uniformly to the function $\alpha f + \beta g: D \to \mathbb{R}$.

7. For each natural number n, let the function $f_n: \mathbb{R} \to \mathbb{R}$ be bounded. Suppose that the sequence $\{f_n: \mathbb{R} \to \mathbb{R}\}$ converges uniformly to $f: \mathbb{R} \to \mathbb{R}$. Prove that the limit function $f: \mathbb{R} \to \mathbb{R}$ also is bounded.

8. A number x of the form $\ell/2^k$, where ℓ and k are integers, is called a *dyadic rational*. Prove that the dyadic rationals are dense in $\mathbb{R}$. From this, conclude that the limit function in Example 9.11 is not integrable.

9. For each natural number n and each number x in $(-1, 1)$, define

$$p_n(x) = x + x(1 - x^2) + \cdots + x(1 - x^2)^n.$$

Prove that the sequence $\{p_n: (-1, 1) \to \mathbb{R}\}$ converges pointwise.

10. Let $\{a_n\}$ be a bounded sequence of numbers. For each natural number n and each number x, define

$$f_n(x) = a_0 + a_1 x + \frac{a_2 x^2}{2!} + \cdots + \frac{a_n x^n}{n!}.$$

Prove that for each $r > 0$, the sequence of functions $\{f_n: [-r, r] \to \mathbb{R}\}$ is uniformly convergent.

9.3   The Uniform Limit of Continuous Functions, of Integrable Functions, and of Differentiable Functions

We will now provide some affirmative answers to the three questions raised in Section 9.2, by strengthening the assumption of pointwise convergence to that of uniform convergence.

THEOREM 9.17   Suppose that $\{f_n: D \to \mathbb{R}\}$ is a sequence of continuous functions that converges uniformly to the function $f: D \to \mathbb{R}$. Then the limit function $f: D \to \mathbb{R}$ is also continuous.

Proof Let x_0 be a point in D. We will use the ϵ–δ criterion for continuity in order to prove that the function $f: D \to \mathbb{R}$ is continuous at x_0. Indeed, let $\epsilon > 0$. Since the sequence $\{f_n: D \to \mathbb{R}\}$ converges uniformly to the function $f: D \to \mathbb{R}$, we can choose a natural number N such that

$$|f_n(x) - f(x)| < \frac{\epsilon}{3} \quad \text{for all integers } n \geq N \text{ and all points } x \text{ in } D. \tag{9.13}$$

Using this inequality with $n = N$ and the Triangle Inequality, we see that

$$|f(x) - f(x_0)| = |f(x) - f_N(x) + f_N(x) - f_N(x_0) + f_N(x_0) - f(x_0)|$$
$$\leq |f(x) - f_N(x)| + |f_N(x) - f_N(x_0)| + |f_N(x_0) - f(x_0)|$$
$$< \frac{\epsilon}{3} + |f_N(x) - f_N(x_0)| + \frac{\epsilon}{3} \quad \text{for all points } x \text{ in } D. \tag{9.14}$$

By assumption, the function $f_N: D \to \mathbb{R}$ is continuous at x_0. Hence, we can choose $\delta > 0$ such that

$$|f_N(x) - f_N(x_0)| < \frac{\epsilon}{3} \quad \text{for all points } x \text{ in } D \text{ such that } |x - x_0| < \delta. \tag{9.15}$$

The inequalities (9.14) and (9.15) imply that

$$|f(x) - f(x_0)| < \epsilon \quad \text{for all points } x \text{ in } D \text{ such that } |x - x_0| < \delta.$$

Thus the function $f: D \to \mathbb{R}$ is continuous at the point x_0. ∎

THEOREM 9.18 Suppose that $\{f_n: [a, b] \to \mathbb{R}\}$ is a sequence of integrable functions that converges uniformly to the function $f: [a, b] \to \mathbb{R}$. Then the limit function $f: [a, b] \to \mathbb{R}$ is also integrable. Moreover,

$$\lim_{n \to \infty} \left[\int_a^b f_n \right] = \int_a^b f.$$

Proof We begin with a preliminary observation: It follows directly from the definition of the Darboux sums that if the positive number α and the natural number n have the property that

$$f_n(x) - \alpha \leq f(x) \leq f_n(x) + \alpha \quad \text{for all points } x \text{ in } [a, b], \tag{9.16}$$

then for any partition P of $[a, b]$,

$$L(f_n, P) - \alpha(b - a) \leq L(f, P) \leq U(f, P) \leq U(f_n, P) + \alpha(b - a). \tag{9.17}$$

First, we will use the Integrability Criterion to show that the function $f:[a, b] \to \mathbb{R}$ is integrable. Indeed, let $\epsilon > 0$. Since the sequence $\{f_n:[a, b] \to \mathbb{R}\}$ converges uniformly to the function $f:[a, b] \to \mathbb{R}$ and the number $\epsilon/(b-a)$ is positive, we can choose a natural number N such that (9.16) holds if $n \geq N$ and $\alpha = \epsilon/3(b-a)$, and hence, by the initial observation, for any partition P of the interval $[a, b]$ and any integer $n \geq N$,

$$L(f_n, P) - \frac{\epsilon}{3} \leq L(f, P) \leq U(f, P) \leq U(f_n, P) + \frac{\epsilon}{3}. \tag{9.18}$$

But the function $f_N:[a, b] \to \mathbb{R}$ is integrable, and so, according to the Integrability Criterion, we can choose a partition P_* of $[a, b]$ such that

$$U(f_N, P_*) - L(f_N, P_*) < \frac{\epsilon}{3}. \tag{9.19}$$

Inequalities (9.18) and (9.19) imply that

$$U(f, P_*) - L(f, P_*) < \epsilon.$$

Hence the function $f:[a, b] \to \mathbb{R}$ is integrable.

It remains to be verified that

$$\lim_{n \to \infty}\left[\int_a^b f_n \right] = \int_a^b f.$$

Let $\epsilon > 0$. We need to find a natural number N such that

$$\left| \int_a^b f_n - \int_a^b f \right| < \epsilon \quad \text{for all integers } n \geq N. \tag{9.20}$$

For $\alpha = \epsilon/2(b-a)$, we may choose a natural number N such that (9.16) holds. But using the linearity and monotonicity properties of the integral, (9.16) implies that for each integer $n \geq N$,

$$\int_a^b f_n - \frac{\epsilon}{2} \leq \int_a^b f \leq \int_a^b f_n + \frac{\epsilon}{2},$$

and so

$$\left| \int_a^b f_n - \int_a^b f \right| < \epsilon. \tag{9.21}$$

∎

The answer to Question B of Section 9.2, regarding the differentiability of the limit of differentiable functions, requires more care than the answers to the other two questions. The uniform limit of differentiable functions need not be differentiable (see Exercise 1). However, there are quite reasonable circumstances under which it is differentiable and the derivative of the limit is the limit of the derivatives.

THEOREM 9.19   Let I be an open interval. Suppose that $\{f_n: I \to \mathbb{R}\}$ is a sequence of continuously differentiable functions that has the following two properties:

(i) The sequence $\{f_n: I \to \mathbb{R}\}$ converges pointwise to the function $f: I \to \mathbb{R}$ and

(ii) The sequence of derivatives $\{f_n': I \to \mathbb{R}\}$ converges uniformly to the function $g: I \to \mathbb{R}$.

Then the function $f: I \to \mathbb{R}$ is continuously differentiable and

$$f'(x) = g(x) \quad \text{for all } x \text{ in } [a, b].$$

Proof Fix a point x_0 in I. According to the First Fundamental Theorem of Calculus, for each natural number n and each point x in I,

$$f_n(x) - f_n(x_0) = \int_{x_0}^{x} f_n'. \tag{9.22}$$

Now, Theorem 9.18 implies that for each point x in I,

$$\lim_{n \to \infty} \left[\int_{x_0}^{x} f_n' \right] = \int_{x_0}^{x} g. \tag{9.23}$$

Also, since, by assumption, the sequence $\{f_n: I \to \mathbb{R}\}$ converges pointwise to the function $f: I \to \mathbb{R}$, for each point x in I,

$$\lim_{n \to \infty} [f_n(x) - f_n(x_0)] = f(x) - f(x_0). \tag{9.24}$$

From (9.22), (9.23), and (9.24), it follows that

$$f(x) - f(x_0) = \int_{x_0}^{x} g \quad \text{for all } x \text{ in } I. \tag{9.25}$$

By assumption, for each natural number n the function $f_n': I \to \mathbb{R}$ is continuous, so by Theorem 9.17, the uniform limit $g: I \to \mathbb{R}$ also is continuous. From (9.25) and the Second Fundamental Theorem of Calculus, we see that

$$f'(x) = g(x) \quad \text{for all } x \text{ in } I. \qquad \blacksquare$$

THEOREM 9.20 Let I be an open interval. Suppose that $\{f_n: I \to \mathbb{R}\}$ is a sequence of continuously differentiable functions that has the following two properties:

(i) The sequence $\{f_n: I \to \mathbb{R}\}$ converges pointwise to the function $f: I \to \mathbb{R}$ and

(ii) The sequence of derivatives $\{f_n': I \to \mathbb{R}\}$ is uniformly Cauchy.

Then the function $f: I \to \mathbb{R}$ is continuously differentiable and for each point x in I,

$$\lim_{n \to \infty} f_n'(x) = f'(x).$$

Proof The Weierstrass Uniform Convergence Criterion implies that there is a function $g: I \to \mathbb{R}$ to which the sequence $\{f_n': I \to \mathbb{R}\}$ converges uniformly. The conclusion now follows from Theorem 9.19. $\qquad \blacksquare$

The property of uniform convergence can frequently be verified. However, there are many interesting cases in which a sequence of functions fails to converge uniformly, but nevertheless the limit function inherits properties possessed by the individual functions in the approximation sequence. We will describe one instance of this: the following verification of a classical formula for π.

PROPOSITION   **The Newton-Gregory Formula**
9.21

$$\frac{\pi}{4} = \int_0^1 \frac{1}{1+x^2}\,dx = \sum_{k=0}^{\infty} \frac{(-1)^k}{2k+1}. \tag{9.26}$$

Proof   Since for each number x,

$$\frac{d}{dx}(\arctan x) = \frac{1}{1+x^2},$$

it follows from the First Fundamental Theorem of Calculus that

$$\frac{\pi}{4} = \arctan 1 - \arctan 0 = \int_0^1 \frac{1}{1+x^2}\,dx. \tag{9.27}$$

Let n be a natural number. Substituting $-x^2 = r$ in the Geometric Sum Formula, we see that for each number x,

$$\frac{1}{1+x^2} = 1 - x^2 + \cdots + (-1)^n x^{2n} + \frac{(-1)^{n+1} x^{2n+2}}{1+x^2},$$

so that

$$\int_0^1 \frac{1}{1+x^2}\,dx = 1 - \frac{1}{3} + \cdots + \frac{(-1)^n}{2n+1} + \int_0^1 \frac{(-1)^{n+1} x^{2n+2}}{1+x^2}\,dx. \tag{9.28}$$

The monotonicity property of the integral gives the estimate

$$\left| \int_0^1 \frac{(-1)^{n+1} x^{2n+2}}{1+x^2}\,dx \right| \le \int_0^1 x^{2n+2}\,dx = \frac{1}{2n+3},$$

from which it follows that

$$\lim_{n\to\infty} \left[\int_0^1 \frac{(-1)^{n+1} x^{2n+2}}{1+x^2}\,dx \right] = 0.$$

Thus, (9.26) follows from (9.27) and (9.28).   ∎

For each natural number n and each number x in $[0, 1]$, define

$$f_n(x) = \sum_{k=0}^{n} (-1)^k x^{2k},$$

and define $f(x) = 1/(1+x^2)$. The Newton-Gregory Formula may be restated as

$$\lim_{n\to\infty} \left[\int_0^1 f_n \right] = \int_0^1 f.$$

We proved this without proving that the sequence of functions $\{f_n : [0, 1] \to \mathbb{R}\}$ converges uniformly to the function $f : [0, 1] \to \mathbb{R}$. In fact, we do not even have pointwise convergence on the whole interval $[0, 1]$, since the sequence $\{f_n(1)\}$ does not converge to $f(1)$.

EXERCISES

1. For each natural number n and each number x in $(-1, 1)$, define

$$f_n(x) = \sqrt{x^2 + \frac{1}{n}},$$

and define $f(x) = |x|$. Prove that the sequence $\{f_n: (-1, 1) \to \mathbb{R}\}$ converges uniformly to the function $f: (-1, 1) \to \mathbb{R}$. Check that each function $f_n: (-1, 1) \to \mathbb{R}$ is differentiable, whereas the limit function $f: (-1, 1) \to \mathbb{R}$ is not differentiable. Does this contradict Theorem 9.19?

2. For each natural number n and each number x in $[0, 1]$, define

$$f_n(x) = nxe^{-nx^2}.$$

Prove that the sequence $\{f_n: [0, 1] \to \mathbb{R}\}$ converges pointwise to the constant function 0, but that the sequence of integrals $\{\int_0^1 f_n\}$ does not converge to 0. Does this contradict Theorem 9.18?

3. Prove that if $\{f_n: \mathbb{R} \to \mathbb{R}\}$ is a sequence of differentiable functions such that the sequence of derivatives $\{f_n': \mathbb{R} \to \mathbb{R}\}$ is uniformly convergent and the sequence $\{f_n(0)\}$ is also convergent, then $\{f_n: \mathbb{R} \to \mathbb{R}\}$ is pointwise convergent. Is the assumption that the sequence $\{f_n(0)\}$ converges necessary?

4. Give an example of a sequence of differentiable functions $\{f_n: (-1, 1) \to \mathbb{R}\}$ that converges uniformly but for which $\{f_n'(0)\}$ is unbounded.

5. Under the assumptions of Theorem 9.19, show that for each interval $[\alpha, \beta]$ contained in I, the sequence $\{f_n: [\alpha, \beta] \to \mathbb{R}\}$ converges uniformly to $f: [\alpha, \beta] \to \mathbb{R}$.

9.4 Power Series

In the study of Taylor series, we began with an infinitely differentiable function; we then constructed a Taylor series, which we analyzed for convergence to the given function. We will now change our point of view. In this section we will *define* a function by a power series expansion and study the properties of such a function.

DEFINITION *Given a sequence of real numbers $\{c_k\}$ indexed by the nonnegative integers, we define the domain of convergence of the series $\sum_{k=0}^{\infty} c_k x^k$ to be the set of all numbers x such that the series $\sum_{k=0}^{\infty} c_k x^k$ converges. Denote the domain of convergence by D. We then define a function $f: D \to \mathbb{R}$ by*

$$f(x) = \lim_{n \to \infty} \left[\sum_{k=0}^{n} c_k x^k \right] = \sum_{k=0}^{\infty} c_k x^k \quad \text{for all } x \text{ in } D. \tag{9.29}$$

We will refer to (9.29) as a power series expansion, and will call the set D the domain of convergence of the expansion.

EXAMPLE 9.15 Consider the series

$$\sum_{k=0}^{\infty} \frac{(-1)^k x^k}{k+2}. \tag{9.30}$$

Fix a number x. Since

$$\lim_{k \to \infty} \left| \frac{(-1)^{k+1} x^{k+1}}{k+3} \middle/ \frac{(-1)^k x^k}{k+2} \right| = |x|,$$

it follows from the Ratio Test for Series that (9.30) converges if $|x| < 1$ and diverges if $|x| > 1$. For $x = 1$, from the Alternating Series Test we conclude that (9.30) converges. For $x = -1$, the Integral Test shows that the series diverges. Thus the domain of convergence of the power series (9.30) is the interval $(-1, 1]$. $\square$

EXAMPLE 9.16 Consider the series

$$\sum_{k=0}^{\infty} k! x^k.$$

For any nonzero number x, the terms of the series $\sum_{k=0}^{\infty} k! x^k$ do not converge to 0, and hence the series does not converge. Thus the domain of convergence of the power series $\sum_{k=0}^{\infty} k! x^k$ consists of the single point $x = 0$. $\square$

EXAMPLE 9.17 Consider the series

$$\sum_{k=0}^{\infty} \frac{1}{(1+k!)} x^k.$$

Fix a number x. Since

$$\lim_{k \to \infty} \left[\frac{1}{(1+(k+1)!)} x^{k+1} \middle/ \frac{1}{(1+k!)} x^k \right] = 0,$$

the Ratio Test for Series shows that the domain of convergence of this series is the set of all real numbers. $\square$

A principal objective of this section is to show that if the function $f: (-r, r) \to \mathbb{R}$ is defined by the power series expansion

$$f(x) = \lim_{n \to \infty} \left[\sum_{k=0}^{n} c_k x^k \right] = \sum_{k=0}^{\infty} c_k x^k \quad \text{for } |x| < r,$$

then $f: (-r, r) \to \mathbb{R}$ is differentiable and, moreover,

$$f'(x) = \frac{d}{dx}\left[\lim_{n\to\infty}\sum_{k=0}^{n} c_k x^k\right]$$

$$= \lim_{n\to\infty}\left[\frac{d}{dx}\left[\sum_{k=0}^{n} c_k x^k\right]\right]$$

$$= \lim_{n\to\infty}\left[\sum_{k=1}^{n} k c_k x^{k-1}\right]$$

$$= \sum_{k=1}^{\infty} k c_k x^{k-1} \quad \text{if} \quad |x| < r. \tag{9.31}$$

The above computation is known as *term-by-term differentiation* of a series expansion. It is not at all obvious that the passage from the first line to the second is justified. Once this computation is justified, it follows easily that the function $f:(-r, r) \to \mathbb{R}$ has derivatives of all orders and that term-by-term differentiation of all orders is valid.

For sequences of functions, we have distinguished between pointwise convergence and uniform convergence. It is necessary to make a similar distinction for the convergence of power series.

DEFINITION *Let A be a subset of the domain of convergence of the power series $\sum_{k=0}^{\infty} c_k x^k$. Define the function $f: A \to \mathbb{R}$ by*

$$f(x) = \sum_{k=0}^{\infty} c_k x^k \quad \text{for all } x \text{ in } A, \tag{9.32}$$

and for each natural number n, define the function $s_n: A \to \mathbb{R}$ by

$$s_n(x) = \sum_{k=0}^{n} c_k x^k \quad \text{for all } x \text{ in } A.$$

The series $\sum_{k=0}^{\infty} c_k x^k$ is said to be uniformly convergent on the set A provided that the sequence of partial sums $\{s_n: A \to \mathbb{R}\}$ converges uniformly to the function $f: A \to \mathbb{R}$.

LEMMA 9.22 The power series $\sum_{k=0}^{\infty} c_k x^k$ is uniformly convergent on the set A provided that the following condition holds:

There is a positive number M and a number α with $0 \le \alpha < 1$ such that for each natural number k,

$$|c_k x^k| \le M\alpha^k \quad \text{for all } x \text{ in } A. \tag{9.33}$$

Proof Define $\{s_n: A \to \mathbb{R}\}$ to be the sequence of partial sums for the series $\sum_{k=0}^{\infty} c_k x^k$ on the set A. By the very definition of uniform convergence on a set, we must show that the sequence of functions $\{s_n: A \to \mathbb{R}\}$ is uniformly convergent. However, the Weierstrass Uniform Convergence Criterion asserts that a sequence of functions converges uniformly if and only if the sequence is uniformly Cauchy. Thus it suffices to show that the sequence of partial sums is uniformly Cauchy.

Let $\epsilon > 0$. We need to find a natural number N such that for each integer $n \geq N$ and every natural number k,

$$|s_{n+k}(x) - s_n(x)| < \epsilon \qquad \text{for all } x \text{ in } A. \tag{9.34}$$

However, from the definition of the partial sums, the Triangle Inequality, and the Geometric Sum Formula, we see that for any pair of natural numbers k and n,

$$|s_{n+k}(x) - s_n(x)| = |c_{n+k}x^{n+k} + \cdots + c_{n+1}x^{n+1}|$$

$$\leq |c_{n+k}x^{n+k}| + \cdots + |c_{n+1}x^{n+1}|$$

$$\leq M[\alpha^{n+k} + \cdots + \alpha^{n+1}]$$

$$= M\alpha^{n+1}[1 + \cdots + \alpha^{k-1}]$$

$$= M\alpha^{n+1}\left[\frac{1 - \alpha^k}{1 - \alpha}\right]$$

$$\leq M\alpha^{n+1}\left[\frac{1}{1 - \alpha}\right] \qquad \text{for all } x \text{ in } A. \tag{9.35}$$

Since $\lim_{n \to \infty} \alpha^n = 0$, we may choose a natural number N such that

$$\alpha^n < \frac{\epsilon}{M}(1 - \alpha) \qquad \text{for all integers } n \geq N.$$

With this choice of N it follows from (9.35) that the required inequality (9.34) holds.

∎

In order to use the above lemma to justify term-by-term differentiation of a power series, it is useful to observe that if α is a number with $0 \leq \alpha < 1$, then there is a number c such that

$$k\alpha^k \leq c(\sqrt{\alpha})^k \qquad \text{for every nonnegative integer } k.$$

Indeed, to see this, we write $k\alpha^k = k\sqrt{\alpha}^k \cdot \sqrt{\alpha}^k$ and then choose c to be any upper bound for the sequence $\{k\sqrt{\alpha}^k\}$; there is such an upper bound, because the sequence $\{k\sqrt{\alpha}^k\}$ converges to 0.

THEOREM 9.23   Suppose that the nonzero number x_0 is in the domain of convergence of the power series $\sum_{k=0}^{\infty} c_k x^k$. Let r be any positive number less than $|x_0|$. Then the interval $[-r, r]$ is in the domain of convergence of the power series $\sum_{k=0}^{\infty} c_k x^k$ and also in the domain of convergence of the derived power series $\sum_{k=1}^{\infty} kc_k x^{k-1}$. Moreover, each of the power series

$$\sum_{k=0}^{\infty} c_k x^k \quad \text{and} \quad \sum_{k=1}^{\infty} kc_k x^{k-1}$$

converges uniformly on the interval $[-r, r]$.

Proof   First, we show that the power series $\sum_{k=0}^{\infty} c_k x^k$ converges uniformly on the interval $[-r, r]$. Since the series $\sum_{k=0}^{\infty} c_k x_0^k$ converges, the terms of this series converge to 0, so, in particular, the terms are bounded. Thus we can choose a number M such that

$$|c_k x_0^k| \leq M \quad \text{for every natural number } k.$$

Define $\alpha = r/|x_0|$ and observe that $0 \leq \alpha < 1$. Moreover, writing x as $x = (x/x_0)x_0$, we see that for every natural number k,

$$|c_k x|^k \leq M\alpha^k \quad \text{if} \quad |x| \leq r. \tag{9.36}$$

The uniform convergence of the series $\sum_{k=0}^{\infty} c_k x^k$ on the interval $[-r, r]$ now follows from Lemma 9.22.

Now we consider the derived series $\sum_{k=1}^{\infty} k c_k x^{k-1}$. It is convenient to write this series as $\sum_{k=0}^{\infty} a_k x^k$, where $a_k = (k+1)c_{k+1}$ for every nonnegative integer k. To show that the series converges uniformly on the interval $[-r, r]$, we will again use Lemma 9.22. In order to do so, observe that for each x in the interval $[-r, r]$ and each natural number k,

$$|a_k x^k| = |(k+1)c_{k+1}x^k| = \frac{(k+1)}{k|x_0|}\left|c_{k+1}x_0^{k+1} K \left(\frac{x}{x_0}\right)^k\right|. \tag{9.37}$$

As we observed above, letting $\beta = \sqrt{\alpha}$, there is a number c such that for every natural number k,

$$k\alpha^k \leq c\beta^k.$$

Using this and (9.37), we see that for each natural number k,

$$|a_k x^k| \leq c'\beta^k \quad \text{if} \quad |x| \leq r,$$

where $c' = 2Mc/|x_0|$. The uniform convergence of the series $\sum_{k=1}^{\infty} k c_k x^{k-1}$ on the interval $[-r, r]$ now follows from Lemma 9.22.   ∎

Let D be the domain of convergence of the power series expansion $\sum_{k=0}^{\infty} c_k x^k$. From Theorem 9.23, it follows that $D = \mathbb{R}$ if D is unbounded. If D is bounded, we define

$$r = \sup D,$$

and it follows that

$$(-r, r) \subseteq D \subseteq [r, r].$$

Because of this, we call the number r the *radius of convergence* of the series $\sum_{k=0}^{\infty} c_k x^k$.

We leave it as an exercise for the reader to verify that if the sequence $\{|a_n|^{1/n}\}$ converges to α, then $D = \mathbb{R}$ if $\alpha = 0$, and $r = \alpha^{-1}$ if $\alpha > 0$ (see Exercise 14).

THEOREM 9.24 Let r be a positive number such that the interval $(-r, r)$ lies in the domain of convergence of the series $\sum_{k=0}^{\infty} c_k x^k$. Define

$$f(x) = \sum_{k=0}^{\infty} c_k x^k \quad \text{if } |x| < r.$$

Then the function $f: (-r, r) \to \mathbb{R}$ has derivatives of all orders. For each natural number n,

$$\frac{d^n}{dx^n}[f(x)] = \sum_{k=0}^{\infty} \frac{d^n}{dx^n}[c_k x^k] \quad \text{if} \quad |x| < r,$$

so that, in particular,

$$\frac{f^{(n)}(0)}{n!} = c_n.$$

Proof It is clear that it will be sufficient to prove that

$$f'(x) = \sum_{k=0}^{\infty} \frac{d}{dx}(c_k x^k) \quad \text{if} \quad |x| < r$$

and hence $$f'(0) = c_1.$$

The general result follows by induction, since according to Theorem 9.23, the derived series also converges on $(-r, r)$.

Choose R to be any positive number less than r. Since the series $\sum_{k=0}^{\infty} c_k x^k$ converges at each point between R and r, according to Theorem 9.23, each of the series

$$\sum_{k=0}^{\infty} c_k x^k \quad \text{and} \quad \sum_{k=0}^{\infty} k c_k x^{k-1}$$

converges uniformly on the interval $[-R, R]$.

For each natural number n, define

$$s_n(x) = \sum_{k=0}^{n} c_k x^k \quad \text{if} \quad |x| < R.$$

Then each of the sequences of functions

$$\{s_n : (-R, R) \to \mathbb{R}\} \quad \text{and} \quad \{s_n' : (-R, R) \to \mathbb{R}\}$$

is uniformly convergent. Theorem 9.20 implies that

$$\lim_{n \to \infty} s_n'(x) = f'(x) \quad \text{if} \quad |x| < R;$$

that is, $$\sum_{k=0}^{\infty} k c_k x^{k-1} = f'(x) \quad \text{if} \quad |x| < R.$$

Since for each point x in the interval $(-r, r)$ we can choose a positive number R less than r with $|x| < R$, it follows that

$$f'(x) = \sum_{k=0}^{\infty} kc_k x^{k-1} \quad \text{for all points } x \text{ in the interval } (-r, r). \qquad \blacksquare$$

The above theorem implies that a function defined by a power series expansion on the interval $(-r, r)$ coincides with its Taylor series expansion about 0; this is a uniqueness result for the coefficients of a power series expansion.

Recall that in Section 5.2 we *assumed* that the differential equation

$$\begin{cases} F''(x) + F(x) = 0 & \text{for all } x \\ F(0) = 1, \quad F'(0) = 0 \end{cases} \qquad (9.38)$$

had a solution. It is a consequence of Theorem 8.11 that this assumed solution of (9.38) must necessarily have the following Taylor series expansion:

$$F(x) = \sum_{k=0}^{\infty} \frac{(-1)^k}{(2k)!} x^{2k} \quad \text{for all } x. \qquad (9.39)$$

We will now prove that the power series expansion (9.39) does indeed define the unique solution of (9.38).

THEOREM 9.25 For each number x, the series

$$\sum_{k=0}^{\infty} \frac{(-1)^k}{(2k)!} x^{2k}$$

converges. Define

$$F(x) = \sum_{k=0}^{\infty} \frac{(-1)^k}{(2k)!} x^{2k} \quad \text{for all } x. \qquad (9.40)$$

Then the function $F: \mathbb{R} \to \mathbb{R}$ has derivatives of all orders and satisfies the differential equation (9.38).

Proof From the Ratio Test for Series, it follows that the domain of convergence of the series $\sum_{k=0}^{\infty}[(-1)^k/(2k)!]x^{2k}$ is the set of all real numbers. Thus, the above function $F: \mathbb{R} \to \mathbb{R}$ is properly defined. Moreover, by Theorem 9.24, it follows that for all x,

$$F'(x) = \sum_{k=1}^{\infty} \frac{(-1)^k}{(2k-1)!} x^{2k-1}$$

and

$$F''(x) = \sum_{k=2}^{\infty} \frac{(-1)^k}{(2k-2)!} x^{2k-2} = -F(x).$$

Thus the power series expansion (9.40) defines a function $F: \mathbb{R} \to \mathbb{R}$ that satisfies the differential equation (9.38). $\blacksquare$

For any number x_0, the substitution of $x - x_0$ for x reduces the study of power series expansions of the form $\sum_{k=0}^{\infty} c_k(x - x_0)^k$ to the case in which $x_0 = 0$.

EXERCISES   **1.** Determine the domains of convergence of each of the following power series:

$$\text{(a)} \ \sum_{k=1}^{\infty} \frac{x^k}{k5^k} \qquad \text{(b)} \ \sum_{k=1}^{\infty} k! x^k \qquad \text{(c)} \ \sum_{k=0}^{\infty} \frac{(-1)^k x^{2k-1}}{(2k+1)!}$$

2. Prove that

$$\frac{1}{(1+x)} = \sum_{k=0}^{\infty} (-1)^k x^k \quad \text{if} \quad |x| < 1.$$

3. Prove that

$$\frac{1}{(1+x)^2} = \sum_{k=0}^{\infty} (-1)^k k x^{k-1} \quad \text{if} \quad |x| < 1.$$

4. Prove that

$$\frac{1}{(1+x^2)^2} = \sum_{k=0}^{\infty} (-1)^k k x^{2k-2} \quad \text{if} \quad |x| < 1.$$

5. Prove that

$$x = \sum_{k=0}^{\infty} \left(1 - \frac{1}{x}\right)^k \quad \text{if} \quad |1 - x| < |x|.$$

6. Define $f(x) = 1/(1-x)^3$, if $|x| < 1$. Find a power series expansion for the function $f: (-1, 1) \to \mathbb{R}$.

7. Suppose that the domain of convergence of the power series $\sum_{k=0}^{\infty} c_k x^k$ contains the interval $(-r, r)$. Define

$$f(x) = \sum_{k=0}^{\infty} c_k x^k \quad \text{if} \quad |x| < r.$$

Let the interval $[a, b]$ be contained in the interval $(-r, r)$. Prove that

$$\int_a^b f(x)\, dx = \sum_{k=0}^{\infty} \frac{c_k}{k+1} [b^{k+1} - a^{k+1}].$$

8. Obtain a series expansion for the integral

$$\int_0^{1/2} 1/(1 + x^4)\, dx$$

and justify your calculation.

9. For each number x, define

$$h(x) = \sum_{k=0}^{\infty} \frac{x^{2k}}{(2k)!} \quad \text{and} \quad g(x) = \sum_{k=0}^{\infty} \frac{x^{2k+1}}{(2k+1)!}.$$

Prove that for any pair of numbers α and β, the function

$$f = \alpha h + \beta g : \mathbb{R} \to \mathbb{R}$$

is a solution of the differential equation

$$\begin{cases} f''(x) - f(x) = 0, & x \text{ in } \mathbb{R} \\ f(0) = \alpha \quad \text{and} \quad f'(0) = \beta. \end{cases}$$

10. Use Bernoulli's Inequality to show that if α is a number with $0 \le \alpha < 1$, then for every natural number k,

$$k\alpha^k \le \left[\frac{\sqrt{\alpha}}{1 - \sqrt{\alpha}}\right](\sqrt{\alpha})^k.$$

11. Prove that if $0 \le \alpha < 1$, then $\lim_{n\to\infty} k\alpha^k = 0$.

12. Rewrite the Geometric Sum Formula as follows: For each natural number n,

$$\frac{1}{1-x} - (1 + x + \cdots + x^n) = \frac{x^{n+1}}{1-x} \quad \text{if} \quad x \ne 1.$$

Differentiate this identity to obtain

$$\frac{d}{dx}\left(\frac{1}{1-x}\right) - [1 + 2x + \cdots + nx^{n-1}] = \frac{(n+1)x^n - nx^{n+1}}{(1-x)^2}.$$

Now use this identity and Exercise 11 to directly justify term-by-term differentiation of the Geometric Series.

13. Prove that the series

$$\sum_{k=0}^{\infty} \frac{1}{1 + |x|^k}$$

converges if and only if $|x| > 1$. In particular, show that the series converges at $x = 2$ but not at $x = 1$. Does this contradict Theorem 9.23? (*Hint:* This is not a power series.)

14. Suppose that $\lim_{n\to\infty} |a_n|^{1/n} = \alpha$.
    (a) If $\alpha > 0$, show that $\sum_{k=0}^{\infty} a_n x^n$ converges if $|x| < 1/\alpha$ and diverges if $|x| > 1/\alpha$.
    (b) If $\alpha = 0$, show that $\sum_{k=0}^{\infty} a_n x^n$ converges for all $x \ne 0$.

9.5   A Continuous Function That Fails at Each Point to Be Differentiable

Weierstrass presented the first example of a continuous function $f: \mathbb{R} \to \mathbb{R}$ that has the remarkable property that there is no point at which it is differentiable. We will analyze such an example, where $f: \mathbb{R} \to \mathbb{R}$ is defined by an expansion

$$f(x) = \sum_{k=1}^{\infty} h_k(x) \quad \text{for all } x$$

and the function $f: \mathbb{R} \to \mathbb{R}$ inherits all of the nondifferentiability possessed by the individual h_k''s.

Define $h(x) = |x|$ if $|x| \le 1/2$ and then extend the function $h: [-1/2, 1/2] \to \mathbb{R}$ to $h: \mathbb{R} \to \mathbb{R}$ so that $h: \mathbb{R} \to \mathbb{R}$ has period 1. The function $h: \mathbb{R} \to \mathbb{R}$ is a so-called "saw-toothed" function, the "teeth" of which have base length equal to 1 and depth equal to $1/2$.

For each natural number k, define the function $h_k: \mathbb{R} \to \mathbb{R}$ by

$$h_k(x) = \left(\frac{1}{4}\right)^{k-1} h(4^{k-1}x) \quad \text{for all } x.$$

Then the function $h_k : \mathbb{R} \to \mathbb{R}$ is also a "saw-toothed" function, the "teeth" of which have base length equal to $1/4^{k-1}$ and depth equal to $1/(2 \cdot 4^{k-1})$. Also, the function $h_k : \mathbb{R} \to \mathbb{R}$ has period $(1/4)^{k-1}$. Furthermore,

$$|h_k(x)| \leq \frac{1}{2} \left(\frac{1}{4} \right)^{k-1} \qquad \text{for all } x. \tag{9.41}$$

FIGURE 9.5

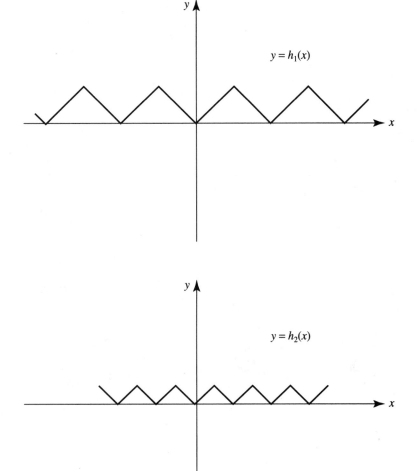

LEMMA 9.26   For each number x, define

$$f(x) = \lim_{n \to \infty} \left[\sum_{k=1}^{n} h_k(x) \right] = \sum_{k=1}^{\infty} h_k(x). \tag{9.42}$$

Then the function $f : \mathbb{R} \to \mathbb{R}$ is continuous.

Proof For each number x and each natural number n, define

$$f_n(x) = \sum_{k=1}^{n} h_k(x).$$

Since each function $h_k : \mathbb{R} \to \mathbb{R}$ is continuous, each function $f_n : \mathbb{R} \to \mathbb{R}$ is also continuous. We will prove that the sequence of functions $\{f_n : \mathbb{R} \to \mathbb{R}\}$ is uniformly Cauchy. Once this is proven, it follows from the Weierstrass Uniform Convergence Criterion that it converges uniformly. Then, by Theorem 9.17, we may conclude that the limit function is also continuous.

To verify the Cauchy property, observe that from the Triangle Inequality, inequality (9.41), and the Geometric Sum Formula it follows that for any pair of natural numbers k and n and any number x,

$$|f_{n+k}(x) - f_n(x)| = |h_{n+k}(x) + \cdots + h_{n+1}(x)|$$

$$\leq |h_{n+k}(x)| + \cdots + |h_{n+1}(x)|$$

$$\leq \left(\frac{1}{2}\right)\left[\left(\frac{1}{4}\right)^{n+k-1} + \cdots + \left(\frac{1}{4}\right)^{n}\right]$$

$$= \left(\frac{1}{4^n}\right)\left(\frac{1}{2}\right)\left[1 + \cdots + \left(\frac{1}{4}\right)^{k-1}\right]$$

$$\leq \frac{1}{4^n}.$$

Since $\lim_{n\to\infty} 1/4^n = 0$, it follows from this inequality that the sequence of functions $\{f_n : \mathbb{R} \to \mathbb{R}\}$ is uniformly Cauchy. ∎

THEOREM 9.27 Define the function $f : \mathbb{R} \to \mathbb{R}$ by

$$f(x) = \sum_{k=1}^{\infty} h_k(x) \text{ for all } x.$$

Then

(i) The function $f : \mathbb{R} \to \mathbb{R}$ is continuous, but

(ii) There is no point at which the function $f : \mathbb{R} \to \mathbb{R}$ is differentiable.

Proof We have already proven that the function $f : \mathbb{R} \to \mathbb{R}$ is continuous.

Let x_0 be any number. We will show that $f : \mathbb{R} \to \mathbb{R}$ is not differentiable at x_0 by choosing a sequence of numbers $\{x_n\}$, with each $x_n \neq x_0$, that converges to x_0 but for which the limit

$$\lim_{n\to\infty} \frac{f(x_n) - f(x_0)}{x_n - x_0}$$

does not exist.

Let n be a natural number. Observe that for an integer m, the interval

$$I_m = \left[m \left(\frac{1}{2} \right) \left(\frac{1}{4} \right)^{n-1}, \; (m+1) \left(\frac{1}{2} \right) \left(\frac{1}{4} \right)^{n-1} \right]$$

has length equal to $1/(2 \cdot 4^{n-1})$ and, moreover, the union of such intervals equals all of $\mathbb{R}$. Thus, we may choose an integer m such that either

(i) the interval $[x_0, \; x_0 + (1/4)^n]$ is contained in I_m, or

(ii) the interval $[x_0 - (1/4)^n, \; x_0]$ is contained in I_m.

If the first possibility occurs, define $x_n = x_0 + (1/4)^n$; otherwise, define $x_n = x_0 - (1/4)^n$. Now, if $1 \le k \le n$, the function $h_k \colon \mathbb{R} \to \mathbb{R}$ on the interval I_m is either strictly increasing with slope 1 or strictly decreasing with slope -1 (see Exercise 1). Thus,

$$\left| \frac{h_k(x_n) - h_k(x_0)}{x_n - x_0} \right| = 1 \quad \text{if} \quad 1 \le k \le n.$$

On the other hand, since each $h_k \colon \mathbb{R} \to \mathbb{R}$ has period $(1/4)^{k-1}$, we see that

$$\frac{h_k(x_n) - h_k(x_0)}{x_n - x_0} = 0 \quad \text{if} \quad k > n.$$

Thus,

$$\frac{f(x_n) - f(x_0)}{x_n - x_0} = \sum_{k=1}^{\infty} \frac{h_k(x_n) - h_k(x_0)}{x_n - x_0} = \sum_{k=1}^{n} \frac{h_k(x_n) - h_k(x_0)}{x_n - x_0}$$

is an integer, which is odd if n is odd and is even if n is even. As a consequence, the limit

$$\lim_{n \to \infty} \frac{f(x_n) - f(x_0)}{x_n - x_0}$$

does not exist, so the function $f \colon \mathbb{R} \to \mathbb{R}$ is not differentiable at the point x_0. ∎

In the following exercises, the functions $h_k \colon \mathbb{R} \to \mathbb{R}$ and $f \colon \mathbb{R} \to \mathbb{R}$ are those defined above.

EXERCISES

1. (a) Show that for each integer k,

$$\frac{h_k(u) - h_k(v)}{u - v} = \begin{cases} 1 & \text{if } 0 \le u < v \le (1/2)\,(1/4)^{k-1} \\ -1 & \text{if } -(1/2)\,(1/4)^{k-1} \le u < v \le 0. \end{cases}$$

   (b) Use (a) to show that for each integer m, each natural number n, and each natural number k with $1 \le k \le n$,

$$\left| \frac{h_k(u) - h_k(v)}{u - v} \right| = 1$$

   if $\quad m \left(\frac{1}{2} \right) \left(\frac{1}{4} \right)^{n-1} \le u < v \le (m+1) \left(\frac{1}{2} \right) \left(\frac{1}{4} \right)^{n-1}$.

2. Let $r > 0$. Prove that for each number x_0 there is an integer m such that either the interval $[x_0, x_0 + r/2]$ is contained in the interval $[mr, (m+1)r]$ or the interval $[x_0 - r/2, x_0]$ is contained in the interval $[mr, (m+1)r]$.

3. Suppose that the function $g: \mathbb{R} \to \mathbb{R}$ has period $T > 0$. Show that for each natural number n, the function $g: \mathbb{R} \to \mathbb{R}$ also has period nT.

4. For each natural number n, define

$$u_n = -\left(\frac{1}{2}\right)\left(\frac{1}{4}\right)^{n-1} \quad \text{and} \quad v_n = \left(\frac{1}{2}\right)\left(\frac{1}{4}\right)^{n-1}.$$

Show that

$$h_k(u_n) = 0 = h_k(v_n) \quad \text{if} \quad k > n,$$

whereas

$$h_k(u_n) > 0 \quad \text{and} \quad h_k(v_n) > 0 \quad \text{if} \quad 1 \leq k \leq n.$$

Conclude that $f(u_n) > 0$ and $f(v_n) > 0$, and hence that there is no interval I containing the point 0 on which the function $f: I \to \mathbb{R}$ is monotonic.

5. Use Exercise 4 to show that there is no interval I on which the function $f: I \to \mathbb{R}$ is monotonic.

6. Find a function $g: \mathbb{R} \to \mathbb{R}$ that is continuously differentiable, but for which there is no point at which it has a second derivative.

A
Consequences of the Field and Positivity Axioms

In the Preliminaries, we stated the Field Axioms and the Positivity Axioms for the real numbers and made various assertions regarding elementary consequences of these axioms. In this first appendix, we will verify some of these assertions.

For convenience, we will restate the Field Axioms. For each pair of real numbers a and b, a real number called the *sum* of a and b is defined and is denoted by $a + b$, and a real number called the *product* of a and b is defined and is denoted by ab. These operations satisfy the following collection of axioms:

The Field Axioms

Commutativity of Addition: For all real numbers a and b,

$$a + b = b + a.$$

Associativity of Addition: For all real numbers a, b, and c,

$$(a + b) + c = a + (b + c).$$

The Additive Identity: There is a real number, denoted by 0, such that

$$0 + a = a \quad \text{for all real numbers } a.$$

The Additive Inverse: For each real number a, there is a real number b such that

$$a + b = 0.$$

Commutativity of Multiplication: For all real numbers a and b,

$$ab = ba.$$

Associativity of Multiplication: For all real numbers a, b, and c,

$$(ab)c = a(bc).$$

The Multiplicative Identity: There is a real number, denoted by 1, such that

$$1a = a \quad \text{for all real numbers } a.$$

The Multiplicative Inverse: For each real number $a \neq 0$, there is a real number b such that

$$ab = 1.$$

The Distributive Property: For all real numbers a, b, and c,

$$a(b + c) = ab + ac.$$

The Nontriviality Assumption:

$$1 \neq 0.$$

First, observe that there is only one number that has the property asserted in the additive identity axiom. Indeed, if $0'$ also has the property that

$$0' + a = a \quad \text{for all real numbers } a,$$

then in particular we have

$$0' + 0 = 0.$$

But by the commutative property of addition and the definition of 0 as an additive identity,

$$0' + 0 = 0 + 0' = 0'.$$

Thus $0 = 0'$, so there is only one additive identity.

**PROPOSITION
1**

For each real number a,

$$a0 = 0a = 0.$$

Proof   Observe that

$$0 + 0 = 0.$$

Thus, by the Distributive Axiom,

$$0a + 0a = 0a.$$

If we add the additive inverse of $0a$ to each side and use the associativity of addition, we obtain $0a = 0$, and from this and the commutative property of multiplication it also follows that $a0 = 0$. ∎

**PROPOSITION
2**

For any pair of real numbers a and b, if

$$ab = 0,$$

then $a = 0$ or $b = 0$.

Proof   If $a = 0$, the proof is complete. So suppose that $a \neq 0$. We must show that $b = 0$. Since $a \neq 0$, by the multiplicative inverse axiom we can select a number d such that $da = 1$. Since $ab = 0$, it follows from Proposition 1 that

$$d(ab) = d0 = 0.$$

On the other hand, by the associative and commutative properties of multiplication, and by the definition of 1 as the multiplicative identity, it follows that

$$d(ab) = (da)b = 1b = b.$$

Thus $b = 0$.   ■

The additive inverse axiom asserts that for each number a, there is a number b such that $a + b = 0$. In fact, there is only one such number; it is called the *additive inverse* of a. To see why there is only one such number, suppose that b' also has the property that $a + b' = 0$. Then

$$
\begin{aligned}
b' &= 0 + b' \\
&= (a + b) + b' && \text{by the choice of } b \\
&= (b + a) + b' && \text{by commutativity of addition} \\
&= b + (a + b') && \text{by associativity of addition} \\
&= b + 0 && \text{by the choice of } b' \\
&= 0 + b && \text{by commutativity of addition} \\
&= b && \text{by the definition of } 0.
\end{aligned}
$$

Thus $b = b'$. Of course, we denote the additive inverse of a by $-a$. The additive inverse possesses the following familiar properties:

PROPOSITION 3

For all real numbers a and b,

   (i) $-(-a) = a$

   (ii) $-a = (-1)a$

   (iii) $-ab = (-a)b$

   (iv) $ab = (-a)(-b)$

   (v) $1 = (-1)(-1)$.

Proof   Part (i) follows from the fact that $-(-a)$ is the unique number that when added to $-a$ equals 0 and from the observation that a has this property. To verify (ii), we must show that

$$a + (-1)a = 0.$$

But since 1 is the multiplicative identity,

$$a + (-1)a = 1a + (-1)a$$

$$= (1 + (-1))a \qquad \text{by the distributive property}$$

$$= 0a \qquad \text{since } -1 \text{ is the additive inverse of } 1$$

$$= 0 \qquad \text{by Proposition 1.}$$

To verify (iii), observe that

$$-ab = (-1)ab \qquad \text{by (ii)}$$

$$= ((-1)a)b \qquad \text{by associativity of multiplication}$$

$$= (-a)b \qquad \text{again by (ii)}$$

To verify (iv), observe that

$$ab = -(-ab) \qquad \text{by (i)}$$

$$= -((-a)b) \qquad \text{by (iii)}$$

$$= -(b(-a)) \qquad \text{by commutativity of multiplication}$$

$$= (-b)(-a) \qquad \text{by (iii)}$$

$$= (-a)(-b) \qquad \text{by commutativity of multiplication.}$$

Finally, observe that (v) follows from (iv) when we set $a = b = 1$. ■

For numbers a and b, we define the *difference* $a - b$ by

$$a - b \equiv a + (-b).$$

Using the preceding proposition, it is not difficult to verify that for any numbers a, b, and c,

$$a(b - c) = ab - ac \quad \text{and} \quad -(b - c) = -b + c.$$

Let us now examine some consequences of the multiplication axioms. Just as we have shown that the additive identity is unique, a similar argument shows that the multiplicative identity is unique. Also, an argument similar to the one that showed that the additive inverse is unique shows that for a nonzero number a, its multiplicative inverse is unique; the multiplicative inverse of a is, of course, denoted by a^{-1}. The multiplicative inverse possesses the following familiar properties:

**PROPOSITION
4**
For any nonzero real numbers a and b,

(i) $(a^{-1})^{-1} = a$

(ii) $(-a)^{-1} = -a^{-1}$

(iii) $(ab)^{-1} = a^{-1}b^{-1}.$

Proof To verify (i), observe that $(a^{-1})^{-1}$ is the unique number that has the property that when it is multiplied with a^{-1}, the product is 1, and that the number a has this property. To verify (ii), we must show that

$$(-a)(-a^{-1}) = 1.$$

However, by part (iv) of Proposition 3, we have

$$(-a)(-a^{-1}) = (a)(a^{-1}) = 1.$$

Finally, to verify (iii), we must show that

$$(ab)(a^{-1}b^{-1}) = 1.$$

However, by the commutative and associative properties of multiplication,

$$(ab)(a^{-1}b^{-1}) = (aa^{-1})(bb^{-1}) = 1 \cdot 1 = 1. \qquad \blacksquare$$

For any two numbers a and b, with $b \neq 0$, we define

$$\frac{a}{b} = ab^{-1}.$$

Directly from the definition of division and the distributive property, it follows that for any numbers a, b, and c, with $c \neq 0$,

$$\frac{a+b}{c} = \frac{a}{c} + \frac{b}{c}.$$

The Positivity Axioms for the Real Numbers

In the real numbers, there is a natural notion of order—that is, of *greater than*, *less than*, and so forth. A convenient way to codify these properties is by specifying axioms that are satisfied by the set of positive numbers.

The Positivity Axioms

There is a set of real numbers denoted by $\mathcal{P}$, called the set of *positive numbers*, that has the following two properties:

> **P1** If a and b are positive, then ab and $a + b$ are also positive.

> **P2** For a real number a, exactly one of the following three alternatives is true:
>
> $$a \text{ is positive}, \quad -a \text{ is positive}, \quad a = 0.$$

The positivity axioms lead in a natural way to an ordering of the real numbers: For real numbers a and b, we define $a > b$ to mean that $a - b$ is positive, and $a \geq b$ to mean that $a > b$ or $a = b$. We then define $a < b$ to mean that $b > a$, and $a \leq b$ to mean that $b \geq a$.

PROPOSITION
5

For each real number $a \neq 0$, $a^2 > 0$. In particular, $1 > 0$.

Proof Since $a \neq 0$, it follows from the second positivity axiom that either a or $-a$ is positive. If a is positive, then since the product of positive numbers is again positive, a^2 is positive. Similarly, if $-a$ is positive, so is $(-a)(-a)$. But by part (iv) of Proposition 3, $(-a)(-a) = a^2$. Thus again, in this case, a^2 is positive. In particular, since by the nontriviality axiom $1 \neq 0$, $1 = 1 \cdot 1$ is positive. ∎

PROPOSITION 6 For each positive number a, its multiplicative inverse a^{-1} is also positive.

Proof Since $a \cdot a^{-1} = 1 \neq 0$, it follows from Proposition 2 that $a^{-1} \neq 0$. By the first positivity axiom, either a^{-1} or $-a^{-1}$ is positive. But it is not possible for $-a^{-1}$ to be positive, since then $a \cdot (-a^{-1}) = -1$ would also be positive, and this contradicts Proposition 5. Thus a^{-1} is positive. ∎

PROPOSITION 7 If $a > b$, then

$$ac > bc \quad \text{if} \quad c > 0$$

and

$$ac < bc \quad \text{if} \quad c < 0.$$

Proof The number $a - b$ is positive. If c is positive, then the product $(a - b)c = ab - ac$ is also positive; that is, $ac > bc$. On the other hand, if $c < 0$, then $-c$ is positive, so $(a - b)(-c)$ also is positive. However, $(a - b)(-c) = bc - ac$, so $ac < bc$. ∎

EXERCISES

1. Prove that for any numbers a, b, and c,
$$a(b - c) = ab - ac \quad \text{and} \quad -(b - c) = -b + c.$$

2. Prove that the multiplicative identity is unique.
3. Prove that each number $a \neq 0$ has a unique multiplicative inverse.
4. Prove that for any numbers a and b, with $b \neq 0$,
$$-\frac{a}{b} = \frac{-a}{b} = \frac{a}{-b}.$$

Answers to Selected Problems

SECTION 1.1

2. Argue by contradiction: If the set A contains two points u and v with $u < v$, then
$$\inf A \le u < v \le \sup A.$$

3. Note that $x^2 - c = (x + \sqrt{c})(x - \sqrt{c})$. Thus, if $0 = x^2 - c$, then $x = \sqrt{c}$ or $x = -\sqrt{c}$.

9. Hint: Show that if $0 \le x \le 1$, then x is in S, and if $x > 1$, then x is not in S.

SECTION 1.2

3. (a) 0 is a lower bound and the Archimedean Property asserts it is the greatest lower bound; the set has no minimum. The maximum is 1.

   (b) $\sqrt{2}$ is the least upper bound, and $-\sqrt{2}$ is the greatest lower bound. The set has no maximum and no minimum.

5. Hint: Use the density of the rationals.

7. If $a < 0 < b$, then, by the case already considered, there is a rational number and an irrational number in the interval $(0, b)$, and the interval $(0, b)$ is contained in (a, b). If $a < b \le 0$, consider the interval $(-b, -a)$ and reflect.

SECTION 1.3

2. Hint: The Reverse Triangle Inequality implies that $|a| - |b| \le |a - b|$.

8. Hint: Use the Difference of Powers Formula, and note that
$$a^{n-1-k}b^k \ge b^{n-1} \text{ for } 0 \le k \le n - 1.$$

10. (b) Hint: Use Cauchy's Inequality from Exercise 9 and the identity $abc = \sqrt{ab}\sqrt{bc}\sqrt{ca}$.

13. Use mathematical induction for both. To prove the second inequality, first show that if a and b are positive, them $a/b + b/a \ge 2$.

14. (a) Substitute $r = 1/(1 + x^2)$ in the first formula.

(b) Use the first formula with $n = 2$ and $r = 1 - a$.

17. Hint: Use mathematical induction, and make use of Exercise 15.

SECTION 2.1

1. (a) Hint: Let $\epsilon > 0$. Since $\epsilon^2 > 0$, by the Archimedean Property there is a natural number N such that $N > \epsilon^2$, so that $1/\sqrt{n} < \epsilon$ if $n \geq N$.

   (b) Hint: $1/(n+5) \leq 1/n$.

6. Hint: If $a > 0$, then
$$|\sqrt{a_n} - \sqrt{a}| = |a_n - a|/(\sqrt{a_n} + \sqrt{a}) \leq (1/\sqrt{a})|a_n - a| \text{ for all } n.$$
   If $a = 0$, then
$$|\sqrt{a_n} - \sqrt{0}| = \sqrt{a_n} \leq a_n \text{ if } a_n \leq 1. ??$$

7. No: Consider the sequence $\{(-1)^n\}$.

9. Hint: Show that each $\alpha_n \geq 0$, and use the Binomial Formula as follows:
$$(1 + \alpha_n)^n = \binom{n}{0}1^n\alpha_n^0 + \binom{n}{1}1^{n-1}\alpha_n^1 + \binom{n}{2}1^{n-2}\alpha_n^2 + \cdots \geq \binom{n}{0}1^n\alpha_n^0 + \binom{n}{2}1^{n-2}\alpha_n^2.$$

14. Hint: Use the identity $\sqrt{n+1} - \sqrt{n} = 1/(\sqrt{n+1} + \sqrt{n})$.

17. Hint: First show that, since $|a| < (1 + |a|)/2$, a natural number N can be chosen such that
$$|a_n| \leq (1 + |a|)/2 < 1 \text{ for } n \geq N.$$

18. (a) For $\epsilon = 1, a = 1$, and $\{a_n\} = \{1/n\}$, this criterion holds; but $\lim_{n\to\infty} 1/n \neq 1$.

    (b) Show that this criterion holds if and only if $a_n = a$ for all natural numbers n.

    (c) Show that this criterion holds if and only if there is a natural number N such that $a_n = a$ for $n \geq N$.

19. Hint: Use mathematical induction.

SECTION 2.2

1. (a) monotone (b) not monotone (c) not monotone.

3. Hint: Show that for each natural number n,
$$1 + \frac{1}{2!} + \cdots + \frac{1}{n!} \leq 1 + \frac{1}{2} + \cdots + \frac{1}{2^n}.$$
   Now use the Geometric Sum Formula and the Monotone Convergence Theorem.

5. Hint: Use the Geometric Sum Formula to estimate the terms.

8. Hint: Consider the cases $x_1 = x_2, x_1 < x_2$, and $x_1 > x_2$ in order to verify monotonicity of $\{x_n\}$. Then show boundedness and apply the Monotone Convergence Theorem.

12. (b) The set $[0, 1)$ is not compact since $\{1 - 1/n\}$ is a sequence in $[0, 1)$ such that it, and hence all of its subsequences, converge to the number 1, which is not in $[0, 1)$.

    (c) The whole set of real numbers is not compact, since the sequence $\{n\}$ has the property that every subsequence is unbounded and hence every subsequence fails to converge.

SECTION 3.1

2. Hint: Use Exercise 1.

4. Hint: The density of the rationals implies that for any number x, there is a sequence of rational number $\{x_n\}$ that converges to x.

5. Hint: The function is continuous at $x = 0$ since $|f(x)| = |x^2|$ for all x. The density of the rationals and the irrationals implies it is not continuous at any other point.

8. (a) Hint: Prove, by induction, that $f(nz) = nf(z)$, for any z and any natural number n. In particular, $f(1) = f(n \cdot 1/n) = nf(1/n)$, so $f(1/n) = (1/n)f(1)$.

   (b) Hint: Use the density of the rationals.

SECTION 3.2

1. (a) Show that the function $f: [0,1] \to \mathbb{R}$ is increasing, so the maximizer is $x = 1$.

   (c) Show that the function $h: [-1,1] \to \mathbb{R}$ is decreasing, so the maximizer is $x = -1$.

3. (e) The set of rational numbers in $[0,1]$ is not compact, since there is a sequence in the set that converges to the irrational number $\sqrt{2}/2$ which is not in the set.

7. Hint: Define $x_0 = \inf \{x \text{ in } [0,1] \mid f(x) = 0\}$ and prove that $x_0 > 0$.

SECTION 3.3

1. Hint: Define $f(x) = x^9 + x^2 + 4$ for all x; find points at which the function $f: \mathbb{R} \to \mathbb{R}$ attains positive and negative values, and apply the Intermediate Value Theorem.

4. Hint: Define $g(x) = x - f(x)$ for $0 \leq x \leq 1$, and apply the Intermediate Value Theorem to the function $g: [0,1] \to \mathbb{R}$.

7. Hint: The average of the n numbers $f(x_1), \ldots, f(x_n)$ lies between the largest and the smallest of these numbers. Apply the Intermediate Value Theorem.

10. Hint: Use the density of the irrationals and the Intermediate Value Theorem.

SECTION 3.4

1. Hint: First use the Difference of Powers formula to show that the function is strictly increasing on $(-\infty, 0]$ and on $[0, \infty)$.

6. The inverse is not continuous at $x = 1$. This does not contradict Theorem 3.10, since the domain D is not an interval.

8. Hint: First show that the sequence $\{a_n\}$ is both monotone and bounded.

SECTION 3.5

2. Hint: To verify continuity at $x = 4$, first show that for all $x > 0$,
$$|\sqrt{x} - \sqrt{4}| = |x - 4|/(\sqrt{x} + \sqrt{4}) \leq (1/2)|x - 4|.$$

6. Hint: First show that for all u and v,
$$|h(u) - h(v)| = \left| \frac{u + v}{(1 + u^2)(1 + v^2)} \right| |u - v| \leq 2|u - v|.$$

8. Hint: First show that for all u and v in the interval $[1/100, 1]$,

$$|f(u) - f(v)| = \left| \frac{u - v}{uv} \right| \leq 100^2 |u - v|.$$

10. Let $\epsilon = 1$. Use the difference of cubes formula to show that no matter what $\delta > 0$ is chosen, there are points u and v with $|u - v| < \delta$, but $|u^3 - v^3| > 1$.

14. Uniform continuity follows from Theorem 3.14. To prove that it is not Lipschitz, show that there is no number c such that

$$|\sqrt{x} - \sqrt{0}| \leq c|x - 0| \text{ for all } x \text{ in } [0, 1].$$

16. Hint: Let $\epsilon = 1$. Choose $\delta > 0$ such $|f(u) - f(v)| \leq 1$ for all u and v in (a, b) such that $|u - v| < \delta$. Then observe that the function is bounded on any subinterval of length less than δ. Express (a, b) as the union of finitely many such subintervals.

SECTION 3.6

2. (a) Hint: For $x \neq 1$, observe that $(x^4 - 1)/(x - 1) = x^3 + x^2 + x + 1$.

   (b) Hint: For $x > 0, x \neq 1$ observe that $(\sqrt{x} - 1)/(x - 1) = 1/(\sqrt{x} + 1)$.

5. No conclusion can be reached: for instance, set $g(x) = -f(x)$ for all x in D, so that $\lim_{x \to x_0} [f(x) + g(x)] = 0$, but nothing is known about $\lim_{x \to x_o} f(x)$.

11. (a)

$$\lim_{x \to x_0, x < x_0} f(x) = \begin{cases} f(x_0) & \text{if } x_0 \text{ is not an integer} \\ f(x_0) - 1 & \text{if } x_0 \text{ is an integer.} \end{cases}$$

   (b)

$$\lim_{x \to x_0, x > x_0} f(x) = f(x_0) \text{ for all } x_0.$$

12. Hint: Use the Difference of Powers formula.

14. Hint at the right end-point: Choose any sequence $\{x_n\}$ in (a, b) that converges to b. Show that $\{f(x_n)\}$ converges; define ℓ to be the limit of this sequence and use monotonicity to show that $\lim_{x \to b} f(x) = \ell$.

SECTION 4.1

2. $y = 14x - 15$.

4. (a) 0.   (b) 4.

6. Hint: Show that if $x \neq 0$, then

$$\left| \frac{f(x) - f(0)}{x - 0} \right| \leq |x|.$$

8. Use difference quotients directly in order to show that (a) $f'(0) = 0$, (b) $g'(0) = 0$.

13. Hint: For $h \neq 0$, write

$$\frac{f(x_0 + h) - f(x_0 - h)}{h} = \frac{f(x_0 + h) - f(x_0)}{h} + \frac{f(x_0 - h) - f(x_0)}{-h}.$$

14. Hint: Write $xf(x_0) - x_0 f(x) = x[f(x_0) - f(x)] + f(x)[x - x_0]$.

15. If $g(0) \neq 0$, then the function $|g|: \mathbb{R} \to \mathbb{R}$ is differentiable at $x = 0$. If $g(0) = 0$, then the function $|g|: \mathbb{R} \to \mathbb{R}$ is differentiable at $x = 0$ if and only if $g'(0) = 0$.

SECTION 4.2

1. Use the composition property of limits by noting that for $x_0 > 0$ and $x > 0, x \neq x_0$,
$$\frac{g(x) - g(x_0)}{x - x_0} = c \left[\frac{f(cx) - f(cx_0)}{cx - cx_0} \right]$$

4. No: Consider $f(x) = x$ for all x.

8. Hint: By the Bolzano-Weierstrass Theorem, a subsequence of $\{x_n\}$ converges to a number x_0. First, show that $f(x_0) = 0$, and then show that $f'(x_0) = 0$.

SECTION 4.3

4. Hint: Define $f(x) = x^5 + 5x + 1$ for $-1 < x < 0$. Show that the derivative of $f:(-1,0) \to \mathbb{R}$ is positive and that this function attains positive and negative values.

5. Hint: To show there are at most two solutions, define $f(x) = x^4 + 2x^2 - 6x + 2$ for all x. Since $f''(x) > 0$ for all x, Rolle's Theorem implies that the equation cannot have three solutions.

8. No: Define $f(x) = g(x) = 0$ for all $x > 0$, $f(x) = 0$ for $x < 0$, and $g(x) = 1$ for $x < 0$.

12. Define $g(x) = -\sqrt{1 - x^2} + 26$ for $-1 < x < 1$. The function $g:(-1,1) \to \mathbb{R}$ is a solution, and the Identity Criterion implies it is the only solution.

13. Define $h(x) = f(x)/g(x)$ for all x. Show that $h: \mathbb{R} \to \mathbb{R}$ is constant, since its derivative is identically 0.

SECTION 4.4

2. Hint: Use Theorem 4.21.

4. (b) Show that for $0 < c < 1$, if $f(1) - f(0) = f'(c)(1 - 0)$, then $c = 1/2$. On the other hand, if $g(1) - g(0) = g'(c)(1 - 0)$, then $c = \sqrt{1/3}$.

6. Hint: Use Theorem 4.21.

9. Hint: Prove Leibnitz' Formula by induction, using the product rule for differentiation together with the following identity for binomial coefficients:
$$\binom{n + 1}{k} = \binom{n}{k - 1} + \binom{n}{k}$$

SECTION 4.5

1. By the Identity Criterion, $F(x) = x^2 + x^4/4 + 7/4$ for all x. Thus $F(-1) = 3$.

4. The Identity Criterion implies that there are constants c_1 and c_2 such that $F(x) = x^2/2 + c_1$ for $x > 0$, and $F(x) = x^3/3 + c_2$ for $x < 0$. Since $F: \mathbb{R} \to \mathbb{R}$ is continuous at $x = 0$, $F(0) = c_1 = c_2$, and since $F(2) = 4$, $c_1 = c_2 = 4 - 8/3$.

5. Hint: The density of the irrationals and Darboux's Theorem imply that the derivative of $F: \mathbb{R} \to \mathbb{R}$ is constant. Now apply the Identity Criterion.

SECTION 5.1

2. Hint: Use the very definition of the derivative at $x = 0$ of the function $f : \mathbb{R} \to \mathbb{R}$ defined by $f(x) = a^x$ for all x: $\lim_{n \to \infty} n[f(1/n) - f(0)] = f'(0)$.

3. Hint: Apply the Lagrange Mean Value Theorem to the natural logarithm on the interval $[a, b]$.

7. Hint: Define $f(x) = xe^x - 2$ for $0 < x < 1$. First show that the function $f : (0, 1) \to \mathbb{R}$ is strictly increasing. Then show that the function attains both positive ($e > 2$) and negative values.

9. Hint: First show that $h(0) = 1$, and then, for any x and any $t \neq 0$, observe that
$$\frac{h(x + t) - h(x)}{t} = h(x) \left[\frac{h(t) - h(0)}{t} \right].$$

SECTION 5.2

4. Hint: Define $f(x) = e^{2x} + \cos x + x$ for all x. Show that the derivative of the function $f : \mathbb{R} \to \mathbb{R}$ is always positive and that $f : \mathbb{R} \to \mathbb{R}$ attains both positive and negative values.

8. Hint: Define $g(x) = k^2 [f(x)]^2 + [f'(x)]^2$ for all x. Show that the derivative of $g : \mathbb{R} \to \mathbb{R}$ is identically 0 and $g(0) = 0$. Then note that $0 \le k^2 [f(x)]^2 \le g(x)$ for all x.

10. Hint: First consider the case $a \ge 0$ and $b \ge 0$, and $0 \le \theta \le \pi/2$. Do the other cases based on the oddness of the sine and the evenness of the cosine.

12. Hint: Choose θ_0 such that $\cos \theta_0 = c_1$ and $\sin \theta_0 = c_2$.

14. No; otherwise, since $f'(0) > 0$, there would be a symmetric neighborhood of 0 on which the derivative is positive, and so on which the function is strictly increasing.

SECTION 5.3

1. Hint: Use the Identity Criterion.

6. Hint: Use the Mean Value Theorem.

SECTION 6.2

2. Hint: Since $f : [0, 1] \to \mathbb{R}$ is increasing, for each i, $m_i = (i - 1)^2/n^2$ and $M_i = i^2/n^2$, so that
$$L(f, P_n) - U(f, P_n) = (1/n^3) \left[\sum_{i=1}^{n} i^2 - \sum_{i=1}^{n} (i - i)^2 \right].$$

4. For the partition $P = \{a, b\}$, $m_1 \ge 0$. Thus, $L(f, P) = m_1(b - a) \ge 0$. Hence, $0 \le L(f, P) \le \int_a^b f$.

7. Hint: For $P = \{x_1, \ldots, x_n\}$ a partition of $[a, b]$, and $1 \le i \le n$, by the density of the rationals, $m_i \le 0 \le M_i$, so $L(f, P) \le 0 \le U(f, P)$. Now use the very definition of the integral.

13. In general, no. However, the sum of monotone increasing (resp. decreasing) functions is monotone increasing (decreasing). If one of the functions only attains values of one sign, the product of monotone functions is monotone.

16. Hint: Argue by contradiction. If there is a point x_0 in $[a, b]$ at which $f(x_0) > 0$, then since the function is continuous, there is an interval $[c, d]$ containing x_0 and contained in $[a, b]$, with $c < d$, such that $f(x) > f(x_0)/2$ for all x in $[c, d]$. From the definition of the integral it follows that $\int_c^d f \ge (f(x_0)/2)(d - c) > 0$.

SECTION 6.3

1. (b) For each n, $L(f, P_n) = 1 + 4(n-1)n/2n^2$ and $U(f, P_n) = 1 + 4n(n+1)/2n^2$:

$$\lim_{n \to \infty} \left[1 + 4(n-1)n/2n^2\right] = \lim_{n \to \infty} \left[1 + 4n(n+1)/2n^2\right] = 3.$$

3. (c) Use the identity $x\sqrt{10-x} = 10\sqrt{10-x} - (10-x)^{3/2}$ and the First Fundamental Theorem.

SECTION 6.4

3. This is the limit of Riemann sums for the function defined by $f(x) = 1/(1+x)$ for $0 \le x \le 1$, based on regular partitions of $[0, 1]$. By the Riemann Sum Convergence Criterion and the First Fundamental Theorem, the limit is $\ln 2$.

5. The limit equals $\lim_{n \to \infty} 1/\sqrt{n \cdot n} + \lim_{n \to \infty} R_n$, where the second limit is the limit of Riemann sums for $f(x) = 1/\sqrt{1+x}$ for $0 \le x \le 1$, based on regular partitions of $[0.1]$. By the Riemann Sum Convergence Criterion and the First Fundamental Theorem, the limit is $2(\sqrt{2}-1)$.

8. Hint: For an interval $[x_{i-1}, x_i]$ in the partition P and a point c_i in $[x_{i-1}, x_i]$, show that for all x in $[x_{i-1}, x_i]$,

$$f(c_i) - c\|P\| \le f(x) \le f(c_i) + c\|P\|.$$

SECTION 6.5

4. Hint: For all real numbers λ, by the monotonicity and linearity of the integral,

$$0 \le \int_a^b [\lambda g - f]^2 = \lambda^2 \int_a^b g^2 - 2\lambda \int_a^b gf + \int_a^b f^2 \equiv a\lambda^2 + b\lambda + c.$$

For this quadratic polynomial in the variable λ to be nonnegative, its discriminant must be nonpositive.

5. (a) By the Cauchy-Schwarz Inequality for Integrals,

$$\int_0^1 \sqrt{1+x^4}\, dx = \int_0^1 \sqrt{1+x^4} \cdot 1\, dx \le \sqrt{\int_0^1 [1+x^4]\, dx} \cdot \sqrt{\int_0^1 1\, dx} = \sqrt{\frac{6}{5}}.$$

7. Define $h(x) = x - \sin x$ and $g(x) = \sin x - (2/\pi)x$ for all x. Since $h(0) = 0$ and $h'(x) > 0$ for $0 < x < \pi/2$, $h(x) > 0$ for $0 < x < \pi/2$. This proves the right-hand inequality. Since $g(0) = g(\pi/2) = 0$ and $g''(x) = -\sin x \ne 0$, for $0 < x < \pi/2$, it follows from the Mean Value Theorem that $g(x) \ne 0$ for $0 < x < \pi/2$. But $g'(0) > 0$, so $g(x) > 0$ for $x > 0$ sufficiently small. Thus, by the Intermediate Value Theorem, $g(x) > 0$ for all for $0 < x < \pi/2$. This proves the left-hand inequality. The integral inequality follows from the monotonicity of the integral.

SECTION 7.1

1. (a)

$$\frac{d}{dx}\left(\int_0^x x^2 t^2\, dt\right) = \frac{d}{dx}\left(x^2 \int_0^x t^2\, dt\right) = (5/3)x^4.$$

(c)

$$\frac{d}{dx}\left(\int_{-x}^x e^{t^2}\, dt\right) = \frac{d}{dx}\left(\int_0^x e^{t^2}\, dt - \int_0^{-x} e^{t^2}\, dt\right) = 2e^{x^2}.$$

8. Consider the function $f:[0,1] \to \mathbb{R}$ that has the value -1 on $[0,1/2]$ and the value 1 on the interval $(1/2,1]$. Then $\int_0^1 f = 0$, but there is no point x in $[0,1]$ at which $f(0) = 0$.

9. Show that $\int_0^1 p(x)\,dx = 0$ and then apply the Mean Value Theorem for Integrals.

SECTION 7.2

1. (a) By Theorem 7.10 and the First Fundamental Theorem,
$$F(x) = e^{-x} + e^{-x} \int_0^x e^t t\,dt = 2e^{-x} + x - 1.$$

5. Show that $f'(x) - f(x) = 0$ for all x, and that $f(0) = 0$; then apply Proposition 7.9.

7. Hint: Show that $h'(x) = 1/g(x)$ for all x and that $f'(x) = 1/h'(f(x))$ for all x in J.

SECTION 7.3

1. (c) $4e^9 - (3/2)e^4$.

2. (b) $-1 - 2\ln(4/3)$.

4. Observe that the formula holds at $x = a$. Then differentiate each side of the formula and apply the Identity Criterion.

9. (a) Hint: (A diagram will help) Choose c such that $f(c) = b$. Consider the cases $a = c, a < c$, and $a > c$. For instance, if $a < c$, then $f(x) \le b$ for $a \le x \le c$, so using Exercise 8,
$$ab = cf(c) - (c-a)b \le F(a) + G(b) + \int_a^c f - (a-c)b \le F(a) + G(b).$$

SECTION 7.4

1. (c) $\int_0^1 x^4\,dx = 1/5$; the Trapezoid Approximation based on the partition $\{0,1\}$ is $1/2$; the error estimate from Theorem 7.14 is 1. For Simpson's Rule based on the partition $\{0,1\}$ the value is $5/24$; the error estimate from Theorem 7.17 is $24/2880$.

6. The Simpson Rule approximation of $\ln 2 = \int_1^2 1/t\,dt$ based on the partition $\{1,3/2,2\}$ is
$$1/12[f(1) + 4f(5/4) + 2f(3/2) + 4f(7/4) + f(2)] = 1747/2520,$$
where $f(t) = 1/t$. Since $\|P\| = 1/2$ and $|f^{(4)}(t)| \le 24$ for $1 \le t \le 2$, the error estimate from Theorem 7.19 is $24/(2^4 \cdot 2880)$.

SECTION 8.1

1. (a) Highest order of contact is 0. (c) Highest order of contact is 2.

2. (a) $p_3(x) = x - x^3/3$.

4. Hint: Show that $f(0) > 0, f'(0) > 0$, and $f''(0) < 0$, and then use continuity of the function and its first two derivatives at $x = 0$.

SECTION 8.2

1. Hint: Find the first Taylor polynomial for $f(x) = \sqrt{1+x}$ at $x_0 = 0$ and estimate the remainder.

5. Hint: Find the first Taylor polynomial for $f(x) = \sin x$ at $x_0 = a$, and use this to estimate $\sin(a+b)$.

7. Hint: A polynomial of degree n is identically equal to its nth Taylor polynomial at $x = x_0$.

SECTION 8.3

1. In (a) and (b), the estimate (8.12) holds with $M = 1$.

4. Hint: Argue by induction that the function $F: \mathbb{R} \to \mathbb{R}$ has derivatives of all orders and that for each natural number n,

$$F^{(n+2)}(x) - F^{(n+1)}(x) - F^{(n)}(x) = 0.$$

Use this formula to show that on each interval $[-r, r]$ the estimate (8.12) holds where $M = 2(1 + c)$ and c is chosen so that $|F'(x)| \leq c$ and $|F''(x)| \leq c$, for $|x| \leq r$.

SECTION 8.4

5. Hint: By the Lagrange Remainder Theorem, for $x > -1, x \neq 0$, there is a point c, strictly between 0 and x, such that

$$\ln(1 + x) - p_n(x) = \frac{(-1)^{n+1}}{(n+1)(1+c)^{n+1}} x^{n+1} = \frac{(-1)^{n+1}}{(n+1)} \left(\frac{x}{1+c} \right)^{n+1}$$

Show that $|x|/(1 + c) \leq 1$ if $-1/2 \leq x \leq 1$. Thus, the Lagrange Remainder Theorem implies the validity of the expansion for $-1/2 \leq x \leq 1$.

SECTION 8.5

4. Hint: Let x_m and x_M be minimizers and maximizers of $g: [a, b] \to \mathbb{R}$. Then, by the monotonicity of the integral,

$$g(x_m) \int_a^b h(x)\, dx \leq \int_a^b g(x) h(x)\, dx \leq g(x_M) \int_a^b h(x)\, dx.$$

If $\int_a^b h(x)\, dx > 0$, divide the above inequality by the integral and apply the Intermediate Value Theorem.

7. Hint: Show that for $0 < c < x < 1$, since $(1 + c)^{\beta - k} \leq (1 + c)^\beta$,

$$\left| \frac{f^{(k)}(c)}{k!} x^k \right| = \left| (1 + c)^{\beta - k} \binom{\beta}{k} x^k \right| \leq (1 + c)^\beta \binom{\beta}{k} |x|^k,$$

and use Lemma 8.18.

SECTION 8.6

2. Argue by contradiction: if there is such an estimate, then from Theorem 8.11 it follows that the Taylor series expansion converges to the function at every point.

4. Hint: Argue by induction. By assumption, $g(0) = 0$. Let n be a natural number, and suppose that for $0 \leq k \leq n - 1$, $g^{(k)}(0) = 0$. Then by the Lagrange Remainder Theorem, for each x there is a point c between 0 and x such that $g(x) = (g^{(n)}(c)/n!) x^n$. The estimate $|g(x)| \leq c_{n+1} |x|^{n+1}$ for $|x| < \delta_n$, and the continuity of the nth derivative, imply that $g^{(n)}(0) = 0$.

SECTION 8.7

4. Hint: Argue by contradiction. Suppose, for instance, that there is a polynomial $p: \mathbb{R} \to \mathbb{R}$ such that $|e^x - p(x)| \leq 1$ for all x. Let the degree of this polynomial be k. Show that this is inconsistent with the fact that $e^x \geq x^{k+1}/(k+1)!$ for all $x > 0$.

7. By the Weierstrass Approximation Theorem, for each natural number k, we may choose a polynomial $q_k(x)$ such that $|q_k(x) - f(x)| \le 1/k$ for all x in $[-1, 1]$. For x in $[-1, 1]$, define $p_1(x) = q_1(x)$ and $p_n(x) = q_n(x) - q_{n-1}(x)$ if $n > 1$. Show that $f(x) = \sum_{n=1}^{\infty} p_n(x)$ for all x.

SECTION 9.1

1. (d) Converges; either find the exact formula for the partial sums or compare with $\sum_{k=1}^{\infty} 1/k^2$.
   (e) Converges; the Integral Test. (g) Diverges; the terms do not converge to 0.

6. The sequence of partial sums of the series $\sum_{k=1}^{\infty} (a_{2k} + a_{2k-1})$ is a *subsequence* of the sequence of partial sums of the series $\sum_{k=1}^{\infty} a_k$.

SECTION 9.2

1. The sequence converges pointwise to the function $f: \mathbb{R} \to \mathbb{R}$ with $f(x) = 1$ for $|x| < 1$, $f(x) = -1$ for $|x| > 1$ and $f(\pm 1) = 0$.

3. The sequence converges pointwise to the function that is identically 0.

7. Hint: Choose n such that $|f(x) - f_n(x)| \le 1$ for all x in $\mathbb{R}$. Thus, $|f(x)| \le |f_n(x)| + 1$ for all x in $\mathbb{R}$. The boundedness of $f_n: \mathbb{R} \to \mathbb{R}$ implies the boundedness of $f: \mathbb{R} \to \mathbb{R}$.

10. Hint: For all natural numbers n and k,

$$|f_{n+k}(x) - f_n(x)| \le \sum_{j=n+1}^{n+k} \frac{a_j}{j!} r^j \text{ for } |x| \le r.$$

This, together with the Weierstrass Uniform Convergence Criterion and the convergence of $\sum_{j=1}^{\infty} (a_j/j!) r^j$, implies uniform convergence.

SECTION 9.3

2. Hint: Since $e^t \ge t^2/2$ for all $t > 0$, $|f_n(x)| \le (2/n|x|^3)$ for all x in $(0, 1]$ and all natural numbers n. This implies pointwise convergence to the function $f: [0, 1] \to \mathbb{R}$ that is identically 0. For each n, on the other hand, $\int_0^1 f_n = (1/2)[1 - e^{-n}]$. Thus, $\lim_{n \to \infty} \int_0^1 f_n = 1/2 \ne \int_0^1 f$. There is no contradiction, because the convergence is not uniform.

4. For a natural number n and any x in $(-1, 1)$, define $f_n(x) = (1/n) \sin(n^2 x)$. Then $|f_n(x)| \le 1/n$ for all n, and all x in $(-1, 1)$, so the sequence $f_n: (-1, 1) \to \mathbb{R}$ converges pointwise to the function that is identically 0. Observe that $f'(0) = n$ for each n.

SECTION 9.4

3. Apply Theorem 9.24 to justify term-by-term differentiation of the series in Exercise 2.

5. Substitute $r = (1 - x)/x$ in the Geometric Series.

9. Show convergence of each of these series for all x, and apply Theorem 9.24 to justify term-by-term differentiation.

11. Use Exercise 10.

14. (a) If $|x| < 1/\alpha$, set $r = [1 + |\alpha x|]/2$. Show that since $|\alpha x| < r$, there is a natural number N such that $|a_n x^n| \le r^n$ for $n \ge N$. Since the Geometric Series $\sum_{n=1}^{\infty} r^n$ converges, show that the sequence of partial sums of $\sum_{n=1}^{\infty} a_n x^n$ is a Cauchy sequence.

SECTION 9.5

2. First show that the interval $[x_0/r - 1/2, x_0/r + 1/2]$ contains an integer m. If m is in $[x_0/r - 1/2, x_0/r]$, then $[x_0, x_0 + r]$ is contained in $[mr, (m+1)r]$, while if m is in $[x_0/r, x_0/r + 1/2]$, then $[x_0 - r, x_0]$ is contained in $[(m-1)r, mr]$,

6. Define $F(x) = \int_0^x f$ for each x, where $f: \mathbb{R} \to \mathbb{R}$ is the function defined in Theorem 9.27. The Second Fundamental Theorem implies that $F'(x) = f(x)$ for all x.

Index